COUNSELING THE INVERT

COUNSELING
THE INVERT

JOHN R. CAVANAGH, M.D., F.A.C.P., F.A.P.A., K.S.G.

Special Lecturer, School of Sacred Theology, The Catholic University of America

AUTHOR OF: *Fundamental Psychiatry* (with James B. McGoldrick, Ph.D.); *Fundamental Marriage Counseling; Pastoral Counseling; The Popes, the Pill, and the People*

THE BRUCE PUBLISHING COMPANY

MILWAUKEE

NIHIL OBSTAT:
   JUSTIN FURMAN, M.S.SS.T.
   Censor Deputatus

IMPRIMATUR:
   ✠ PATRICK A. O'BOYLE
   Archbishop of Washington
   April 29, 1965

Library of Congress Catalog Card Number: 66–18318

© 1966 THE BRUCE PUBLISHING COMPANY

MADE IN THE UNITED STATES OF AMERICA
      (Second printing — 1967)

Preface

Sex is a little understood subject. In recent years an effort has been made to overcome this difficulty in regard to heterosexuality, and as a result a great deal has been written on that subject. Some of the serious writing has been very good, some of the romantic writing very poor. There has been, however, no lack of good material. In regard to homosexuality this has not been true. In fact there has been very little serious effort to illuminate this area of deviant sexuality.

Clergymen who wield so much influence over the lives of others have not been well informed. Problems of the marriage of inverts, their entry into seminaries, and their employment have been blind spots.

This book attempts to provide the information which is needed to answer some of the questions in this area. It makes no attempt to tell all that is known about inversion. It does make an effort to supply those who need to know with enough background information to do their jobs well. For the invert himself it may help him to have some information about the development of his disorder, and not only what is necessary to eliminate it but also the knowledge that it can be treated.

For the counselor suggestions are made in the text as to methods of handling problems as they arise and also technics of long-term treatment. For the clinical psychologist and the psychiatrist, in addition to the suggestions for counseling, there is a discussion of methods of physical and psychotherapeutic treatment.

An attempt to provide a treatment of the subject of interest to such diverse groups may seem presumptuous. It would have been a few years ago. Today, however, clergymen, social workers, probation officers, clinical psychologists, and others are well versed in psychology and psychopathology. Almost daily they are confronted with psychological problems. In this book an effort is made to give them in one source the information for which they would otherwise have to delve through the bookshelves.

The various sections are called "clinics" even though until very recently this term was reserved to medical matters. Basically I believe that homosexuality is a medical-psychiatric problem and is best studied as a psychiatric problem. I have no illusions, however, that any high percentage of inverts will ever seek psychiatric help. It is the duty of the medical profession to supply those who will see the homosexual with whatever information will be helpful in his management. This I shall attempt to do in these clinics. No effort has been made to exhaust the subject, but I hope that a fair cross section has been presented.

I wish to thank all those authors and publishers who have given permission to quote from their works.

JOHN R. CAVANAGH, M.D.

Of all of the difficult problems which confront physicians, clergymen, and others of the "care-taking" professions homosexuality stands high on the list. Although the problem is as old as recorded history, efforts to understand and treat the disorder seem to have been sporadic and few. Little, if anything, has been taught about it in medical schools; at best it was mentioned in passing and only recently have psychiatrists and psychologists seriously turned their attention to it. Heretofore the attitude seemed to be that the problem belonged to somebody else and, besides, not much could be done about it anyhow. Like other distortions of the emotional life, the subject was generally avoided and people acted as though, if they kept quiet, it might go away, unless, of course, they were intent upon putting someone in jail because of inversion, which would not help the individual but might salve some consciences, but not for long.

It is obvious, therefore, that for many reasons there is a need for Dr. Cavanagh's book, a need to have the problem delineated and defined, a need especially to advise physicians and clergymen as to what to do and what not to do upon encountering the problem, a need to advise the pastor in counseling the hapless individual who appeals to him for help.

There will be general agreement with the author that homosexuality is not a disease per se, but rather it is the result of a personality or character problem in which the sexual orientation of the individual becomes fixated at an early age. While the inversion may at times be symptomatic of an underlying neurosis or psychosis, this type of reaction generally represents the individual's reaction to society, or society's reaction to him.

The writer divides his chapters into what he calls "clinics," for he believes homosexuality is a medicopsychologic problem which is best treated psychiatrically. There are 18 clinics in all. Clinics 11, 16, and 17 are directly slanted toward the pastor, for it is recognized that in a large number of cases he is the first person consulted by the individual or his family when the problem comes to light or becomes pressing. Clinic 12 concerns "Homosexuality and Governmental Agencies," a much-needed discussion, for at intervals there is a flurry in Washington about allegations or suspicions of the presence of homosexuals in some department or so-called "sensitive" agency and Congress gets roiled either of its own accord or because of the receipt of indignant letters. The agency in question is publicly criticized and, as a result, usually sets up or reactivates screening tests for its applicants. Then there are more indignant letters and more congressional indignation because in the screening tests there are questions about sex and this, it is said, violates the individual's privacy. Hearings are held, committees of experts called, the experts make recommendations, but by that time the criticism has cooled and nothing much is done about the problem, which will arise again in a few years and then the routine starts all over again.

One can certainly agree with the author of this volume that inverts do not belong in the military services because of the constant strain that an all-male population puts upon them. This can become a serious problem and it is only recently that the military has begun to show wisdom rather than abhorrence in its handling, although I fear it is still incumbent upon chaplains and psychiatrists to report inversion, even though the person involved confided to them in secret. This is a serious invasion of medical and clerical privilege in communication and is probably illegal.

It is probable, also, that this regulation, if it is still in force, is only honored in the breech, unless a criminal act has occurred. If an invert has seduced a younger person or attacked someone, then, understandably, society demands that he be punished. But if a person with homosexual tendencies is innocent of overt acts and appeals to a chaplain or a physician for help because of the stress his condition puts upon him, it is grossly unfair to turn this man in, for he may be separated from the service with an undesirable discharge; this was done regularly in World War II.

This action, to the mind of this observer, put the government in the peculiar role of drafting a man who was self-supporting, even if only making a marginal adjustment, inducting him into the service, where, because of his condition, he was placed in circumstances of inordinate stress. If he applied to the chaplain or medical service for help to keep from getting into trouble and he was recommended for discharge, he was usually given a "yellow ticket," which would ensure that he would have trouble in getting a job and sustaining himself in the future. This man, it would seem, was betrayed by professional people, punished for something he did not do, and the punishment was made to carry indefinitely into the future because of the type of discharge he was given. During the war, efforts to correct this situation came to naught. Also, it should be recognized that, while the homosexual has no place in the armed services, it is because of the nature of his sex drives and not because he is a particular security risk. It is undoubtedly true that blackmail and fear of exposure exist and could possibly lead to a security break, but this chance also exists in other persons, particularly in those poorly motivated and seeking financial reward.

Dr. Cavanagh examines the problem of female homosexuality but this, for a number of obvious reasons, does not call forth the serious reactions that male inversion seems to carry in its wake. For one thing, its detection is much more difficult and it rarely eventuates in a tragedy or public scandal.

The author also gives a fair and reasoned explanation of the etiology and clinical features of inversion and discusses the difficult problems of "Marriage and the Homosexual" and "Homosexuality and the Law" in the light of canon law and recent legislative decisions and the Wolfenden Report. He considers most sex offenders as nuisances rather than as dangers to the community. Many laws concerning these individuals, he notes, are outdated, having been promulgated in anger in response to public demand following upon some sexual crime.

Unlike some psychiatrists, the author does not approve of the Durham Act; he feels it leads to more confusion. However, it is not necessary to agree with all of the author's statements to conclude that this is a well-written, sensible, and timely work. Clinic 9, entitled "A Homosexual Speaks," is poignant in parts; from it one can only come to look upon a large portion of the sufferers from inversion with compassion. There is also included a chapter on moral responsibility, which chapter, like the one on homosexual organizations and publications, is an innovation in a work of this kind.

This is an important book and it will profit theologians and physicians to read it. In fact, the information it contains could be communicated to seminarians, medical students, and to all individuals or organizations which have to do with young adults. The knowledge gained might in some instances prove to be a deterrent to tragedy.

FRANCIS J. BRACELAND, M.D.

Contents

COUNSELING THE INVERT

The Community and the Invert

Every human being has two ways of dealing with things outside himself. He may either assimilate them into himself or he may go outside himself to them. Examples of this assimilation are observed in the process of eating and knowing. When something is eaten it becomes part of us. When we know a thing we incorporate its characteristics into ourselves. There are, of course, varying degrees of such incorporation. There is no comparison, for example, between merely knowing and really understanding that same thing.

In the matter of sex we have an example of going outward to things about us. When one experiences the *whole* sexual relation — not just the physical act — he becomes aware of this outgoing. We offer ourselves to the one beloved and the beloved offers himself to us. We achieve a commingling of personalities. The two persons in love are like two mirrors which reflect the light shone upon each other. Human sex and all the emotions that are its sequelae are more than bodily pleasure. It is a giving and a having of the whole complex person. The man contributes his strength and masculinity, the woman contributes her beauty and femininity. The end result is a psychological situation which neither the man nor the woman alone could produce.

This complementary oneness of man and woman has been given expression time and again in world literature. In the Old Testament there is the account of how Eve was created out of Adam's side. There is a similar story in the Upanishads. In Plato's *Banquet,* there is the story of how man and woman were once a single being who was cut in two by an angry god, and the two parts ever since have been trying to reunite in one.[1]

Homosexuality is an imperfect copy of this more natural male and female relationship. It is an attempt to establish contact with reality no matter how minimal it may be. It is a parody on the heterosexual union which results in an unhappy and transient relationship.[2]

Homosexuality is a disturbing word. No one, not even the affected individual, really relishes what it describes. For the heterosexual person the word implies an abnormality; for the homosexual it represents either fear, guilt, or conflict. The ill-informed heterosexual may look upon the homosexual as a depraved individual. A better informed heterosexual will, I hope, appreciate the condition as a distortion of the emotional life and will realize that the deviation is primarily confined to the sexual life.

The homosexual himself is not, as a rule, at ease with his condition. He may have reconciled himself to the moral issues involved, or he may have distorted his outlook upon morality to such a point that he pictures himself as a courageous pioneer of a new morality. In any case he will realize that he is fighting against the normal current of society. This in itself may make him feel like an outcast. In some instances he pictures himself as a crusader. He may accept the condition and join with others in homosexual ghettos which can be found in any large city. There is, at the other extreme, the homosexual whose whole life is a torture because he is pursued with guilt arising from his conduct.

One would expect that such an unhappy state would be embraced by only a few and would soon be extinct through a process of attrition. On the contrary, homosexuality is as old as recorded history and more common today than ever before. The Laws of Hammurabi (2067–2025 B.C.) are said to mention it with disfavor.[3] According to Ellis, however, even though the Hammurabi Code gives indication that homosexuality was practiced in Assyria at that time, its extant portions do not mention this fact, and nothing contained in it can be construed as implying any reference to it.[4]

HOMOSEXUALITY IN THE BIBLE

The earliest mention of homosexuality in the Bible is the Sodom and Gomorrah account (Gn 19:4–11). From this the sin of sodomy derives its name. This account is now controverted, although in past ages it was assumed to be the *locus classicus* of the divine condemnation of homosexual acts as the most heinous sin.[5] Unfortunately the "traditional" interpretation of this story has given the impression that homosexuals are moral monsters for whom God has selected special punishments. St. Paul, however, mentions other kinds of sins which deprive one of the kingdom of God (cf. 1 Cor 6:10, Rom 1:28–32, and Gal 5:19–21).

The Genesis account is as follows:

> They [the two angels] had not yet retired when the townsmen, the men of Sodom, all the people from every quarter, both young and old, surrounded the house, and called Lot, and said to him, "Where are the men who came to your house tonight? Bring them out that we may abuse them." Lot went out to the men, and shut the door behind him, and said, "I entreat you, brethren, do not act wickedly. I have two daughters that have not known man. Let me bring them out to you; do as you please with them. Only do nothing to these men, for they have come under the shelter of my roof."

In spite of other references to Sodom and Gomorrah in the New Testament, e.g., Matthew 10:14–15, 2 Peter 2:6, Luke 10:12, there is only one which specifically refers to the reason for the destruction of Sodom and Gomorrah. This reference is Jude 7:

> Just as Sodom and Gomorrah, and the neighboring cities which like them committed sins of immorality and practiced unnatural vice, have been made an example, undergoing the punishment of eternal fire.

Another biblical story apparently referring to inversion and more likely than the Sodom story, I am told,[6] to be historically accurate is found in Judges 19:15–25:

> When he noticed the traveler in the public square of the city, the old man asked where he was going, and whence he had come. He said to him, "We are traveling from Bethlehem of Juda far up into the mountain region of Ephraim, where I belong. I have been to Bethlehem of Juda and am now going back home; but no one has offered us the shelter of his house. We have straw and fodder for our asses, and bread and wine for the woman and for our servant; there is nothing else we need." "You are welcome," the old man said to him, "but let me provide for all your needs, and do not spend the night in the public square." So he led them to his house and provided fodder for the asses. Then they washed their feet, and ate and drank.

> While they were enjoying themselves, the men of the city, who were corrupt, surrounded the house and beat on the door. They said to the old man whose house it was, "Bring out your guest that we may abuse him." The owner of the house went out to them and said, "No, my brothers; do not be so wicked. Since this man is my guest, do not commit this crime. Rather let me bring out my maiden daughter or his concubine. Ravish them or do whatever you want with them; but against the man you must not commit this wanton crime." When the men would not listen to his host, the husband seized his concubine and thrust her outside to them. They had relations with her and abused her all night until the following dawn, when they let her go.

THE KORAN
(Arabic transliteration: *Qur'an*, i.e., "recitation")

Since two versions of this story have been mentioned, it may be of interest to note that the Koran also relates a similar description of events in Sodom.

Koran is the name for the sacred writings of Islam, regarded by Moslems as the word of God. The Koran itself tells how it originated. It was communicated, piecemeal at various times, from heaven to Mohammed (A.D. 570?–632) through the intermediation of an angel (sometimes called Gabriel). Its contents are extremely varied. It deals with dogma and morals. Many passages concern various religious ordinances, e.g., prayers, fasting, pilgrimage, and matters dealing with civil or criminal laws.

The Koran uses Christian, Jewish, and Arabic "sources" for its material in many instances. Mohammed frequently cites stories from both the Old and New Testaments as examples to corroborate his teaching, but takes these stories and facts not from the Bible itself, but rather from the legendary writings of the Jews and Apocryphal Gospels. It is a rare passage in the Koran which shows a *verbal* resemblance to the Old or New Testaments.

The Koran has 114 chapters (*suras*) of very unequal length, arranged with the shortest first. In all, the Koran contains 6226 verses.

Mohammed sometimes revoked earlier statements, ordering them to be canceled out. It seems, though, that they were not, and so the Koran has different laws or directions telling one how to act in the same situation:

> (80) And when our messengers came to Lot, he was grieved for them; but his arm was straitened for them, and he said, "This is a troublesome day!" And his people came to him, rushing at him, for before that they used to work evil. He said, "O my people! here are my daughters, they are purer for you; then, fear God, and do not disgrace me through my guests; is there not among you one right-thinking man?"

> They said, "Thou knowest that we have no claim on thy daughters; verily thou knowest what we want!" He said, "Had I but power over you; or could I but resort to some strong column . . . !" [The angels] said, "O Lot! verily, we are the messengers of thy Lord, they shall certainly not reach thee; then travel with thy people in the darkness of thy wife: verily, there shall befall her what befalls them. Verily, their appointment is for the morning! and is not the morning nigh?"

> And when our bidding came, we made their high parts their low parts.

And we rained down upon them stones and baked clay one after another, marked, from thy Lord, and these are not so far from the unjust! (E. H. Palmer, *The Qur'an,* Parts I and II, Sacred Books of the East, Oxford: Clarendon Press, 1880, Vol. VI, p. 213.)

OTHER REFERENCES

Other references in the Old Testament are more specific. For example, in the Book of Leviticus it is stated:

You shall not lie with a male as with a woman; such a thing is an abomination (Lv 18:22).

If a man lies with a male as with a woman, both of them shall be put to death for their abominable deed; they have forfeited their lives (Lv 20:13).

In the New Testament St. Paul makes frequent references to homosexuality. His clearest and most unmistakable statement is in his Epistle to the Romans:

For this cause has given them up to shameful lusts; for their women have exchanged the natural use for that which is against nature, and in like manner the men also, having abandoned the natural use of the woman, have burned in their lusts one towards another, men with men doing shameless things and receiving in themselves the fitting recompense of their perversity (Rom 1:26–27).

Other Pauline references are found in 1 Corinthians 6:9–10 and 1 Timothy 1:9–10.

COMMENTARY

Asked to comment on these biblical references, Father Nathan Kay, M.S.SS.T., stated:

Sacred Scripture explicitly mentions many causes for the destruction of Sodom and her sister cities. In fact, if statistics mean anything — and here they are not of much significance — non-sexual causes by far outnumber the sexual, to say nothing of unnatural sex (e.g., Ecclus. 16/8; Wisdom 10/6–8; and especially Ezechiel 16/49). This, for one thing, should temper any statement which implies that Scripture condemned these cities only and expressly for unnatural sex.

The Sodom story (Genesis 18/20–19/29) begins with God's conversation with Abraham; it is a composite and edited account about God's righteousness, Abraham's privileged position, Lot's failure despite God's grace (Lot's biography is resumed from Chapter 13) — all of which is centered about a city which is presented as being on trial, charged with being totally corrupt.

Obviously, were one to say that the whole purpose of the narrative was to show the city was sodomistic, he would be very narrow.

There is no reason to doubt that the story tells of an attempted act of unnatural sex. When the men of the city (from the oldest to the youngest) ask for Lot's visitors, it is for the purpose of "knowing them," a common circumlocution for sexual intercourse. Furthermore, Lot offers instead, as a compromise, his two daughters.

To me it seems that attempted unnatural sex play is not the only contemplated offense mentioned here. There is the sacred and inviolable law of hospitality which will be broken if the guests are surrendered. I hesitate to hazard a guess as to which, according to the Israelite mentality of the time, was judged more sacred. Leviticus condemns homosexuality with the death penalty; but the same penalty is prescribed for other sins, e.g., the striking of parents. Still Lot is willing to sacrifice his daughters rather than have the law of hospitality violated (Gen. 19/8).

Because so many different causes are given in Sacred Scripture (especially among the prophets: pride, neglect of the poor, thoughtless ease, etc.), perhaps we have here in Genesis a tradition about Sodom which is distinct from the one common among the Israelites. On the other hand, because Sodom and Gomorrah (and the rest at times) were always an example of supreme degradation, it would be easy and quite in order for a later writer to particularize the nature of the sin according to the circumstances of his time, as for example, Ezechiel may have done.

With all this as background it is easier to make some sort of judgment about Jude 7.

A very literal translation of the text would read: "As Sodom and Gomorrah and the neighboring cities, in like manner having given themselves to fornication and going after other flesh, were made an example, suffering the punishment of eternal fire."

". . . having given themselves to fornication. . . ." Some translate this as "indulged in immorality." The Greek can mean "to dedicate oneself to illicit sex"; or metaphorically, "to go whoring." The latter idea was frequently applied to Israel which is described as "whoring after false gods, i.e., committing idolatry."

So it has both ideas: sex and the generic idea of idolatry with all its attendant abuses.

". . . going after other flesh. . . ." Some translate this as ". . . unnatural vice" or "unnatural lusts" or "different flesh" or "strange flesh." Or to "follow, go after (also with the idea of eagerness) flesh to which one has no right." It *suggests* a use which is contrary to nature, and because of the Genesis incident for one, there are grounds for translating it as something "unnatural."

So, there is no doubt that Jude intends to use Sodom and Gomorrah as examples of gross immorality which was divinely punished. It fits in perfectly with the purpose of his letter — a warning to a group of Christians because of the dangers resulting from the false doctrines and immoral conduct of some sort of early Gnostics who were infiltrating or defecting from the Church and who were quite famous for their sexual immorality, as we learn from another source.

However, I would judge that Jude has more in mind than mere sex play when he uses the word "fornicate." He certainly was aware of all the causes attributed to the Sodom and Gomorrah destruction and even how Israel itself was likened to these cities because basically it was a spouse unfaithful to God's laws.

This "going after other flesh" certainly does suggest Genesis, and at least the Sodom incident.

One modern commentator sees these verses (Jude 5–7) figuratively: the "angels and Sodom and Gomorrah" are the leaders of this group of early Gnostics who are causing all the trouble; "fornication" refers to idolatry; "flesh" denotes human society and its violent attempts at self-exaltation. All of which is good, but it does not detract from the basic meaning of the Sodom and Gomorrah story as Jude would have known it.

So, if Jude is the only place in the New Testament where Sodom and Gomorrah are condemned outright because of unnatural sex, he must be interpreted in this light, at least. On the other hand, unnatural sex is certainly at least one implicit cause given in Genesis for the destruction of Sodom.

Still, as was said in the beginning, if someone says flatly that sodomy is the *only* cause given in Sacred Scripture for the destruction of Sodom, he is not right.

THE TEACHINGS OF THE FATHERS

Bailey[7] discusses at length not only the biblical descriptions but also the statements of the early Fathers and of the Councils. For a detailed treatment of the subject in English, reference should be made to his work. He concludes that the consistent teaching of the Fathers was that homosexuality is objectively illicit.

As an example of the early writers, Tertullian referred to homosexual acts as "acts of frenzied lust." Tertullian also stated that such vices should be banished "not only from the threshold but also from all shelter of the Church, for they are not sins so much as monstrosities."[8]

St. Augustine spoke out strongly against inversion:

Therefore are those foul offenses which are against nature to be everywhere and at all times detested and punished; such as were those of the men of Sodom: which should all nations commit, they should all stand guilty of the same crime, by the law of God, which hath not so made men that they should so abuse one another. For even that intercourse which should be between God and us is violated when that same nature, of which He is Author, is polluted by the perversity of lust.[9]

St. John Chrysostom referred to homosexual acts as "of the last degree of corruptness."[10]

St. Thomas Aquinas, whose treatment of inversion is studied and considerate, states that this sin is the gravest sin of all:

> On the contrary, Augustine says (*De adult. conjug.*) that of all these, namely the sins belonging to lust, that which is against nature is the worst.
>
> I answer that, in every genus, worst of all is the corruption of the principle on which the rest depend. Now the principles of reason are those things that are according to nature, because reason presupposes things as determined by nature, before disposing of other things according as it is fitting. This may be observed both in speculative and in practical matters. Wherefore just as in speculative matters the most grievous and shameful error is that which is about things the knowledge of which is naturally bestowed on man, so in matters of action it is most grave and shameful to act against things as determined by nature. Therefore, since by the unnatural vices man transgresses that which has been determined by nature with regard to the use of venereal actions, it follows that in this matter this sin is the gravest of all.[11]

From the objective standpoint there seems little doubt that moralists and lawmakers through the ages have considered acts of inversion as immoral and illegal.

POPULAR WRITINGS

In spite of its antiquity little that is of real value has been written on homosexuality until very recent years.[12] However little has been done to study its psychopathological aspects, there has been even less discussion of the subject in ethicoreligious literature. This in spite of the fact that the religious counselor should have a clear, sound knowledge of the subject. The sparseness of literature was not confined, however, to its religious aspects. There has been a general ignorance of the subject. Only recently has an effort been made to change this. Changed it has been, but when confronted with traditional attitudes the average lay reader is left confused.

Popular Articles

Popular magazines have brought some knowledge of the subject to a wide audience, although much of it is sensational. Readers were told, for example, that the pagan Greek society of Plato and Sappho regarded inversion as an established, honored relationship, while Christian British society made "sodomy a crime."[13]

In the United States, "homosexual relationships between males constitute a criminal offense in 46 of the States."[14] The reader cannot help some degree of confusion when faced with these contrasts.

Homosexuality, it was noted, is found in all classes of people. A leading London newspaper said in regard to inversion:

> We are in no doubt that homosexuality is widespread, that it extends to people in high positions here and abroad and that its eruption in such offenses as importuning, corrupting boys, or public indecency is today a serious and growing criminal problem.[15]

Famous names were mentioned. Weinstock stated that the tragic life of Piotr Tchaikovsky was mainly due to his homosexual yearnings. In a letter to his brother, Modest, who was also a homosexual, Piotr wrote:

> I have sunk so deeply in the mire of my tastes and habits that to discard them at once, as one discards an old glove, is impossible. Besides, I am far from being the possessor of an iron character. Since my recent letters to you, I have already succumbed to my natural inclinations three times.[16]

Oscar Wilde, a successful English dramatist, was an invert whose eroticism in later life brought his singularly brilliant career to a melancholy end. "Wilde was sentenced to two years' imprisonment with hard labour for offenses under the Criminal Law Amendment Act."[17]

The recent cases of homoeroticism of Edward, Baron Montague of Beaulieu, a rising young Tory of the House of Lords; of the Shakespearean actor, Sir John Gielgud; and of the Laborite, W. F. Field, were also described in the press.[18]

The following testimony of Roy E. Blick, Washington, D. C., Vice Squad head for eighteen years, appeared in a weekly magazine:

> "There are 5,000 homosexuals in the District of Columbia," he testified; "3,750 of them work for the government. Between 300 and 400 suspects still work for the State Department," he said.[19]

From what has been said, it is obvious that homosexuals come from all levels of society. They are not confined solely to the class of the illiterate, the unlearned, or the squalid.

Yet, unfortunately, one of the better recent articles on homosexuality published in a popular magazine[20] tends to perpetuate this
concept. The article concentrates on the "gay world" of "brawny
young men in leather caps, shirts, jackets and pants." The whole
tone of the article gives a "murky" picture of the subject.

This fact — that homosexuality is not confined to dark bars and
"gay spots" — is emphasized by these statements which were selected
from case histories in Army files:

> They topped the average soldier in intelligence, education, and rating;
> at least ten per cent were college graduates; more than fifty per cent
> had finished high school. Only a handful were illiterate.

> Including all ages, there were more whites than negroes in this group.
> They came mostly from the cities rather than from the country.

> Although the majority had no family history of nervous or mental
> diseases, many were from homes broken by divorce or separation.

> As a whole, these men were law-abiding and hard-working. In spite of
> nervous, unstable, and often hysterical temperament, they performed
> admirably as office workers.[21]

A further insight into the homosexual personality is provided by
this comment of Anomaly, himself an invert:

> They are good citizens, useful members of the community, many of
> them — especially in the artistic sphere — extremely talented, and
> often models of social respectability. Contrary to popular supposition,
> they may be conventional in their dress and behavior.[22]

This information has value in making the average individual aware
of the real nature of homosexuality and tends to correct mistaken
ideas which may have arisen from the concept that it was the "unspeakable crime." This type of insight has value not only for the
public but also for the homosexual so that both the heterosexual
and the invert may begin to understand that the disorder is not
present through the deviate's own fault and is to some extent con-
trollable. A combination of such understanding with psychological
and religious insights is the most helpful means of adjustment for
the deviate.

TRADITIONAL ATTITUDES TOWARD HOMOSEXUALITY

An unworthy prejudice against the homosexual has existed from
the days when homosexuality was "that horrible sin, not to be
mentioned among Christians."[23] This attitude is imperfectly under-

stood by many counselors and helps to perpetuate the concept that the homosexual is a being set apart as evil and unclean. This is usually not true.

Such a prejudice probably arose from a variety of causes. The Catholic Church has traditionally condemned homosexual acts as contrary to nature and, therefore, as "unnatural." Sodomy as related to the sin of the inhabitants of Sodom constituted what was considered ample biblical proof for this belief. Since biologically the purpose of the sex act is procreation it is clear that homosexual acts bring about a frustration of this generative function. Bailey states this quite well:

> Starting from the universally accepted premise that the primary purpose of the sexual organs is procreation — from which it followed that they may only be used legitimately for such acts as do not exclude the possibility (though they may not express the intention) of generation — he [St. Thomas Aquinas] found no difficulty in showing that all homosexual practices are *ex hypothesi* unnatural, lustful, and sinful. Thus he established the principal argument upon which moral theologians were to rely in the future when treating of venereal acts between members of the same sex.[24]

From this traditional background many counselors look upon the homosexual with mixed feelings. They have been known to be fearful, mistrusting, resentful, and sometimes overcome by feelings of inadequacy. Many have frightened the deviate away with their rudeness and hostility. They may associate all homosexuals with willful depravity, seduction of the young, effeminacy, and moral perversion:

> The tragic reception which many a homosexual has received from a well-meaning but uninformed priest, or ineffectual or sometimes even hostile priest at least partially explains how so many of these unfortunates leave the Church in frustrated rebellion or deep despair. . . . it is easy for him to conclude that the Church has abandoned him too.[25]

Because of these attitudes many homosexuals do not seek advice, which may lead some counselors to believe that homosexuality is a rare thing. I have been told by priests of over twenty years' experience that they have never seen a homosexual.

THE INCIDENCE OF HOMOSEXUALITY

The frequency of homosexuality in the population as a whole is very difficult to determine. There seems, however, to be no lack of

sexual companions for sex deviates. The exact incidence of homosexuality is not known.

In primitive societies Ford and Beach found that 49 percent of
seventy-six societies which they studied considered that homosexual
behavior was normal and socially acceptable. The usual custom was
to allow the male to dress like a woman and vice versa. Males
dressed as women were also permitted to perform sodomy in many
societies. In other societies the male invert was considered to have
magical powers. In still others the majority or, in some instances, all
the male population practiced homosexuality. In others sodomy was
part of the puberty rites. It was, as a matter of fact, considered
necessary for the health of the growing boy.

In twenty-eight of the seventy-six societies studied, homosexual
behavior was condemned and disapproved. In these societies children
who showed any such tendency were punished. In adults penalties
ranged from ridicule and social condemnation to death.[26]

Magnus Hirschfeld stated in 1903 that if homosexuality were
defined as an abiding sexual interest only in members of the self-
sex, the number of homosexuals was probably 1.5 percent of the
population of Germany. Hirschfeld also maintained that if inclu-
sion were made of persons whose interest was predominantly in
members of their own sex, the percentage would approximate 2.3.[27]

The Kinsey Report on the male, although greatly criticized for
statistical and other errors, cannot be completely put aside. Kinsey's
study of 5300 American males revealed some interesting figures.
Using as his criterion "physical contact to the point of orgasm,"
his study revealed that, if projected to the whole population, 37
percent of American males have had "some homosexual experience"
between adolescence and old age. Further, his figures showed (1)
50 percent of males single to the age of 35 had had homosexual
experience, (2) 25 percent had experience, or reaction, for at least
three years between ages 16 and 35 years, (3) 10 percent of males
were more or less exclusively homosexual between the age of 16 and
55 years, (4) 8 percent of males were exclusively homosexual for
at least three years between age 16 to 55 years, (5) 4 percent of
males were exclusively homosexual throughout their active sex life.[28]
If the male population of the United States over 14 years of age is
60,364,000,[29] this would mean that there were 2,414,560 practicing
homosexuals in the United States in 1958.

K. B. Davis[30] in 1929 stated that 38 percent of college women and 15 percent of noncollege women showed homosexual responses. G. V. Hamilton[31] in the same year maintained that 26 percent of the women tested show intense homosexual emotional responses. Hamilton at the same time reported that 17 percent of the male population was homosexual. Ramsey[32] wrote that in 1929 30 percent of 291 junior high school boys were homosexual. Finger[33] concluded in 1947 that 27 percent of 111 college men were homosexual. G. Th. Kempe[34] estimated that in 1954 there were at least 100,000 manifestly homosexual men and women in the Netherlands, aged 18 and older. Havelock Ellis[35] estimated that in 1928 England had slightly over 2 percent.

More recent figures concerning the incidence of homosexuality were given by the Wolfenden Committee. This committee estimated that a very large segment of the British population was homosexual and in its report gave the impression that the controversial Kinsey estimates for the United States might be quite applicable to Great Britain.[36]

Waring and Bryce report that the Mattachine Society had some startling figures in the June, 1960, issue of its *Review*. In that issue it was stated that there are approximately 1,000,000 homosexuals over 15 years of age in the state of California alone. The *Review* estimated that there were 50,000 male and 40,000 female homosexuals in San Francisco.[37]

It can be seen from these figures that there is no accurate estimate of the number of homosexuals. Oliven summarizes the incidence in these words:

> Best available estimates indicate that approximately 4 to 5 percent of adult men in the civilized Western world have predominantly or exclusively homosexual inclinations of one clinical type or another. Types of "facultative" homosexuality are more frequent, and in some regions of the world (Levant, Eurasian Middle East and elsewhere) it seems to be traditionally "endemic."[38]

THE ATTITUDE OF THE COUNSELOR

What should the pastoral counselor's attitude be when confronted with the problem? First of all the pastor should acquire a certain degree of knowledge and understanding of the subject. The counselor does not need a degree in psychology or psychiatry, but he should be well informed; he should have some knowledge of the nature of homosexuality and the different theories advanced by psychologists and psychiatrists. He should, of course, note that the theories advanced on the causality of homosexuality are as yet unproved.

For those who believe that a study of inversion is undesirable, Father Larere has this advice:

> There are anomalies and perversions which appear so contrary to the common laws of nature and to the demands of the Christian life that it often seems best to pass over them in silence, for fear of arousing unhealthy curiosity or even of uncovering to man certain profound disorders of his personality. This policy of silence is not called for. when the audience is one of doctors, medical students, and priests, whose social and spiritual duties not only demand that they should be conversant with the psychology of inverts, but also oblige them to intervene in the therapeutic field and in that of the direction of consciences in order to cure such inverts.[39]

I would add to the list of Father Larere all those who deal with people, such as social workers. Without such knowledge the counselor, whatever his orientation, has a blind spot.

Much of the ignorance of certain clergymen with regard to inversion is due to the lack of treatment of this subject in moral manuals. Most such manuals merely mention that there is such a thing as inversion, give some divisions of it, mention the heinousness of the sin — and then pass on to some other topic. A similar outline is followed by most books dealing *ex professo* with pastoral care — commonly referred to as pastoral theology. In fact the latest text in pastoral medicine available to me — *Handbuch der speziellen Pastoral-medizin* by Dr. Albert Niedermeyer — covers the homosexual problems in less than four pages *out of six volumes*. Even then, most of the author's words are devoted to criminal cases and listings of punishments which are inflicted by the Austrian government on offenders.

The literature on homosexuality ranges from the pornographic to the literary and scientific and only occasionally to the ethicoreligious aspects of the problem. Even an uncritical survey of this literature reveals the most discouraging dearth of useful or even factual material in the latter category. Yet, of all men, surely the religious counselor has the greatest need of clear, sound ideas on this frequently occurring condition. These clinics, I hope, may point to some of the difficulties and indicate certain directions for their solution. They will have fulfilled their aim if they serve to convince those who need to be convinced, that to be uninformed in this matter is to run the risk of personal enbarrassment and, what is inestimably graver, of irreparable harm to people. The spiritual guide can never lose sight of the fact that he is not dealing with a mere case or statistic, but with a *soul* for whose ransom Christ shed His blood.

Perhaps the most fundamental principle to be learned from a moral point of view is that a clear distinction must be made between homosexual *tendency* and *practice*. Rudimentary as this may seem, the ignorance of some counselors (and often of the homosexual himself) in this regard is ample justification for emphasizing this statement in the very beginning. In the vocabulary of many clergymen, "homosexuality" is a synonym for "sodomy." But even in those cases where tendency and practice are adequately distinguished, the moral nonimputability of the homosexual attitude is frequently only imperfectly appreciated.[40]

These topics we could pursue indefinitely. Enough has been said, I hope, to help the reader realize that there is much ambivalence about the condition, even among those who should know better.

CLINIC 1 — NOTES

1. As Plato speaks through Aristophanes, he describes it in these words: "Each of us then is the mere broken tally of a man, the result of a bisection which has reduced us to a condition like that of flat fish, and each of us is perpetually in search of his corresponding tally. Those men who are halves of a being of the common sex, which was called, as I told you, hermaphrodite, are lovers of women, and most adulterers come from this class, as also do women who are mad about men and sexually promiscuous. Women who are halves of a female whole direct their affections towards women and pay little attention to men; Lesbians belong to this category. But those who are halves of a male whole pursue males, and being slices, so to speak, of the male, love men throughout their boyhood, and take pleasure in physical contact with men. Such boys and lads are the best of their generation, because they are the most manly" (Plato, *The Symposium*, trans. W. Hamilton, Penguin Books, L24, Baltimore, 1962, par. 191–192). See also Sandor Rado, "A Critical Examination of the Concept of Bisexuality," *Psychoanalytic Medicine II*, October 4, 1940, p. 459.
2. Charles Berg, M.D., and Clifford Allen, M.D., *The Problem of Homosexuality* (New York: The Citadel Press, 1958), p. 54.
3. Derrick S. Bailey, *Homosexuality and the Western Christian Tradition* (London: Longmans, 1955), p. 33.
4. *Ibid.*
5. *Ibid.*, pp. 1–28.
6. Personal discussion with biblical scholars.
7. *Op. cit.*, Chapters II, III, IV.
8. *De Pudic*, C, IV, PL 2, 1032.
9. St. Augustine, *The Confessions*, Book iii, Chapter VIII, 15. See also iii, XVI, 3, in *City of God*.
10. In *Epist. ad Rom.*, IV, 60, 415–422.

11. St. Thomas Aquinas, *Summa Theologica*, Vol. II (Quest. 154, Art. 12, Obj. 4).
12. In ten years the *Journal of the American Psychiatric Association* published less than an article a year.
13. "The Unspeakable Crime," *Time*, November 16, 1953, p. 36.
14. "A Delicate Problem," *Newsweek*, June 14, 1954, p. 99. Actually today (1965) 49 states and the District of Columbia punish overt acts.
15. "The Unspeakable Crime," *loc. cit.*, quoting the *London Times*.
16. Herbert Weinstock, *Tchaikovsky* (New York: Alfred A. Knopf, 1943), p. 123.
17. *Encyclopaedia Britannica* (1961 ed.), Vol. XXIII, p. 596.
18. "The Unspeakable Crime," *loc. cit.*
19. "New Shocker," *Newsweek*, May 29, 1950, p. 18.
20. "Homosexuality in America," *Life* (International), Vol. XXXVII, No. 2, pp. 44–58.
21. "Homosexuals in Uniform," *Newsweek*, June 9, 1947, p. 54.
22. Tudor Rees and Harley V. Usill, *They Stand Apart* (New York: The Macmillan Co., 1955), p. 80.
23. K. Bowman and B. Engle, "A Psychiatric Evaluation of the Laws of Homosexuality," *The American Journal of Psychiatry*, Vol. 112, No. 8 (February, 1956), pp. 577–578.
24. Bailey, *op. cit.*, p. 118.
25. George Hagmaier, C.S.P., and Robert Gleason, S.J., *Counselling the Catholic* (New York: Sheed and Ward, 1959), p. 94.
26. Quoted by Berg and Allen, *op. cit.*, pp. 20–21.
27. Magnus Hirschfeld, *Die Homosexualitat des Mannes und des Weibes* (2 ed.) (Berlin: L. Marcus Verladsbuchjandlung, 1920). Quoted by Kinsey *et al.*, *Sexual Behavior in the Human Male* (Philadelphia and London: W. B. Saunders Company, 1948), p. 619.
28. A. C. Kinsey *et al.*, *Sexual Behavior of the Human Male* (Philadelphia: Saunders, 1948), p. 624.
29. United States Statistical Abstract, 1958 (81st annual edition), prepared under the direction of Edwin D. Goldfield, Chief, Statistical Reports Division, U. S. Department of Commerce (U. S. Government Printing Office, Washington, D. C.).
30. K. B. Davis, *Factors in the Sexual Life of 2200 Women* (New York: Harper, 1929).
31. G. V. Hamilton, *Research in Marriage* (New York: A. C. Boni, 1929).
32. G. V. Ramsey, "The Sexual Development of Boys," *The American Journal of Psychiatry*, Vol. 56 (1943), pp. 217–234.
33. F. W. Finger, "Sex Beliefs and Practices Among Male College Students," *Journal of Abnormal and Social Psychology*, Vol. 42 (1947), pp. 57–67.
34. G. Th. Kempe, "The Homosexual in Society," *The British Journal of Delinquency*, Vol. V (1954–1955), pp. 4–20.
35. Quoted in Robert W. Laidlaw, "A Clinical Approach to Homosexuality," *Marriage and Family Living*, Vol. XIV, No. 1 (February, 1952), pp. 39–45.
36. The British Government in 1954 appointed a "Committee on Homosexual Offences and Prostitution." This committee, which published its report in 1957, was known informally as the *Wolfenden Committee*.
37. Paul Waring and Dean Travis Bryce, "Homosexual Freedom," privately published, 1961, p. 5.
38. John F. Oliven, M.D., *Sexual Hygiene and Pathology* (Philadelphia and Montreal: J. B. Lippincott Company, 1955), pp. 430–431.
39. Rev. Charles Larere, "Passage of the Angel Through Sodom," in *New Problems in Medical Ethics*, Dom Peter Flood, O.S.B. (ed.) (Westminster, Md.: Newman Press, 1953), Vol. I, p. 108.
40. John F. Harvey, O.S.F.S., *Theological Studies*, Vol. XVI (March, 1955), p. 86.

Definitions

HOMOSEXUALITY

Before attempting to decide exactly what constitutes homosexuality, it is important to emphasize that until recently practically nothing was known of the *state of being a homosexual,* although there was knowledge of homosexual acts. The derivation of the term itself was not known. The term *homo* is from the Greek meaning "same," not from the Latin *homo* meaning "man." Since only homosexual acts were known, it led to the belief that all homosexual individuals were perverts. This is not the case. Homosexuals may be perverted, but they are not necessarily so. A *pervert* is an individual, homosexual or heterosexual, who finds his complete sexual satisfaction in a manner which deviates from the usual or accepted way of performing the sex act. It differs, for example, from the way in which the sex act is performed in the society or culture in which the individual lives. In ordinary usage among Catholics, it would also refer to those acts which in a positive way exclude procreation.

It is important to realize that perversion refers to complete physical satisfaction, not merely to the use of various means of sensory stimulation for sexual arousal which are often employed as preliminaries to sex acts. It is not perversion, for example, when any act which is desired or acceptable to both male and female partners is employed as part of the sex play prior to sexual intercourse. This is true only as long as the act ends with the deposition of the semen in the vault of the vagina in such a way that there is no interference with penile-vaginal intercourse.

A homosexual, therefore, is not a pervert, unless he performs perverse acts; that is to say, the chaste homosexual should not be considered a pervert. It is important to accept the concept that *homosexuality is a way of thinking and feeling; not merely a way of acting.* The performance of homosexual acts is, therefore, not, in itself, evidence of homosexuality. As I will explain in a future

17

clinic, homosexuality is not a disease entity but is merely a symptom of a personality disorder (see Clinic 3). Salzman expresses this same thought:

> A definition in terms of behavior is preferable, since homosexuality is a symptom of underlying personality distortion and not of a single integrated psychiatric syndrome.[1]

More of this later. The condition, however, is sufficiently clear-cut as a behavior disorder that it may be defined and described *per se*.

Definition

As a working definition, *homosexuality may be defined as a persistent, postadolescent state in which the sexual object is a person of the same sex and in which there is a concomitant aversion or abhorrence, in varying degrees, to sexual relations with members of the opposite sex.*

This aversion and abhorrence should not be understood to mean a total absence of ability to have heterosexual relations on the part of all homosexuals. It is not uncommon to see an individual who is known to be a homosexual pushing a baby carriage. Even in the presence of disgust and revulsion one may carry out an unpleasant task, and although with practice it may become more tolerable, as long as the condition persists it never becomes wholly acceptable. In the case of the homosexual the task may become more acceptable by fantasying a homosexual companion. Disgust and aversion for heterosexual contacts will persist, especially in the male homosexual, as long as he is an invert.

Oliven emphasizes these feelings of aversion:

> These men are attracted exclusively toward men. Erotic situations involving an attractive woman leave them indifferent or even fill them with repugnance or vague fear.[2]

The term "homosexuality" is often used indiscriminately to include such nonsexual concepts as dependency, aggression, competition, domination, and submission. The term should, however, be restricted only to behavior which has orgiastic satisfaction as its object.[3]

Another definition of homosexuality is given by Anomaly. Since frequent references will be made to this book, I would like to call attention to the fact that the name "Anomaly" is a pseudonym used by the author of a small book called *The Invert*. It was published by the Williams and Wilkins Company of Baltimore (1948). Anomaly states that he is a male homosexual who is a Catholic. The book gives excellent insights into homosexuality from the standpoint of a nonprofessional homosexual. It is a book which could be recommended to the homosexual for his own use.

Anomaly gives this definition:

A homosexual person (or invert) is one who, though apparently physically normal, is entirely unsusceptible to the sexual and emotional attraction of the opposite sex, but is susceptible to the sexual and emotional attraction of his, or her, own sex.[4]

Another definition is that given by The Group for the Advancement of Psychiatry:

Homosexuality is a sexual pattern in which there is an erotic interest in one's own sex, replacing to a greater or lesser degree heterosexual interest and behavior. An individual should be considered to be a homosexual, who after adolescence repeatedly or exclusively prefers sexual activity with the same sex.[5]

Reverend William Tobin, a canon lawyer, offers this definition:

Homosexuality may be described as that condition of psychosexual immaturity characterized by a predominant erotic attraction for a sexual object of the same sex. It constitutes a sexual anomaly that is not an either-or condition but admits of great variations. Le Moal has indicated that erotic attraction for the same sex is the *conditio-sine-qua-non* of this disorder. In its rare, extreme form, this condition includes a complete absence of attraction towards the opposite sex together with a concomitant positive disgust for sexual relations with the opposite sex.[6]

Dr. Oliven emphasizes other aspects of the homosexual state:

This is a chronic, usually life-long disorder of the total personality, although in a number of cases its only apparent manifestation is the abnormal direction of the sex drive. Homosexuality is basically a medical (probably chiefly psychiatric) problem. But because of its relative incurability, the fairly frequent tendency of these patients to seduce others, and because of the almost instinctive animosity the homosexual inspires in many normal people, in practice it has remained rather more a social than a strictly medical problem.[7]

Classification of Homosexuality

You may ask, is there more than one type of homosexual? This question is difficult to answer because by the definition given it would appear that homosexuals are an autonomous group. Even within

that group we could, however, specify several subgroups; for example:
1. Adolescent pseudohomosexuals
2. Active adult homosexuals
3. Passive adult homosexuals
4. Chaste homosexuals

Laidlaw describes these psychological types of homosexuals:

1a. Promiscuous: needs a different partner each time he commits the act, and has no use for one after the act.
1b. Faithful to a complete involvement with only one person — comparable to heterosexual love.
2a. Purely physical expression — act is tossed off and forgotten.
2b. Deep feeling and love — really meaningful to the individual.
3a. No conflict in personality.
3b. Violent conflict in personality.[8]

Homosexuals are usually classified as:
1. *True homosexuals,* also called manifest, obligatory, exclusive homosexuals.[9]
2. *Pseudohomosexuals,* sometimes also called bisexuals, ambisexuals, facultative, substitute, or circumstantial homosexuals.
3. *Constitutional homosexuals.*

True homosexuality or psychosexual homosexuality is the condition defined above. True homosexuals have no real sexual interest in members of the opposite sex. They may, however, seek them out as intellectual or social companions. This condition is usually considered to be acquired in early life and to be psychogenic in nature. *It is this condition with which we are concerned when discussing the homosexual state.*

Pseudohomosexuality, sometimes erroneously called *bisexuality,* is a condition in which the individual so affected may be sexually interested in members of both sexes. It occurs usually when he is isolated from the preferred sex and because of a strong, poorly discriminating sex drive, he may sexually accept either sex. This is most likely to occur in prisons, isolated military posts, and similar situations. This is not true homosexuality and resembles it only in its externals. Such individuals usually prefer the heterosexual object if it is available. The term *bisexual* is derived from the biological fact that the urogenital tracts of the two sexes derive from a common embryonic origin. Because the embryo contained cell material from the glands of both sexes it was originally called *hermaphroditic.* This unfortunate description opened the door to indiscriminate speculation on man's bisexuality and appeared to offer a scientific basis for an explanation of homosexuality. Krafft-Ebing (1840–1903) adopted this idea and introduced it into psychiatry. In 1905 when Freud published his "Contributions to the Theory of Sex," he followed the lead of Krafft-Ebing. Freud later changed some of his ideas, and as late as 1933 he stated that he had merely "carried over the notion of bisexuality into the mental life."[10] This biological concept has withered away and is seldom seriously considered, at the present time, as representative of the genesis of homosexuality (see Clinic 4).

Constitutional homosexuality is a term used by those who feel that the condition is inborn or hereditary. There is little or no scientific proof of this theory.

Definitions

Before proceeding further with a discussion of homosexuality, it is important to pause briefly for the unpleasant but necessary task of defining some terms. These are terms which are requisite for an understanding of our future clinics as well as for an easier comprehension of the books and articles which should be read to extend your knowledge of this subject. These definitions should be committed to memory, but for the time being, until you have done so, they will be listed alphabetically for ease of reference.

Absolute inversion. Freud speaks of those who are "absolutely inverted; i.e., their sexual object must always be of the same sex, while the opposite sex can never be to them an object of sexual longing, but leaves them indifferent or . . . may even evoke sexual repugnance."[11]

Active homosexual. This term refers to the more aggressive homosexual partner who usually assumes the male role, the one who instigates the act, the one who makes the first suggestion.

Amphigenous inversion. Certain individuals are "amphigenously inverted (psychosexually hermaphroditic); i.e., their sexual object may belong indifferently to either the same or to the other sex. The inversion lacks here the character of exclusiveness."[12] These have been described as pseudohomosexuals or bisexuals.

Anomaly, sexual. See *Perversion (sexual).*

Buggery. A legal term still commonly used in England although archaic in the United States. It refers to the insertion of the penis into the anus or rubbing it between the folds of the buttocks. When the penis is that of an adult, and the anus is that of a child, the perversion is called "pederasty."

Cunnilingus. The practice of applying the lips, tongue, or mouth to the vulva or to any part of the external genital organs of the female. This may serve as a source of complete satisfaction to the one who employs the practice.

Patient I is an American-born, European-educated white male of 45 years. He is married, but has no children. His best description sexually is that he is a "hard-core homosexual." He is well educated and perceptive. He was given a copy of this manuscript to read and he made some comments about it. In regard to cunnilingus he said:

> I find more and more men indulging in this, until it becomes the whole end in itself of the sex act, and would like to note that these men are very often homosexuals, who from this kind of relation with women come to men. I suppose the desire to do this is in itself a sign of latent homosexuality. I have so often run into this type who gives one a vivid picture of the pleasure he gets from this act with women, but unfortunately it is not always easy to arrive at, as many women object, but one can do the same with men.

Exhibitionism. Exhibitionism is the derivation of sexual pleasure or gratification from the display of the genitals to another person. In many cases the preference is for this person to be a child. By modification, to make the exhibition more socially acceptable, the tendency may be unconsciously displaced from the genitals to the body as a whole, to clothes, to dramatics, etc. The person to whom the tendency is directed may be either homosexual or heterosexual, depending on the orientation of the exhibitor.

Fellatio (Mod. L. — *fellare,* "to suck."). Fellatio is the application of the mouth to the penis. The mucous membrane of the lips and mouth were regarded by Freud as a primary erotogenic zone. "An intense activity of this erotogenic zone at an early age thus determines the subsequent presence of a somatic compliance on the part of the tract of mucous membrane which begins at the lips." The original object of the lips and mouth is the nipple. "It then needs very little creative power to substitute the sexual object of the moment (the penis) for the original object (the nipple) or for the finger which did duty for it later on, and to place the current sexual object in the situation in which gratification was originally obtained. So we see that this excessively repulsive and perverted phantasy of sucking at a penis has the most innocent origin."[13]

Fellator. One who practices fellatio.

Fellator, self (autofellatio). The practice of putting the male genital organ into the individual's own mouth. "While he occasionally practices self-irrumination (self-fellatio) to relieve sexual tension that has already been aroused, he more often employs it to stimulate sexual excitement in himself."[14]

Fellatrice. A female who takes the oral part in fellatio.

Fetishism. This is a condition in which the individual gains sexual satisfaction by contact with, or possession of, a part of the clothing or portion of the body of the loved object. This erotic feeling may be heterosexual or homosexual. The fetish may be used as a means of sexual stimulation or as a sexual object in itself. For example, a lock of hair may be held in the same esteem as would be the person from whom it is taken.

Hermaphrodite. A *true hermaphrodite* is an individual who has the complete sex glands of both sexes and frequently the external organs of both sexes as well. A *pseudohermaphrodite* is one in whom, although there may be the external organs of both sexes, the glands of only one sex are present. There is no necessary relation between homosexuality and hermaphroditism.

Homosexual panic (also called Kempff's Disease). An acute schizophrenic-like episode characterized by intense fear, marked excitement, and paranoid ideas, usually of short duration, occurring in individuals whose homosexuality is unconscious.

Incest. A term for sexual relations between persons related within the degrees wherein marriage is prohibited by law. It may be homosexual or heterosexual.

Inversion. A term used for homosexuality indicating that the sex drive has been turned to the self-sex. The expression "sexual inversion" is usually used today in psychiatry in its psychoanalytic sense:

> The popular theory of the sexual instinct corresponds closely to the poetic fable of dividing the person into two halves — man and woman — who strive to become reunited through love. It is, therefore, very surprising to find that there are men for whom the sexual object is not the woman but the man, and that there are women for whom it is not man but woman. Such persons are designated as contrary sexuals, or better, inverts, and the situation of such a relationship is called inversion.[15]

A few writers reserve the words "invert" and "inversion" for a special use: for them, an invert is an individual who desires or seeks homosexual relations and at the same time tries to adopt the complete sex role of a member of the other sex.[16]

> In spite of the work of Kinsey and others there has been an attempt to divide homosexuals into "inverts" and "perverts." This was put forward in the Church of England's *The Problem of Homosexuality* in 1954, and was used by the counselor in the Montague trial. It was suggested that "an invert is a man who from accident or birth has unnatural desires . . . whereas a pervert is a man who either from lust or wickedness will get desires for either natural or unnatural functions."[17]

The Wolfenden Report comments:

> Some writers on the subject, and some of our witnesses, have drawn a distinction between the "invert" and the "pervert." We have not found this distinction very useful. It suggests that it is possible to distinguish between two men who commit the same offense, the one as the result of his constitution, and the other from a perverse and deliberate choice, with the further suggestion that the former is in some sense less culpable than the latter. To make this distinction as a matter of definition seems to prejudge a very difficult question.[18]

In spite of these comments I shall use the terms "homosexual" and "invert" and "homosexuality" and "inversion" as synonyms.

Kempff's Disease. See *Homosexual panic.*

Latent homosexuality. This term is usually used to indicate a tendency to, or a condition of, homosexuality of which the individual affected is not fully conscious. There has been a good deal of discussion lately as to the real significance of the term which will be discussed later (see Clinic 6).

Lesbian. This term is used for the female homosexual. It derives from the ancient inhabitants of the Island of Lesbos in the Aegean Sea who were said to favor homosexuality.

Masturbation. Masturbation refers to all forms of sexual self-gratification. The impulse to such an act may occur as the result of psychic stimuli, either homosexual or heterosexual, or local physical stimulation of the genital parts. It occurs in both sexes at all ages. Masturbation is not uncommon in small children. Many writers believe that the practice is universal, but there is no proof of this. It is more frequent in boys than in girls. In small infants, the process should not be called masturbation because it has nothing specifically to do with sex but is merely part of the child's exploration of his body. He finds a part which is pleasurable when touched and consequently he tends to touch it repeatedly because of the pleasure involved. Forcible attempts at repression of masturbation may lead to thumb-sucking, nail-biting, tics, or other neurotic disorders, among which might be the development of compulsive masturbation. Masturbation is more frequent in women after middle life and in males during adolescence.

Masturbation may be solitary or be performed with one or more partners. The latter form is referred to as mutual masturbation. It is probably the most common sexual practice between female homosexuals.

Overt homosexuality. A condition in which the individual consciously thinks, feels, and may act in a homosexual manner.

Paraphilia. Another term for sexual perversion (q.v.).

Passive homosexual. This is the partner who is acted upon, who assumes the passive, female role. This term must not be taken to indicate that a homosexual is necessarily always either active or passive. The roles may be interchangeable. An individual may be active at one time and passive at another. A passive homosexual may be more a source of disturbance than the one who is more aggressive, because he is responsive to the demands made on him. Such individuals have a seductive attractiveness while retaining the appearance of innocence.

Perversions, sexual (also called sex deviations, paraphilias, or psychosexual abnormalities). Methods of sex gratification, mainly or exclusively, without penile-vaginal intercourse. Perversion may occur by the individual's selection of an abnormal sexual object or by engaging in abnormal relations with a usual sex object.[19]

Since the term "perversion" carries with it a connotation of serious basic psychopathology, it would be helpful in many cases to employ a term less suggestive of pathology. *Sexual anomaly* is surely a more meaningful term. Behavior in the sexual sphere that deviates rather sharply from the average is not necessarily pathological. The term *sexual anomaly* is proposed as a substitute for "sexual perversion," on the ground that evidence is lacking that perversions are intrinsically pathological and that a less condemnatory term is socially desirable. This term must be distinguished from sex anomaly which refers properly to anatomical deviation.[20]

Sapphism. This term is derived from the name of Sappho, a native of Lesbos. It is a less commonly used term for female homosexuality.

Sodomy. This term is probably derived from Sodom, an ancient Palestinian city which was destroyed, according to Genesis 18 and 19, because of the prevalence there of unnatural sex relations. The term today is most commonly used to designate *coitus per anum*, performed between homosexual partners. It may, however, take place between heterosexual partners, so it is not, therefore, an exclusively homosexual act. If it is performed with a person of the same sex, it is called — by the moralists — perfect sodomy; when it occurs between persons of the opposite sex, imperfect sodomy. In some modern texts the term is used for *coitus of humans with animals.*[21] A better and more commonly used term for this is bestiality (see *Buggery,* p. 21).

Transsexualism. An extreme form of transvestitism where in addition to cross-dressing, the wish for emasculation is present (see p. 95).

Transvestitism. A condition in which the subject prefers to wear the clothes and live the life of the opposite sex. It may be, but is not always, associated with overt homosexuality. In some instances, however, the mere wearing of the clothing satisfies the individual's erotic needs (see p. 93).

Tribadism. A term frequently used to indicate female homosexuality. More specifically it refers to a practice consisting of the mutual friction of the genitals between women.

Voyeurism is a condition in which the individual derives sexual pleasure or gratification by looking at the genitals of another. The *voyeur* is known as a "peeping Tom." This condition is also known as scopophilia. It may be homosexually, as well as heterosexually, directed.

Although this list in not exhaustive, it includes most of the terms ordinarily used. For other terms reference should be made to a standard psychiatric dictionary such as that published by Leland E. Hinsie, M.D., and Jacob Shatsky, Ph.D.,[22] from which some of the above definitions were taken.

Homosexual Jargon

In addition to these technical terms, some colloquialisms may be of value for understanding the language used by inverts in reference to sex. Alphabetically listed, some of these terms are:

Busted. Arrested.

Butch. Usually used in the sense of "be butch," i.e., to act masculine. Occasionally used to refer to a masculine type of Lesbian.

Camp it up. To act "gay" without inhibitions.

Camping. To flaunt the mannerisms of the other sex.

Cruising. Looking for a "pickup," whether because of lonesomeness or for purposes of prostitution.

Dike or *dyke.* A Lesbian.

Drag. Dressed and made up like a woman.

Drag act. A vaudeville act of female impersonators.

Drag balls. Dances to which guests may come dressed as women.

Fag. A derogatory term for a homosexual.

Faggot. An obvious homosexual.

Fairy. A derogatory term for a homosexual.

Gay. A term frequently used as a synonym for homosexual — sometimes used in the sense of "be gay" or to act effeminately.

Gay trade. One in which many homosexuals may be employed, e.g., hairdressing.

Pansy. A derogatory term for a homosexual.

Pimp. A procurer.

Queen. A transvestite.

Screaming queen. A very obvious queen.

Square. A heterosexual.

Straight. To act like a heterosexual; to be a heterosexual.

Swish. A derogatory term for a homosexual.

Summary

This is an important clinic. There is so much difference of opinion about homosexuality that there will probably be authors who will disagree with some of the definitions given. Those given, however, should be studied carefully to understand future clinics.

CLINIC 2 — NOTES

1. Leon Salzman, "The Concept of Latent Homosexuality," *American Journal of Psychoanalysis,* Vol. XVII, No. 2 (1957), p. 167.
2. John F. Oliven, M.D., *Sexual Hygiene and Pathology* (Philadelphia and Montreal: J. B. Lippincott Company, 1955), p. 431.
3. Lionel Ovesey, "The Homosexual Conflict," *Psychiatry,* Vol. XVII, No. 3 (August, 1954), p. 245.
4. Anomaly, *The Invert* (Baltimore: Williams and Wilkins Company, 1948), p. 6.
5. "Report on Homosexuality With Particular Emphasis on This Problem in Governmental Agencies," compiled by the Group for the Advancement of Psychiatry

(3617 W. 6th Ave., Topeka, Kansas), Report No. 30, January, 1955.

6. Rev. William J. Tobin, *Homosexuality and Marriage* (Rome: The Catholic Book Agency, 1964), pp. 22–23.

7. Oliven, *op. cit.*, p. 430.

8. Robert W. Laidlaw, "A Clinical Approach to Homosexuality," *Marriage and Family Living*, Vol. XIV, No. 1 (February, 1952), p. 42.

9. Oesterle states that homosexuality is such that in relation to persons of the opposite sex the subject is absolutely impotent (Gerard Oesterle, "De Relatione Homosexualitatis ad Matrimonium," *Revista Espanola de Derecho Canonico*, X [1955], No. 28, p. 23). The term will not be used in this sense in this text. It will be considered as a synonym of "true" inversion.

10. Sigmund Freud, *New Introductory Lectures on Psycho-analysis*, Lecture 33 in volume on The Major Works of Sigmund Freud in Great Books of the Western World (Chicago: Encyclopaedia Britannica, Inc., 1952), p. 854.

11. Sigmund Freud, *The Basic Writings of Sigmund Freud*, trans. A. A. Brill (New York: Random House, 1938). Quoted by Leland E. Hinsie, M.D., and Jacob Shatsky, Ph.D., *Psychiatric Dictionary* (New York: Oxford University Press, 1953), p. 304.

12. *Ibid.*

13. Sigmund Freud, *Collected Papers*, Vol. III, trans. A. and J. Strachey, London: Leonard and Virginia Woolf, 1952, quoted by Leland E. Hinsie, M.D., and Jacob Shatzky, Ph.D., *Psychiatric Dictionary* (New York: Oxford University Press, 1953), p. 222.

14. E. Kahn and E. G. Lion, *American Journal of Psychiatry*, Vol. XCV (1935), p. 132.

15. *The Basic Writings of Sigmund Freud*, quoted by Hinsie and Shatsky, *op. cit.*, p. 304.

16. *The Encyclopedia of Sexual Behavior*, Albert Ellis and Albert Abarbanel (eds.) (New York: Hawthorn Books, Inc., 1961), Vol. I, p. 485.

17. Clifford Allen, *A Textbook of Psychosexual Disorders* (London: Oxford University Press, 1962), p. 172.

18. *The Wolfenden Report*, authorized American edition with Introduction by Karl Menninger, M.D. (New York: Stein and Day, 1963), pp. 35–36.

19. Ellis and Abarbanel, *op. cit.*, Vol. II, p. 802.

20. English and English, *A Comprehensive Dictionary of Psychological and Psychoanalytical Terms* (New York: Longmans, Green and Company, 1958), p. 498.

21. Hinsie and Shatsky, *op. cit.*, p. 493.

22. *Loc. cit.*, fn. 11.

Is Homosexuality a Disease?

What is homosexuality? A disease? A symptom? A neurosis? A personality disorder? Answers to these questions vary. I have myself over the years held different opinions. That which I express at this time probably represents my final conclusion. My present opinion is that homosexuality is not a disease *per se* but represents a defective development of the personality with a fixation of the libido at an early age of development.

Some physicians look on the invert as a sick person. If this is so, then the invert would constitute only a medical problem. They make this assertion, although they offer no proof that homosexuality constitutes either a physical or psychological disease. Implicit in this opinion is the belief that since the invert is ill, he has little or no control over the developed malady (see Clinic 16).

In recent years this tendency to regard homosexuality as a disease is being more generally accepted. This is in line with the tendency of some psychiatrists and psychologists to teach that those who habitually break the law, whether moral or civil, are mentally ill.[1] This then would lead to the conclusion that there is no such thing as an immoral person or a criminal, but only a mentally ill or mentally healthy one. As Barbara Wooten says, "The concept of illness expands continually at the expense of the concept of moral failure."[2]

There are also the words of Pope Pius XII, speaking to the psychotherapists in April, 1953, to be considered. The Holy Father repudiated the *general* rule that passion excludes subjective guilt and subjective responsibility. He stated at that time: "It cannot be alleged that the psychic troubles and disorders which disturb the normal functioning of a psychic being represent what usually happens."[3]

Such general assumptions as these repudiated by the Holy Father have entered not only the field of civil law in the United States but also the theological writings of at least one French author. The Durham Decision of the United States Court of Appeals for the Dis-

trict of Columbia is a case of the former. In this instance an attempt
was made to improve upon the "M'Naughton Rule" which has been
widely used for over a hundred years as the criterion for determining
the responsibility of individuals who were mentally ill (Rex *vs.*
M'Naughton, House of Lords Cases, 1843). The danger of the
Durham Decision is that it opens the door too wide. It allows a
psychiatrist to testify to any theory which he may hold. It then leaves
to his persuasive effect upon the jury whether the individual is to
be considered irresponsible or not. It offers nothing specific for the
jury to consider.

One such opinion in the field of Catholic theology was that of
Abbé Marc Oraison whose book, *Vie chretienne et problemes de la
sexualite,* was placed upon the Index of Forbidden Books less than
a year after it was published — although the publication of the fact
of condemnation was not made known until two years later (January,
1955). During this time, to the credit of the Abbé, he had withdrawn
the book from publication and signified through the press his acceptance of the Church's decision. According to his theory:

> Almost all of mankind is so sexually immature and dominated by
> passions, that it may be taken as a general rule that sexual sins must
> be presumed to be only materially grave and thus the person is not
> subjectively guilty.[4]

From this it is evident that the action and reaction brought about
by the teachings of Luther are still being felt within Western culture.
It is only in this framework that one can appreciate the convictions
that are so evident in the field of modern criminology and psychiatry
and almost necessarily in moral theology. Kierkegaard has seen this
and put it to use, although it seems that he has reached what might
be termed the religion-centered extreme with the conclusion that
"only the saint may be called immune against neurosis."[5] The counselor, too, must see this background and be able to judge particular
problems accordingly.

Not all share this view that homosexuality is a disease. Father
Buckley states: "Homosexuality, therefore, is most certainly not a
disease."[6]

Clara Thompson, who shared Harry Stack Sullivan's views, regarded the term "homosexual" as "a wastebasket to which all friendly
and hostile feelings towards members of one's sex are applied." She
considered homosexuality not as a specific entity having characteristic

determinants but only as a symptom of a character problem. In this opinion she and Sullivan are not alone.[7]

According to Dr. Thompson:

> . . . homosexuality is not a clinical entity, but a symptom with different meanings in different personality set-ups. One might compare its place in the neurosis to that of a headache in various diseases. A headache may be the result of a brain tumor, a sinus, a beginning infectious disease, a migraine attack, an emotional disturbance, or a blow on the head. When the underlying disease is treated successfully, the headache disappears.
>
> Similarly, overt homosexuality may express fear of the opposite sex, fear of adult responsibility, a need to defy authority, or an attempt to cope with hatred or of competitive attitudes to members of one's own sex; it may represent a flight from reality into absorption into body stimulation very similar to the autoerotic activities of the schizophrenic, or it may be a symptom of destructiveness of oneself or others. These do not exhaust the possibilities of its meanings.[8]

THE WOLFENDEN REPORT

The Wolfenden Report was presented to the British Parliament by command of her Majesty Elizabeth II. A work of enormous compassion as well as social and psychological insight, *The Wolfenden Report* was written under the auspices of a committee of public persons drawn from the clergy, medicine, sociology, psychology, and the law, and headed by Sir John Wolfenden, C.B.E. The committee gave the following statement of its purpose:

> 1. We were appointed on 24th August, 1954, to consider:
>   (a) the law and practice relating to homosexual offenses and the treatment of persons convicted of such offenses by the courts; and
>   (b) the law and practice relating to offenses against the criminal law in connection with prostitution and solicitation for immoral purposes, and to report what changes, if any, are in our opinion desirable.[9]

The Wolfenden Report also took the position that homosexuality is not a disease. It pointed out that there is no legal definition of "disease" or of "disease of the mind." The committee also pointed out "ill" health and "good" health are merely relative terms, as are "normal" and "abnormal." The *Report* stated that the mere presence of deviant sexuality in an individual showing no other abnormality was not incompatible with "full mental health." The *Report* further indicated that in those homosexual individuals who showed anxiety or other unpleasant symptoms, the symptoms were not necessarily the result of the condition of homosexuality, but quite likely occurred as the consequence of social attitudes. There is, of course, as the *Report* pointed out, no underlying pathological condition, either organic or psychopathological, which would warrant calling the disorder a "disease." None of the various theories formulated to explain the perversion, the *Report* concluded, is conclusive or specific to it, since the postulated or etiologic factors are also found in other psychopathological states.

> There is clear-cut situation in which (homosexuality) invariably occurs. It appears as a symptom in people of diverse types of character structure.[10]

THE AMERICAN PSYCHIATRIC ASSOCIATION

The Diagnostic Nomenclature of the American Psychiatric Association classifies homosexuality under "Personality Disorders." For the sake of those who may not have this text readily available to them, I shall quote rather extensively from the manual so that it can be seen where the diagnosis of homosexuality fits into the classification. It is important to have a clear concept of personality disorders and to distinguish them from neuroses. Unfortunately, there has not been a new edition of this nomenclature since 1952. It is possible that when it is reissued some changes will be made.

PERSONALITY DISORDERS

These disorders are characterized by developmental defects or pathological trends in the personality structure, with minimal subjective anxiety, and little or no sense of distress. In most instances, the disorder is manifested by mental or emotional symptoms. Occasionally, organic diseases of the brain (epidemic encephalitis, head injury, Alzheimer's Disease, etc.) will produce clinical pictures resembling a personality disorder. In such instances, the condition is properly diagnosed as a Chronic Brain Syndrome (of appropriate origin) with behavioral reaction.
. . . Although the groupings are largely descriptive, the division has been made partially on the basis of the dynamics of personality development. The personality pattern disturbances are considered deep seated disturbances, with little room for regression. Personality trait disturbances and sociopathic disturbances under stress may at times regress to a lower level of personality organization and function without development of psychosis.[11]

Personality Disorders are divided into three types:
1. Personality Pattern Disturbance

      2. Personality Trait Disturbance
      3. Sociopathic Personality Disturbance

1. *Personality Pattern Disturbance* (000–x40)

These are more or less cardinal personality types, which can rarely if ever be altered in their inherent structures by any form of therapy. Their functioning may be improved by prolonged therapy, but basic change is seldom accomplished. In some, "constitutional" features are marked and obvious. The depth of the psychopathology here allows these individuals little room to maneuver under conditions of stress, except into actual psychosis. It is subdivided into:

Inadequate Personality (000–x41)

Schizoid Personality (000–x42)

Cyclothymic Personality (000–x43)

Paranoid Personality (000–x44)

2. *Personality Trait Disturbance* (000–x50)

This category applies to individuals who are unable to maintain their emotional equilibrium and independence under minor or major stress because of disturbances in emotional development. Some individuals fall into this group because their personality pattern disturbance is related to fixation and exaggeration of certain character and behavior patterns; others, because their behavior is a regressive reaction due to environmental or endopsychic stress.

This classification will be applied only to cases of personality disorder in which the neurotic features (such as anxiety, conversion, phobia, etc.) are relatively insignificant, and the basic personality maldevelopment is the crucial distinguishing factor. Evidence of physical immaturity may or may not be present. It is subdivided into:

Emotionally Unstable Personality (000–x51)

Passive-Aggressive Personality (000–x52)

Compulsive Personality (000–x53)

Personality Trait Disturbance, Other (000–x54)

3. *Sociopathic Personality Disturbance* (000–x60)

Individuals to be placed in this category are ill primarily in terms of society and of conformity with the prevailing cultural milieu, and not only in terms of personal discomfort and relations with other individuals. However, sociopathic reactions are very often symptomatic of severe underlying personality disorder, neurosis, or psychosis, or occur as the result of organic brain injury or disease. Before a definitive diagnosis in this group is employed, strict attention must be paid to the possibility of the presence of a more primary personality disturbance; such underlying disturbance will be diagnosed when recognized. Reactions will be differentiated as defined below.

Antisocial Reaction (000–x61)

Dyssocial Reaction (000–x62)

Sexual Deviation (000–x63)

This diagnosis [Sexual Deviation] is reserved for deviant sexuality which is not symptomatic of more extensive syndromes, such as schizophrenic or obsessional reactions. [See p. 99.] The term includes most of the cases formerly classed as "psychopathic personality with pathologic sexuality." The diagnosis will specify the type of the pathologic behavior, such as homosexuality, transvestism, pedophilia, fetishism and sexual sadism (including rape, sexual assault, mutilation).[12]

THE KINSEY REPORT

This opinion of the American Psychiatric Association — that homosexuality in itself provides evidence of a psychopathic personality — is challenged, according to the Kinsey Report on the male, by the incidence and frequency data which they elicited. They comment:

> Of the 40 or 50 percent of the male population which has homosexual experience, certainly a high proportion would not be considered psychopathic personalities on the basis of anything else in their histories. It is argued that an individual that is so obtuse to social reactions as to continue his homosexual activity and make it any material portion of his life, therein evidences some social incapacity; but psychiatrists and clinicians in general might very well re-examine their justification for demanding that all persons conform to particular patterns of behavior.

Kinsey adds that there are, of course, some persons with homosexual histories "who are neurotic and in constant difficulty with themselves and not infrequently with society." But he points out that this is also true of heterosexual individuals:

> Some homosexual individuals are so upset that they have difficulty in the accomplishment of their business or professional obligations and reach the point where they find it difficult to make the simplest sort of social contact without friction.

He argues, however, that there is a considerable question, as indicated by Bieber, that these persons are neurotic, and that if they are, their neurotic disturbances are the product of society's reaction to them rather than the result of their sexual behavior.[13]

OTHER OPINIONS

Allen points out that "homosexuality is not the opposite of heterosexuality — as so many people imagine — but a phase in development which some people find it difficult to pass."[14] This, he states, explains the fact that homosexuality is so often found with other sexual abnormalities which are themselves the residues of earlier developmental phases. The oral and anal interests shown by such individuals are only signs of incomplete evolution of the personality.

According to Ovesey, Freud concluded that homosexuality was not a neurosis. Freud's theory of instincts and the libido theory held that neurotic symptoms represented the repression of perverse infantile sexual impulses. "If no repression occurred, the perverse impulses remained conscious, and found direct expression without displacement." This, Ovesey states, led Freud to one of his earliest conclusions, that "neurosis is the negative of a perversion," a dictum which of necessity excluded homosexuality from the neuroses and also, at least, from the realm of psychoanalytic therapy, "since only neuroses were believed susceptible to psychoanalysis."[15]

To better understand how the sexual impulse becomes deviated from its normal adult heterosexual orientation, an understanding of the Freudian concept of sexuality will be helpful. This is admittedly only a hypothetical construct, but it helps to make understandable how the personality can develop in a way compatible with mental health and yet be associated with deviant sexuality.

FREUDIAN CONCEPT OF THE DEVELOPMENT OF SEXUALITY

The hypothesis for the development of sexuality as described by Freud and his followers is probably the best known and most easily understood. Freud was impressed by the frequency with which his patients' productions had a sexual significance. The more he investigated these, the more he was led to the belief that neurotic manifestations were due to conflicts between sexual impulses and resistance to the acceptance of these impulses. Freud's study of the reasons for repression of sexuality led him back to very early childhood, and he concluded that early sexual traumata formed the basis of later neurotic disturbances. He published these findings in 1905 under the title *Three Contributions to the Theories of Sex.*[16]

The Freudian concept of sexuality, particularly his ideas on the oedipal situation, forms an important basis of present thought. It is, therefore, important to discuss this in some detail because it will lead to a better understanding of homosexuality. Freud separated the concept of sexuality from the close association it had previously with the genital organs. He felt that it included "all of those merely affectionate and friendly impulses to which usage applied the exceedingly ambiguous word 'love.'"

He considered pleasure as the goal of the sexual function and felt that this function existed from the beginning of life. These sexual feelings, he taught, were at first diffuse and their object was the subject's own body (autoerotic), as, for example, in masturbation. These feelings later become localized in certain erotogenic zones, the first of these areas being the lips. He considered that the pleasure the infant gets from sucking (oral stage) was sexual in nature. In adult life, a fixation at this level may lead to fellatio or cunnilingus. Later the erotogenic zone shifts to the anus where the sensation arises first in the pleasure of giving feces (anal-erotic stage) and later in withholding feces (anal-sadistic stage). In adult life this feeling may persist and result, for example, in a desire for sodomy. The next shift is to the genitals where it is at first unorganized (phallic stage) but later develops into the adult or genital stage. Between the phallic stage and the genital phase is a latent period during which the child is interested in children of the same sex. For this reason, the period is sometimes known as the "homosexual phase." It must be clearly understood that although this is a normal stage of development, a fixation at this level may lead to adult homosexuality.

PERIOD OF SEXUAL LATENCY

This period of sexual latency lasts from about the sixth year to prepuberty. During this period, the child tends to play with children of the same sex. A boy will liberate his aggressive tendencies by playing rough and tumble games such as "cops and robbers," whereas the girl tends to play with dolls and keep house and thereby expresses her desire to replace her mother. Parents frequently traumatize their children by forcing them into each other's company during this period. Mixed parties for children are frequently arranged by parents during this period, much before the boys and girls are ready for it. Parents should wait until the children naturally seek each other's company before they force dating upon them. The latter part of this period is frequently considered as a "normal" homosexual period during which children of the same sex seek each other's company. It must be emphasized that this is a normal situation and should, with the appearance of adolescence, give way to a proper heterosexual orientation. Having a "crush," or the development of an attitude of hero worship toward some admired figure, usually a teacher or clergyman, also frequently occurs during this period. This should lead to no difficulty if the adult is mature and well balanced. The "crush" usually passes very quickly (see p. 85).

Fixation is a term used to indicate a failure to advance to the next stage of development. For example, a child may become fixated at a homosexual level and fail to progress to a normal heterosexual adjustment. On the contrary, a child may advance to a stage of development and then, by a process of regression due to some traumatic episode, become fixated at a lower level. To explain certain neuroses, Freud stated that the libido (the energy of the sexual instincts) does not move smoothly along with the course of development, but that, as a result of traumatic emotional experience, it may become fixated at any level where pleasure was obtained. The stage of libido fixation, if it occurs, determines the choice of the anomaly. Homosexuality is due, according to this theory, to a fixation at or regression to an earlier level of sexual development.[17]

As may be seen from the above, in accordance with his libido theory, Freud considered unconscious homosexuality as a basic factor in neurosis. More recent analysis, however, has led to the conclusion that inversion is simply a manifestation of a more general personality problem. In a given case, instead of being the causal problem, it is merely one of the symptoms of a character problem and becomes less significant as the more general character disturbance is resolved.

CONCLUSIONS

1. Homosexuality is not a disease *per se.*

2. Deviant sexuality, including homosexuality, is the result of a personality or character problem in which the sexual orientation of the individual becomes fixated at an early age.

3. Homosexuality may be a symptom of a neurosis or psychosis, but in such cases it represents the individual's reaction to society or society's reaction to him.

CLINIC 3 — NOTES

1. Robert G. Gassert, S.J., and Bernard H. Hall, M.D., *Psychiatry and Religious Faith* (New York: The Viking Press, 1964).
2. Barbara Wootton, "Sickness or Sin," *The Twentieth Century*, May, 1956.

3. *The Linacre Quarterly*, Vol. XX, No. 4 (November, 1953), p. 99.
4. In John Ford, S.J., and Gerald Kelly, S.J., *Contemporary Moral Theology* (Westminster, Maryland: The Newman Press, 1958), Vol. I, p. 175.
5. Rudolph Allers, *The Homiletic and Pastoral Review*, April, 1942, p. 642.
6. Rev. Michael J. Buckley, *Morality and the Homosexual* (Westminster, Md.: The Newman Press, 1959), p. 153.
7. Irving Bieber *et al.*, *Homosexuality* (New York: Basic Books, Inc., 1962), p. 9.
8. Clara Thompson, "Changing Aspects of Homosexuality in Psychoanalysis," *Psychiatry*, Vol. X (1947), p. 186.
9. *The Wolfenden Report*, authorized American edition with Introduction by Karl Menninger, M.D. (New York: Stein and Day, 1963), p. 19.
10. Thompson, *op. cit.*, p. 184.
11. *Diagnostic and Statistical Manual of Mental Disorders*, prepared by the Committee on Nomenclature and Statistics of the American Psychiatric Association (Washington, D. C.: A.P.A. Mental Hospital Service, 1952), pp. 34–35.
12. *Ibid.*, pp. 38–39.
13. A. C. Kinsey *et al.*, *Sexual Behavior in the Human Male* (Philadelphia: Saunders, 1948), p. 660.
14. Clifford Allen, "The Meaning of Homosexuality," *International Journal of Sexology*, Vol. VI, pp. 207–212 at p. 209.
15. Lionel Ovesey, "The Homosexual Conflict," *Psychiatry*, Vol. XVII, No. 3 (August, 1954), p. 243.
16. In *The Basic Writings of Sigmund Freud*, ed. A. A. Brill (New York: Modern Library, 1938).
17. John R. Cavanagh, M.D., *Fundamental Pastoral Counseling* (Milwaukee: The Bruce Publishing Company, 1962), p. 140.

The Etiology of Homosexuality

Nowhere in the study of homosexuality does the lack of knowledge about it show up as prominently as in efforts to explain its origin. The George W. Henry Foundation found that a high percentage of the overt homosexuals they studied had been introduced to the activity by older and more experienced devotees of the practice.[1] Such initiations may have been an etiological factor in the case of Patient X (see p. 171). The older group were looking for fresh material, just as in heterosexual matters the same experience may be sought. One of our patients was introduced to the practice by a valet who was seducing the children in the neighborhood unknown to the parents of the children. There were, however, other factors present. The actual seduction explains the immediate initiation into the practice, but what I want to show now are the more remote causes which predispose the child, or the adolescent especially, toward the initial act.

A number of etiological factors have been advanced. These may be grouped into three classes: (1) organic factors; (2) genetic factors; and (3) psychological factors.

According to the organic viewpoint, homosexuality arises from an imbalance in endocrine secretions or from some defect in the physical constitution. Evidence for this position was sought in studies of the physique of known homosexuals. Among male homosexuals there seemed to be a slight tendency toward a female build, such as broader hips. However, this same tendency was not found in female homosexuals (see below). Another fact which has been used to advance the organic viewpoint is the comparative lack of androgen secretion in males and estrogen secretion in females. If this reasoning were correct, it would seem, then, that a homosexual male should be cured by an increase in androgen. But numerous experiments have shown that the increase of androgen does not decrease the homosexual drive. It only increases the libido in its initial direction. The evidence from physical characteristics has not been validated.

Some authors, like Krafft-Ebing, taught that homosexuality might arise from several sources. In some cases he said it was an acquired evil. In other cases, it arose from a failure of the sexual components of the body to develop completely.

Magnus Hirschfeld maintained that homosexuals were the result of constitutional factors; and he spent most of his life in a defense of homosexuality on this basis.

George Henry took the evolutional viewpoint. He insisted that psychosexual deviations were merely manifestations or by-products of human evolution. His view is similar to that of Maranon who suggested that homosexuality resulted from imperfect development of the human embryo.

Havelock Ellis held for a congenital predisposition toward homosexuality which is activated by environmental influences. Ellis puts more emphasis on the environmental factors than he does on heredity. Ellis says that the most important factors are psychological. In this respect he shares the opinion of the majority of psychiatrists today.

While most students agree that the dispositive influence is psychological, or at least dominantly so, they disagree on whether emphasis should be placed on instinctual or on environmental factors.

Before discussing the theories about the origin of homosexuality, the old wive's tale that homosexuality may be caused by excessive masturbation by an adolescent should be refuted. This notion is as unfounded as that which states that masturbation may lead to insanity. Masturbation is never a cause of anything physical. It is a symptom of some underlying disturbance.

ORGANIC FACTORS

There seems no reason to believe, according to available evidence, that true homosexuality is due either to organic or hereditary factors.[2] Since I have not personally made any investigations in this matter, I shall quote from several sources who have either made investigations or reviewed the literature on the subject.

Allen, for example, speaks quite firmly on this point and states somewhat unwillingly:

> I am reluctantly driven to the conclusion that there is, so far, no evidence upon which any reliance can be placed that there is any en-

THE ETIOLOGY OF HOMOSEXUALITY

docrine difference between "normal" and homosexual. This is in accordance with the clinical finding that castration does not cause a man to
be homosexual, nor does it even in all cases, cause cessation of
heterosexual intercourse. Moreover, injection of female hormones fails
to make a man behave homosexually if he has previously been normal.
The endocrine factor may be ancillary, but is not the basic cause.[3]

He then concludes:

It would be wearisome to labor the point. No investigations in any
sphere indicate an organic basis for homosexuality, whether physical,
chemical, cellular, microscopic, or macroscopic.[4]

Father Buckley, whose work suffers somewhat from the fact that
he largely ignores American sources, in his otherwise careful review
of current literature finds no evidence in favor of an organic etiology.
He concludes:

. . . a cursory examination of the British Medical Association report
openly reveals the inadequacy of available medical data to explain
homosexuality on a biological or endocrinological basis. The report
does not even visualize the possibility that all cases of homosexuality
have a medical background.[5]

The theory that homosexuality is a constitutional and, therefore,
natural variation seems to have been advocated by Father Leo Trese
in an article in *Commonweal:* "The homosexual is a freak of nature
as is the albino or midget according to medical science . . . due to
an imbalance of the hormones. . . ."[6] For this there seems to be
no evidence.

PHYSICAL CONSTITUTION

Attempts were made by Weil to determine the physical constitution
of 380 male homosexuals in comparison with 1000 heterosexual
males.[7] Weil's findings were that homosexuals had a slightly wider
breadth of the hips than heterosexuals. It was 32.26 as compared
with 31.41. Weil, however, has been criticized because he did not
describe the method of measurement he used in his experiment. He
states, for example, that some of the homosexuals he measured were
people whom he met socially. He does not state how he determined
these people to be homosexual. Nor does he show that he avoided the
possibility of unconsciously choosing people who fitted into a pattern
he had already designated.

Weil's study, however, is not the only one made on the possibility
of physical factors. Henry and Galbraith concluded that there were

significant physical characteristics: long legs; narrow hips; large
muscles; deficient hair on face, chest, and back; female distribution
of pubic hair; high-pitched voice; small penis and testicles; and
the presence of the scrotal fold. Sometimes there was excessive
fat on shoulders, buttocks, and abdomen. And in some cases the
pelvis was exactly the homosexual build which they postulated —
very large with unusually wide hips.

Female homosexuals, according to Henry and Galbraith, have:

> firm adipose tissue, a lack of fat on the shoulders and abdomen, a
> large amount of hair on the chest, back and legs, male distribution
> of pubic hair, small uterus, either overdeveloped or underdeveloped
> labia and clitoris. Moreover the female homosexual body seems to
> have a shorter trunk, a contracted pelvis, underdeveloped breasts,
> superfluous facial hair and a low-pitched voice.[8]

Wortis[9] made a study of the measurements of a group of 17 male
homosexuals and 16 female homosexuals. This group was compared
to a heterosexual control group of 5 males and 10 females. Wortis
did not find any significant differences between homosexuals and
heterosexuals in this small group. All that Wortis concluded was
that the measurements of male homosexuals were somewhat below
the average of male university students in Berlin, but the Lesbians
were well above the average of female students at the University of
Munich. It need hardly be mentioned that Wortis' group is so small
that no general conclusions should be drawn from it.

Anthropological investigations help to confirm the opinion expressed by Wortis that there are no physical characteristics of
inversion. Coppen, in 1959, stated:

> The androgyny score (i.e. 3 X biacromial = 1 X bi-iliac diameters, in
> centimeters), however, did not differentiate the homosexuals from the
> the controls any better than did the biacromial diameter, which is less
> in these patients. It was concluded that homosexuals have a body-
> build similar to that found in patients with other psychiatric disorders
> and that it could not be specifically related to their sexual disorder.[10]

The validity of the method of testing was confirmed to some
extent by the work of Dixon and Torr. These researchers made oral
tests on 260 normal individuals to determine the chromosomal sex.
They applied the method to 60 cases of abnormal physical and
psychological sexual development. They stated:

> The present series includes cases of true and pseudo-hermaphrodites.
> The method has been particularly useful in separating out those cases

with definite physical abnormalities — for example, Klinefelter's and Turner's syndromes — from those of an essentially psychological nature, without resort to laparotomy. In the psychologically maladjusted group it has been our invariable experience that the physical sex diagnosis is borne out by the chromosomal sex findings.[11]

Pare (1956) by chromatin staining procedures studied 50 homosexual men and 50 control heterosexuals (25 men and 25 women).[12] All male subjects studied were considered biologically male, and all 25 women as female. Other studies by Davidson and Winn confirmed these results.[13]

Barr and Hobbs examined 194 male homosexuals and 5 male transvestites. All of these gave male readings.[14] In any group of homosexuals, the proportion of those having a chromatin sex status inconsistent with their anatomical sex is no greater than among those with normal sexual leanings, according to Raboch and Nedoma.[15]

The possibility of physical factors has been studied in respect to more than body measurements. Studies have also been made on the cell structure of the testes and on the quantity of male and female sex hormones present. Steinach[16] made a microscopic examination of the testes of five homosexuals. His study suggested the possibility of degeneration of the testicles and the presence of certain cells, somewhat like lutein cells in the ovary of a woman. Slotopolsky and Schinz, however, discovered that degeneration in testicles and the presence of these quasi-lutein cells could be found in the testes of heterosexual males as well.[17]

As for the relative quantities of sex hormones, there is evidence that there is relatively less androgen in the urine of male homosexuals than in the urine of male heterosexuals. These were the findings of Glass, Duel, and Wright in 1940.[18] Neustadt and Myerson[19] studied 29 homosexuals in 1940 and found a similar condition and found also that there was a higher amount of estrogen present. The studies of Glass *et al.* were later rejected because of technical errors in their work.[20] Sawyer in 1954 stated that hormonal therapy offered no success in the treatment of cases of homosexuality.[21] Apparently the hormonal substances responsible for the development of the sexual characteristics play little or no part in the direction of the sexual drive.

Clear evidence seems to have been developed in recent research that androgen, the male hormone, is responsible for the function of sexual arousal in both sexes, although in different degrees.[22] Thus sex identification overrides the effects of the various hormones.[23]

After research on the administration of exogenous sex hormones, Waxenburg concluded "that it is the androgens which provide the hormonal basis for the erotic component of human female sexuality."[24]

Krafft-Ebing[25] believed that there were several sources of origin for homosexuality. He believed that in some cases the determining factor was primarily organic and in other cases it was psychic. According to his organic viewpoint all human embryos have rudimentary male and female sexual organs. Normally one of these sexual organs develops and the other disappears. But in the homosexual there is development of one sexual organ without a complete disappearance of the other. This abnormality in development and disappearance of the organs of the other sex will be accompanied by psychological abnormalities as well. If Krafft-Ebing's theory were correct there would be evidence of bodily abnormalities in all homosexuals. But this is not unanimously conceded.

Laidlaw concluded from his study of male homosexuals in New York City that these tended toward a body build varying somewhat toward the female; but that female homosexuals had less inclination toward a male body build.[26]

Some students hold that homosexuality is a natural alternative to heterosexuality; in other words, that the invert is of a third sex, between male and female. This theory may be positively rejected on the grounds that (1) it contradicts revealed truth, (2) it contradicts the conclusions of reason, and (3) it would be contrary to nature.

Father Moore, although he discussed the topic some years ago, gave some conclusions which are still valid on this point:

> The idea of homosexuality as due to some unfathomable force in nature compelling one to act as he does is a creation of the homosexual mind, a parataxis of defense. From an empirical, scientific point of view, the major factors in the occurrence of homosexuality are psychic in their nature rather than organic. From the philosophical and biological point of view, any displacement of the sex drive which makes impossible the attainment of the proper end of the sexual function must of its nature be abnormal. Accordingly, homosexuality and its fruitless acts must be a pathological condition whether the underlying pathology is of a psychic or organic character.[27]

HEREDITY

Studies have been made on the possibility that homosexuality may be transmitted by heredity. Prior to World War II, Theodore Lang made a study of the known homosexuals in Hamburg, Germany, in order to determine whether the relatives of these persons seemed to show evidence of the condition.[28] From this study Lang concluded that the possibility of transmission by genes had to be ruled out. It should be mentioned here that even if he had evidence of homosexuality among the relatives, he would not have been able to rule out the psychological affect.

Since Lang did not see homosexuality as genetic in origin, he considered the possibility of homosexuality as an intersex. According to Lang's final view, the homosexual male is not really a male but a transformed female. That is to say, the homosexual comes about as the result of development just as a new strain of flowers may be developed in a botanical garden. Lang did not derive his ideas from botany but from the work of Goldschmidt[29] who had produced sexual intergrades in butterflies. Lang's fundamental argument, however, is based on a faulty reasoning process which does not give a necessary conclusion. Lang argued as follows: "If it is true that a proportion of male homosexuals are actually transformed females, then an undue preponderance of males must be found among the siblings of male homosexuals." The normal sex ratio of male-female siblings is 106:100. Lang then attempted to show that there was this undue preponderance in inverts. Among the siblings of homosexual fathers, he found a ratio of 121 males to 100 females. His argument falls down, however, when he compares this ratio in the children of homosexual fathers; this turns out to be 106.9 to 100 — which is normal. But this argument is also weak because it does not rule out other possibilities. Therefore, Lang's conclusion should be taken with the possibility of error in mind.

S. Keller has suggested that while Lang's findings are not to be taken conclusively, it might be interesting to make a study of the proportionate number of brothers and sisters among the siblings of homosexuals.[30]

Other studies of the male-female sibling relationship were also inconclusive.[31] Slater studied the families of male exhibitionists, and noted a ratio of 109:144, which he interpreted as an excess of female siblings to form an audience for the exhibitionist brother.[32] Darke studied a small sample consisting of American homosexuals and reported a normal 106:100 ratio.[33]

Franz Kallman[34] made a study of overt male homosexuality in forty pairs of identical twins. He discovered that whenever one was homosexual, the other was also. And the tendency was moderately increased in brothers or fraternal co-twins of overt homosexuals.

I am recording Kallman's study because it is frequently quoted. His findings, however, are not conclusive. It is just as easy to explain the frequency of homosexuality in these fraternal pairs by "psychic infection" as it is in terms of genetics. In every case these children were subjected to the same family conditions. The possibility of psychic influences would have to be eliminated before any of these studies could be accepted conclusively.

Although Kallman's study must be considered, its reliability is generally held to be doubtful. In the first place, it is too perfect. Clinical investigations seldom work out 100 percent. This is not only my opinion. Berg speaks of the study rather skeptically:

> Since the actual clinical data of his paper is very superficial and sketchy and he gives only three case histories because the patients were still subject to New York laws, one feels that the paper, in spite of the elaborate statistical analysis, is dubious and uncertain. Statistical formulas may be impressive, but the basic clinical facts must be completely determined for them to be of any value at all. Obviously one cannot go up to a man and say, "Excuse me, I understand your twin brother is homosexual; do you mind telling me if you are?" It is here that the perilous part comes and it seems possible that sometimes Kallman went more on hearsay than actual investigation.[35]

Berg then concludes:

> Kallman's paper, therefore, stands suspect because (1) his clinical material is not satisfactory; (2) it is contradicted by the experience of others; and (3) it is unusual in medicine to obtain 100% results and one usually encounters some omission or contradiction; and (4) his work has never been confirmed by anyone else.[36]

I find myself in complete agreement with Berg. There is no conclusive evidence that homosexuality is transmissible hereditarily.

Having said this, may I report briefly some relevant comments of Patient I:

> I am thinking about the case of four brothers, friends of mine in Europe — all four of whom were homosexuals, and the individual life of each was unknown to the others until they were already grown. Was it due to being exposed to the same parental situation? Or the same environmental influences?
>
> Also, have you thought of family histories which show certain sexual aberrations appearing generation after generation, sometimes manifesting themselves in open homosexuality, sometimes in other forms? This has

THE ETIOLOGY OF HOMOSEXUALITY

THE ETIOLOGY OF HOMOSEXUALITY

intrigued me in my own family where we have fairly complete information on lives and personalities for some four hundred years. This is not an argument for the heredity theory of homosexuality, but probably indicates a certain tendency for some form of sexual maladjustment. This does not run like a thread through each generation, and would seem to indicate that there appear some individuals incapable of making an adjustment sexually.

A study of certain royal families will show the reappearance generation after generation of this same thing.

Summary

It is generally held that the possibility of genetic causation of homosexuality rests more on faith than on proof.[37]

PSYCHOGENIC FACTORS IN ETIOLOGY

It seems clear, as I hope to demonstrate, that the basic cause of homosexuality is psychological. It seems also clear that this psychological deviation arises early in life. Although the psychopathology is not always apparent in every case, two factors help to confirm its presence: (*a*) when a sufficient search in depth is made such factors can usually be detected; (*b*) there is frequently a good response in psychotherapy.

In approaching the discussion of etiology, I will do so in this order:

1. Theories of origin
   a) The Bisexual Theory
   b) The Ishmael Complex
   c) Homosexuality as an Obsessive-Compulsive Neurosis
   d) Lorand's Theory
   e) Fear of the Genitals of the Other Sex

Bisexuality

So much has been written and said about the role of bisexuality in the development of homosexuality that, although the theory is generally discarded, something should be said about it. Freud was its greatest exponent, although the idea was not original with him.

Freud's concept of bisexuality was borrowed from a nineteenth-century medical background which was in turn derived from a study of human embryology. It was discovered in the nineteenth century that in both the male and female embryos the sexual organs arose from the same source. It was first debated whether this embryonic source should be considered neutral or hermaphroditic. When it was later discovered that the embryonic source contained elements from the sexual apparatus of both males and females, it was immediately called hermaphroditic. Once the embryonic source was called hermaphroditic, it was easy to extend the theorizing to any field where bisexuality was a matter of concern.[38]

Kiernan[39] was the first to bring the new concept into the field of psychiatry. He was followed by others: Lydstrom, Chevalier, Krafft-Ebing, Ellis, and Magnus Hirschfeld.

Krafft-Ebing[40] began his organic theory of inversion on the then new concept of bisexuality. He assumed that if the peripheral structure of the sexual apparatus had a bisexual predisposition, this must be equally true for the brain centers related to sexual activity. From this he concluded that the embryonic cerebrum must also contain male and female centers which ultimately determined the sexual orientation of the human person. Homosexuality, he concluded, therefore, resulted when the female brain center developed in an otherwise male body. Krafft-Ebing was aware that an individual might have a hermaphroditic condition sexually without being bisexual so far as his psychological condition was concerned. Krafft-Ebing was, therefore, forced to conclude that the sexual centers of the brain and the sexual development of the cell structure of the organs were distinct from one another — that each one had its own autonomous development, and these could be independently subject to aberrations in development. It is maintained by Rado that "not a trace of neurological evidence was then or is now available to give credence to Krafft-Ebing's chain of hypotheses."[41]

Freud[42] eventually took over Krafft-Ebing's hypothesis of the bisexual nature of the human embryo. From this he suggested bisexuality as something generally applicable to all human beings. This early biological explanation of bisexuality seems to be passing from the scientific scene today. The psychogenic explanation is being accepted more widely than ever.

Freud's original theory on homosexuality was that every human being possessed both male and female psychosexual attributes. At the outset these have no genital significance — they merely show up as an attribute of activity or passivity.

It is this early predisposition toward either masculine activity or feminine passivity that fundamentally determines the subsequent sexual development of the child. If the child is male and has been endowed with a strong constitutional diathesis toward passivity then he will adopt the feminine sexual role and nothing can be done for him. On the other hand, if the child is male and has only a weak constitutional tendency toward passivity, he may have this neutralized or doubled in intensity by circumstances in his environment. In the latter case he would become homosexual according to this theory.

Freud described the contributing factors of homosexuality in terms of this constitutional predisposition toward activity and passivity and in terms of his libido theory (see p. 35).

Most authors today would reject Freud's emphasis on the constitutional basis for homosexuality and would place greater emphasis upon environmental factors. This does not mean that Freud ignored all environmental factors. He was well aware that they had a role to play. But he put his emphasis on constitutional factors.

For Freud the most significant environmental factor was the Oedipal Situation or Complex. It is so named after the tragedy by Sophocles in which the leading character, Oedipus, unknowingly kills his father and eventually marries his mother. Neither Oedipus nor his mother are aware that they are mother and son because Oedipus had been taken away as a child and had been brought up by a shepherd. Freud said that in the normal family development there is a drama similar to this enacted between the small child and the two parents. The child at the outset is narcissistic — that is to say, the child loves itself. Its activities are centered only on its own interests. The child begins to expand its interests to others. The first person the child loves other than itself is the mother. In the course of time the child becomes aware of another individual in the home — if the home has a healthy psychological atmosphere. This second individual is the father of the family. If the child is a boy, he begins to realize that his mother loves not only him but his father as well. The boy begins to see his father as a rival for his mother's affection. This rivalry is not actually hostility. (Hostility in this situation would be indicative of a neurotic element in the family setup.) The rivalry is merely a desire of the boy to have more time with his mother, to have her exclusively with him some of the time. Eventually the boy appreciates that his father is much stronger and more powerful than he is. Anything the boy can do the father can do better (see "Ishmael Complex," below). When the boy begins to realize this, he gives up an attempt at rivalry and begins to conform himself to his father's pattern of acting. When the boy begins to pattern himself on his father's character, he is said to have resolved the Oedipal crisis. Before he copies his father's attitudes he will probably associate with other boys. Here he is likely to develop an attachment to one or another boy. This is the homosexual stage of development. But the word here refers merely to a direction of affections rather than to genital activity. (It is not until puberty that the flush of hormones through the body concentrates otherwise diffused love interests to actual genital activity.) The boy, under normal circumstances, finally develops himself on the pattern of his father.

The psychosexual development of the female is similar to this. The female child first centers her affections on her mother and eventually becomes aware of her father. She becomes aware that they are physically different. As she begins to learn the difference between herself and her father, she fantasies attempts at the incorporation of her father's penis. But she is also aware that it is only for her mother. She sees her mother as a rival for the father. Like the boy, she realizes that she is no competition for her mother, and so she begins to copy her mother with the hope that she too will in time have a male to complement her lack of a penis.

The Oedipal complex at first seems wholly fantastic to adults who have no recollection of these stages of development. But these earlier fantasies are often brought out during depth therapy. Sometimes they are not as pronounced as I have indicated here, but they are easily recognizable under similar forms. This statement should not be interpreted to mean that I feel the Oedipal conflict is universal. There is no way of knowing this. It is, however, frequent.

Helene Deutsch[43] and Karen Horney[44] have both asserted that whenever there are difficulties in the Oedipal stage (such as excessive rivalry with the mother or a predominance of castration feelings) there is a more or less marked tendency toward homosexuality in women.

The Ishmael Complex

Helen M. Hacker[45] has suggested an interesting and provocative theory on the origin of homosexuality. She feels that too much emphasis has been placed on the importance of the Oedipus complex as an etiological factor in the development of homosexuality. The term "Ishmael" was suggested to her by the opening lines in *Moby Dick,* when the hero exclaims, "Call me Ishmael!" In the course of the story this hero becomes a composite father and mother image to the boy. As with so many names in *Moby Dick* the term "Ishmael" is symbolically significant. Ishmael was the son of Abraham and Hagar, his bondswoman. Because he mocked Isaac, his half brother, he was cast out to wander in the desert.

Hacker points out that in a number of American juvenile classics an interesting situation develops. An American boy finds himself in a primitive and isolated state in association with an older, not too highly civilized, dark-skinned man. There is mutual affection and admiration. This affection is strictly nonsexual. The older man in such cases is portrayed as more or less omnipotent in relation to his environment as well as being a loving protector to the boy. This one figure incorporates the main characteristics usually attributed by a child to both his father and his mother.[46]

In American middle-class groups the father-son relationship does not usually follow the Oedipal pattern, according to Hacker. In this group the father shares the authority in the family with the mother, so that the supremacy of the father is not present. Hacker also points out that in this group the son is expected to surpass the father socially, financially, and educationally. The child does not, therefore, fear and respect the father as he does in European groups. The American father is more affectionate than the European father. There is, therefore, a different father-son relationship in the American and European situations. In the American middle-class setup the child does not form an attachment for the father alone but for the mother as well and, consequently, in Hacker's concept of the *Ishmael stage* of psychic development the child has a parent image which fuses the best attributes of both the father and the mother.

Hacker feels that homosexuality results in those individuals who have been unable to resolve the conflicts which arose during the Ishmael stage. This may come about in cases when the boy's desire for affection from the father has been severely frustrated and/or when the boy's mother is markedly deficient in companionable qualities. If the child does not find this Ishmael image fulfilled by his parents he will grow up with a compulsive urge to find some

object which will fulfill his dream image. Homosexuality arises when
the adult attempts to solidify this image in some individual of his
own sex. But the expression of this feeling in overt homosexual behavior spoils that individual as the embodiment of the Ishmael image
because according to the ideal image the relationship should remain
etherialized. Therefore, the Ishmael myth is not fulfilled in an overt
homosexual act and the homosexual goes on in a never ending
search for the idealized Ishmael object.

Homosexuality as an Obsessive-Compulsive Neurosis

This theory has always appealed to the author as having wide
application to the etiology of homosexuality. It explains quite satisfactorily most of the facts of homosexuality as we know them and
offers a useful therapeutic approach. It was first described by Dr.
Erwin O. Krausz.[47] An *obsessive-compulsive neurosis* is one in which
the individual affected has an almost irresistible impulse to do
something which he knows he should not do. In a negative way
this might result in a firm conviction that one is incapable of doing
what he ought to do. *Krausz finds the basis for his theory of homosexuality in this negative statement.* The homosexual, he feels, is
incapable of imagining himself married or engaging in sexual activity
with a person of the opposite sex; in other words, the male homosexual has an obsessive fear (of the vulva) of women and the Lesbian
has an obsessive fear (of the genital organs) of men (see below,
p. 57).

What the homosexual fails to understand is that he will be
incapable of loving members of the other sex until he has cleared
away the underlying difficulty. According to Krausz, when we probe
to see what this difficulty is we find that the homosexual has a fear
of being compared with members of his own sex. Proper comparison
with members of one's own sex can only be made by members of the
opposite sex. Hence, the homosexual avoids all women.

At the same time, according to Krausz, the homosexual neutralizes
the potential enemies he finds among the members of his own sex
by "loving" them. In "loving" members of his own sex, he eliminates
them as rivals in the eyes of women. From this, of course, we may
conclude that the homosexual "love act" is not an act of love at all,
but is really a hostile act of aggression whereby the homosexual

emasculates a person who would otherwise be a competitor. The perverse character of homosexuality is not that the homosexual loves a member of the same sex but that he loves what he actually hates. In his homosexual activity the homosexual is doing nothing more than utilizing the technique of reification.

There are several ways in which the homosexual may reify* his attitude. He may adopt the "good brother" attitude; that is to say, he acts like a good brother to women. He gets along "fine" with women until they attempt to put the relationship on a sexual basis. In adopting the "good brother" attitude the homosexual is really de-sexualizing the heterosexual individual. A second attempt at reification may be the depreciation of members of the same sex except those in whom he has a "sexual" interest. The third method of reification — which is the homosexual's masterpiece — is his conviction that he can love only members of his own sex. This is the foundation upon which all else rests. This conviction above all must stand because he believes that if this one fails, he will be left with a crushing feeling of utter nothingness.

Lorand approaches the etiology of inversion in a way somewhat similar to that of Krausz. We refer the reader directly to his text.[48]

CLINIC 4 — NOTES

1. Father Buckley agrees with the findings of the Henry Foundation and states that "acquired homosexuality by initiation and indulgence must be admitted as the main causative factor in a large number of homosexual cases" (Rev. Michael Buckley, *Morality and the Homosexual* [Westminster, Md.: The Newman Press, 1959], p. 114). On the contrary, Father Harvey, a long-time student of the disorder, comments: "It has not been proven that a real homosexual tendency is *mainly* the result of initiation" (Rev. John F. Harvey, *Theological Studies*, Vol. XXI, No. 3, September, 1960, p. 493).
2. John R. Cavanagh, M.D., and James B. McGoldrick, S.J., *Fundamental Psychiatry* (2 rev. ed.) (Milwaukee: The Bruce Publishing Company, 1958), p. 552 f.
3. Clifford Allen, *A Textbook of Psychosexual Disorders* (London: Oxford University Press, 1962), p. 169.
4. *Ibid.*, p. 170.
5. Buckley, *op. cit.*, p. 151.
6. Leo Trese, "Muted Tragedy," *Commonweal*, Vol. LI (February 17, 1950), p. 512 ff.
7. A. Weil, "Concerning the Anatomical Fundamentals of the Congenital Homosexual," *Arch. Frauenck-Eugen.*, 10, pp. 23–26. See also: A. Weil, "The Substance of the Expression of Homosexuals About Their Specific Constitution," *Arch. f. Entwicklungsmechanik der Organismen*, 49 (1921), p. 538; J. Vague, G. Favier, and J. Nicolino, "Somatic Aspects of Male and Female Homo-

* Reify — to convert into or regard as a concrete thing.

sexuality," *Sessuologia,* Vol. IV, No. 3 (July–September, 1963), pp. 124–149; L. Muscardin, "Research Into Some Morphological Features in a Group of Homosexuals," *Sessuologia,* Vol. IV, No. 3 (July–September, 1963), pp. 124–149; L. Muscardin, "Research Into Some Morphological Features in a Group of Homosexuals," *Sessuologia,* Vol. IV, No. 3 (July–September, 1963), pp. 150–154.

8. Quoted in Dom Thomas V. Moore, *The Nature and Treatment of Mental Disorders* (New York: Grune & Stratton, 1951), p. 321.

9. J. Wortis, "Intersexuality and Effeminacy in a Male Homosexual," *American Journal of Orthopsychiatry,* 10 (1940), pp. 567–569. See also: J. Wortis, "Note on Body Build of Male Homosexuals," *American Journal of Psychiatry,* 93 (1937), p. 1121.

10. A. J. Coppen, "Body Build of Male Homosexuals," *British Medical Journal,* Vol. II (1959), pp. 1443–1445.

11. A. D. Dixon, and J. B. D. Torr, "Chromosomal Sex and Abnormal Sex Development," *British Medical Journal,* Vol. I (1948), pp. 222–228. See also: G. Lapponi, "Determination of Nuclear Sex. Technical Note and Findings Obtained From a Large-Scale Survey," *Sessuologia,* Vol. IV, No. 3 (July–September, 1963), pp. 120–123; F. Brambilla, "Endocrinal and Chromatinic Pictures of Male Homosexuality," *Sessuologia,* Vol. IV, No. 3 (July–September, 1963), pp. 170–174.

12. C. M. B. Pare, "Homosexuality and Chromosomal Sex," *Journal of Psychosomatic Research,* 1 (1956), pp. 247–251.

13. W. Davidson and S. Winn, *Postgraduate Medical Journal,* 35 (1959), p. 494.

14. M. L. Barr and G. E. Hobbs, *Lancet,* i (1954), p. 1109.

15. J. Raboch and K. Nedoma, "Sex Chromatin and Sexual Behavior: A Study of 36 Men With Female Nuclear Pattern and of 134 Homosexuals," *Psychosomatic Medicine,* Vol. XX (1958), p. 55.

16. Steinach is mentioned only because of his historical interest. His work of rejuvenation of the aging and the treatment of homosexuality by the transplantation of testicles created quite a furor in 1918–1919. For example, in Volume 6 (1921) of the Cumulative Medical Index of Periodical Literature, there were 28 articles listed by different authors. In spite of the interest the results were illusory and the method is no longer employed. A typical article of Steinach on this subject is the following: E. Steinach and R. Lichtenstein, "Umstimmung der Homosexualität durch Austausch der Pubertätsdrusen," *Munchener medizinische Wochenschrift,* Vol. 65 (1918), I, pp. 145–148.

17. Referred to in Moore, *op. cit.,* p. 329.

18. S. J. Glass, H. J. Duel, and C. A. Wright, "Sex Hormone Studies in Male Homosexuals," *Endocrinology,* 26 (1940), pp. 590–594.

19. R. Neustadt and A. Myerson, "Quantitative Sex Hormone Studies in Homosexuality, Childhood and Various Neuropsychiatric Disturbances," *American Journal of Psychiatry,* 97 (1940), pp. 524–551.

20. Cf. Alfred C. Kinsey, *Journal of Clinical Endocrinology,* 1 (1941), p. 424.

21. G. I. M. Sawyer, "Homosexuality: The Endocrinological Aspects," *The Practitioner,* 172 (April, 1954), pp. 374–377. Cf. also: G. I. M. Sawyer, *Lancet,* 2 (December 12, 1959), p. 1077; L. A. Lurie, "The Endocrine Factor in Homosexuality," *American Journal of Medical Science,* 208 (1944), pp. 176–186.

22. Cf. John Money, "Components of Eroticism in Man. I: The Hormones in Relation to Sexual Morphology and Sexual Desire," *Journal of Nervous and Mental Diseases,* 132 (1961), pp. 239–248; "II. The Orgasm and Genital Somesthesia," 132: 289–297; *idem,* "Sex Hormones and Other Variables in Human Eroticism," in W. C. Young (ed.), *Sex and Internal Secretions* (3 ed.) (Baltimore: Williams and Wilkins, 1961), Chap. 22.

23. John Money, *art. cit.,* p. 32. Cf. also: G. I. M. Sawyer, *op. cit.,* pp. 374, 377; J. Tudor Rees and Harley V. Usill (eds.), *They Stand Apart* (New York: The

Macmillan Company, 1955), pp 71–72; L. A. Lurie, *op. cit.;* "Endocrine and Disordered Sexual Behavior," *British Medical Journal*, 1 (March 9, 1957), p. 574.

24. Sheldon E. Waxenburg, "Some Biological Correlatives of Sexual Behavior," in George Winokur (ed.), *Determinants of Human Sexual Behavior* (Springfield, Ill.: Charles C. Thomas, 1963), p. 57. Cf. also: U. Teodori and F. Morabito, "Endocrinological Aspects of Homosexuality," *Sessuologia*, Vol. IV, No. 3 (July–September, 1963), pp. 156–164; M. Tocca and F. Micheli, "The Validity of Hormonal Exploration in the Diagnosis of Homosexual Conditions," *Sessuologia*, Vol. IV, No. 3 (July–September, 1963), pp. 165–169; F. Brambilla, *op. cit.;* A. Marcozzi, "Value of Homosexual Behavior in Adolescence," *Sessuologia*, Vol. IV, No. 3 (July–September, 1963), pp. 175–177; A. Marcozzi, P. Pomini, and N. Caprioli, "Determination of Urinary 17-Ketosteroids in Females With Homosexual Tendencies," *Sessuologia*, Vol. IV, No. 3 (July–September, 1963), pp. 178–179.

25. R. v. Krafft-Ebing, *"Psychopathia-Sexualis* (New York: Physicians and Surgeons Book Company, 1934), p. 282 ff.

26. Robert W. Laidlaw, "A Clinical Approach to Homosexuality," *Marriage and Family Living*, Vol. XIV, No. 1 (February, 1952), pp. 39–45.

27. Dom Thomas V. Moore, O.S.B., "The Pathogenesis and Treatment of Homosexual Disorders," *Journal of Personality*, Vol. XIV, No. 1 (September, 1945), pp. 49–50.

28. Theodore Lang, "Studies on the Genetic Determination of Homosexuality," *Journal of Nervous and Mental Diseases*, Vol. XCII (1940), pp. 55–64.

29. R. Goldschmidt, *The Mechanism and Psychology of Sex Determination* (London: Rd. Methuen, 1924).

30. See Moore, *The Nature and Treatment of Mental Disorders, loc. cit.*, p. 325.

31. K. Jensch, "Zur Genealogie der Homosexualitat," *Archiv für Psychiatrie und Nervenkrankheiten*, 112 (1941), pp. 527–540, 679–696.

32. Eliot Slater, "The Sibs and Children of Homosexuals," in *Symposium on Nuclear Sex* (New York: Interscience Publishers, 1958).

33. R. A. Darke, "Heredity as an Etiological Factor in Homosexuality," *Journal of Nervous and Mental Diseases*, 107 (1948), pp. 251–268.

34. Franz J. Kallman, "Comparative Twin Studies on the Genetic Aspect of Male Homosexuality," *Journal of Nervous and Mental Diseases*, 115 (1952), pp. 283–298. Cf. also L. Gedda, "Genetic Aspects of Homosexuality," *Sessuologia*, Vol. IV, No. 3 (July–September, 1963), pp. 108–119.

35. Charles Berg, M.D., and Clifford Allen, M.D., *The Problem of Homosexuality* (New York: The Citadel Press, 1958), p. 39.

36. *Ibid.*, p. 40.

37. Allen, *op. cit.*, p. 166.

38. Referred to in Sandor Rado, "A Critical Examination of the Concept of Bisexuality," *Psychosomatic Medicine*, II, No. 4 (October, 1940), p. 460.

39. See Rado, *op. cit.*, p. 460 ff.

40. R. v. Krafft-Ebing, *op. cit.*, p. 282 ff.

41. Rado, *op. cit.*, p. 460.

42. Sigmund Freud, *Three Contributions to the Theory of Sex* in *The Basic Writings of Sigmund Freud*, A. A. Brill (ed.) (New York: Modern Library, 1938).

43. Helene Deutsch, "Homosexuality in Women," *Psychoanalytic Quarterly*, October, 1932, pp. 484–510.

44. Karen Horney, "On the Genesis of the Castration Complex in Women," *International Journal of Psychoanalysis*, Vol. V (1924), p. 50.

45. Helen Mayer Hacker, "The Ishmael Complex," *The American Journal of Psychotherapy*, Vol. VI, No. 3 (July, 1952), pp. 494–513.

46. The first footnote to Hacker's article in the *American Journal of Psychotherapy* gives the names of other novels in which she sees elements of the Ishmael

complex; for example, *Moby Dick, Huckleberry Finn, Two Years Before the Mast,* and *The Leatherstocking Tales.*

47. Erwin Krausz, notes distributed as "ditto" copies after the paper was read at a meeting of the American Psychiatric Association. I have not seen it published subsequently.

48. Sandor Lorand, M.D., and Michael Balint, M.D. (eds.), *Perversions, Psychodynamics and Therapy* (New York: Random House, Inc., 1956), pp. 92–94.

The Etiology of Homosexuality (Continued)

FEAR OF THE GENITAL ORGANS OF THE OTHER SEX AS A CAUSE OF HOMOSEXUALITY

Although the theory of Krausz has many appealing features, it would seem that if we carry the theory beyond the concept of an obsessive fear of the other sex a more specific and therapeutically useful foundation for the theory may be formulated. In many cases the individual who becomes a homosexual develops a fear of the genital organs of the other sex as dangerous and destructive. This is more clearly seen in cases of male homosexuality than it is in the Lesbian.

The concept is in line with psychoanalysis which accepts castration anxiety as one of the basic etiological factors in male homosexuality. The knowledge, however acquired and however conscious, that a woman has no penis creates in them a fear of castration. In fact, the vulva may be fantasied in oral-sadistic terms as a castrating instrument.[1] The fetishist and the transvestite consciously deny that the female lacks a penis; the homosexual accepts this fact but feels threatened by it. For this reason, although the majority of male homosexuals are interested in women as intellectual companions, they reject them as sexual (genital) partners.

Freud expressed this conception in somewhat similar terms. As described by Freud, the homosexual man is so insistent on the idea of a penis that he cannot accept its absence in his sexual partner. This could also be expressed negatively by saying: homosexual men are so frightened at the sight of a being without a penis, that they reject any sexual relationships with such a partner.

A great many patients quite clearly bring out these fears in therapy, but probably not in sufficient numbers, certainly not in my experience, to make the assertion that such a fear is universally present. Undoubtedly homosexuality has many causes.

It is, however, a useful concept in therapy and one quite generally accepted by those who have written on the subject. For this reason, instead of merely just listing those authors who have commented on the subject, I would like to take time to quote some of their comments. This coverage is not intended to be exhaustive, but only representative.

First, this passage from Berg and Allen:

> Analysis of homosexual men regularly shows that they are afraid of female genitals. . . . The female genitals, through the connection of castration anxiety with oral anxieties, may be perceived as a castrating instrument capable of biting or tearing off the penis.[2]

Sullivan also recognized that the fear of female genitals may exist in men even though they regard women as pleasurable sexual objects — "a fear amounting to a feeling which is literally uncanny, which is quite paralyzing," and which is able to force the male to escape from this "uncanny feeling" into homosexuality. The origin of this fear, he believed, may derive from the "not me," indicating a serious dissociation in the personality.[3]

Rado attributed homosexuality to the following factors:

> Hidden but incapacitating fears of the opposite sex which result in a homosexual adaptation, which through symbolic processes is in fantasy a heterosexual one, or in which problems of rivalry with isophilic partners who represent father are solved.[4]

Bieber:

> This study provides convincing support for a fundamental contribution by Rado on the subject of male homosexuality: a homosexual adaptation is the result of "hidden but incapacitating fears of the opposite sex."
>
> A considerable amount of data supporting Rado's assumption has been presented as evidence that fear of heterosexuality underlies homosexuality, e.g., the frequent fear of disease or injury to the genitals, significantly associated with fear and aversion to female genitalia; the frequency and depth of anxiety accompanying actual or contemplated heterosexual behavior.[5]

Cory:

> Briefly summarized, the homosexual is definitely emotionally disturbed, *suffering from fear of the other sex*, puritanical distortions about sexuality, self-abnegation, feelings of inadequacy, self-destructive drives, and compulsive desires.[6]

The aim of therapy is to relieve the hostility toward and fear of relationships, sexual and other, with the other sex, rather than to seek to suppress the homosexual interest. The reasons for this are twofold: (1) to aid the homosexual to get at the root of the problem, and not to attack what is merely a symptom — his problem is not so much that he is attached to males, but that *he is in flight from females.*[7]

Adler:

A. Adler has conceived in these cases the hypothesis of a "fear of the sexual partner." This observation certainly holds true in the case of many homosexuals, but it is *not true of all cases.* Nature does not operate in such simple ways and a single key does not unlock the riddle of homosexuality.[8]

Stekel:

May fear of the sexual partner drive a person into homosexuality? We must answer this question in the affirmative inasmuch as we are able to trace that fear in a number of cases.[9]

Bromberg:

Chiefly, homosexuality develops as a psychological defense against unconscious fear of women with subsequent retreat to men for sexual expression. This is the core of the psychoanalytic theory of homosexuality. The mental mechanisms by which the resultant attitude evolves are complicated. In brief, the boy who is destined to become a homosexual develops a strong unconscious identification with the mother, or mother figure, thus laying the psychological groundwork in early life for a pattern of seeking male love objects. In contrast, the normal boy identifies with the father and hence, in time, seeks a female love object. Early fear of women, in homosexually inclined boys, is observed by their identification with women, the "identification with the aggressor" mechanism. Thus, men become psychologically "safe" for them.[10]

Davidman:

Homosexual relationships in neurotics have the underlying psychological goal of achieving a male-female union in a safe way; that is, *free from the disturbing and terrifying genital of the opposite sex and the heightened responsibilities, expectations, demands and reproductive hazards of normal sexuality.* But each participant preserves in his or her imagination a male-female union with a partner. One partner in fantasy attempts a caricature of one sexual role; the other partner attempts the opposite. Though the reality of the situation is thereby impaired, orgiastic pleasure of a minimal sort is obtained. The individual feels safer emotionally than he would with a "real" sexual partner.[11]

A. Ellis:

In seeing these individuals with severe homosexual problems, an active form of psychoanalytically-oriented psychotherapy was employed, and *one of the main therapeutic goals was to help the patient overcome his fear of heterosexual relations* and, through improved sex-love relations with members of the other sex, to minimize his homosexual interests and activities. The therapeutic goal was not that of inducing the patient to forego all homosexual interests because . . . that would be unrealistic.

The abnormality in homosexuality consists of the exclusiveness, the fear, the fetishistic fixation, of the obsessive-compulsiveness which is so often its concomitant. The aim of psychotherapy, therefore, should be to remove these elements: to free the confirmed homosexual of his underlying fear of or antagonism toward heterosexual relations, and to enable him to have satisfying sex-love involvements with members of the other sex.[12]

Allen:

We thus assume that homosexuals are men who in some way experienced a very deep disappointment which turned them against the female sex.[13]

I find that a large number of timid, shy men who have drifted into homosexual relations have done so because they are afraid of women. They have never developed the male aggressiveness, and literally do not know how to make love to a girl. They feel that if they do so she will be shocked.[14]

Cole:

The male homosexual incurs *fears of the vagina*. Incidentally, it is these same fears which underlie the phenomenon known as premature ejaculation. The man is able to insert the penis into the vagina, but he unconsciously desires to get it out as quickly as possible, so that no matter how he may consciously long to be able to prolong the stimulation, he cannot. The orgasm occurs spontaneously and quickly. Premature ejaculation is a psychological, not a physiological problem. But what is only a partial difficulty with the sufferer from premature ejaculation is virtually a total one for the male homosexual. He cannot stand it even to insert the penis, let alone have an orgasm. This fear of the vagina makes it necessary for him to confine his sexual relations to someone of his own sex, someone without the fearful vagina and with the reassuring penis. A similar attitude prevails in the Lesbian, who fears the penetrating penis and can enjoy sex only with someone who does not possess such a frightening organ. The so-called castration complex seems to play an important role in this process.[15]

PROXIMATE FACTORS

Psychogenic factors do not produce their trauma in one day. They are not like a sudden automobile accident. They are slow and persistent like some cancerous growths. After all, there are other ways to produce wounds than a quick jab with a knife. It is just as possible to produce a wound by gently scraping back and forth on the surface of the skin with a dull nail.

The factors so frequently mentioned in case reports are more likely to be precipitating, rather than causative, factors in etiology. Some of those to be mentioned are reported quite frequently; others are much less commonly found in the history of homosexuals. A knowledge of these factors is important from several standpoints — e.g., they are part of the natural history of the disorder, such knowledge may be useful in the prophylaxis and treatment of it, and such knowledge may help the counselor in the development of insight into his client. Actually, a knowledge of these proximate factors may be more important to the counselor than the more basic theories. Anomaly expressed this in a different way:

> A study of the prenatal influences which may have contributed to the condition may be interesting and useful to the professional psychiatrist, but an investigation into the present surroundings and friends of the subject is likely to accomplish more immediate good.[16]

These factors will be discussed under these titles:

1. Disturbances in the interfamily relations
2. Separation of the child from the parents
3. Sexual immaturity
4. Mistreatment of one parent by the other
5. Other situations

1. *Disturbances in the interfamily relations* frequently lead to deviation. Such disturbances usually follow one of several patterns:

a) Rejection of the child by the parent of the opposite sex. "A tragic proportion — eighty percent — of homosexuals owe their inversion to their mothers. It is those who love us most who are capable of doing us the greatest harm."[17]

b) Seduction of the child by the parent of the same or opposite sex.

c) Rejection of the parent of the opposite sex by the child.

In cases of homosexuality there is almost always a history of unhappy parent-sibling relationships. The homosexual comes frequently from a broken home in which the remaining parent is emotionally unstable, rejecting, or overpossessive. Rejection by the parent may be evidenced in actual neglect or in cruel treatment for real or imagined sexual explorations on the part of the child. Rejection may have a secondary important effect. The rejected child is frequently lonesome and will seek companionship. If the companion he seeks turns out to be an invert there is little doubt that seduction will be the result.

Seduction is a common method of introduction to homosexual practices. Such seduction does not always occur outside the home. According to Johnson and Robinson parental seduction of the growing child is quite common. "It may be extremely subtle or as blatant as incest."[18] A frequent though seldom recognized form of seduction is a lack of modesty in the home.

"Momism" is a frequent source of difficulty. In such cases the undue attachment usually starts with an overpossessiveness on the part of a parent, usually the mother, although "Pop" may also be a "Mom." Soon, however, the child may establish an abnormal dependence on the parent so that a two-way "silver cord" may be established. Such situations may be the beginning of homosexual tendencies. Prolonged attachment of the child to the parent of the opposite sex may produce an identification which may later cause the male child to act sexually in imitation of his mother or sister. Another result is possible: the child, if a boy, who develops a close maternal attachment may later experience strong feelings of guilt and by identifying all women as maternal figures find sex possible only with individuals of the same sex. An overprotecting parent may interfere more directly with the child's normal sexual development by refusing heterosexual dates to his children. West writes:

> Homosexual adaptation occurs when heterosexual adaptation proves too difficult. This is why a too puritanical upbringing can be dangerous. A child instilled with disgust for normal sex is all the more likely to try furtive, substitute outlets. The history of sexual perverts, homosexuals and otherwise, suggests strongly that an overmoralistic upbringing can have a most evil influence.[19]

2. *Separation of the child from the parents* for a long period during early years is likely to lead to confusion in regard to his proper sexual role, and homosexual seduction is rendered easy. Early entry of children into boarding schools where they associate exclusively with members of their own sex is especially hazardous. Such children, as they grow, will experience the natural biological evidences of

developing sexuality. Knowing only the self-sex they are likely to associate this erotic feeling with individuals of the same sex. Even when there is no overt activity there are likely to be strong feelings of guilt and a conviction of inversion. Such feelings from whatever cause foster lack of ego strength with consequent feelings of inferiority or inadequacy which may lead to a fear of having one's sexuality subjected to a test and consequent fear of accepting adult responsibilities in marriage. Such feelings might well result in the retention of the already experienced homosexual attraction. Such feelings of inadequacy may foster an already present fear of the opposite sex (see p. 57) especially if the individual has any physical or emotional handicap.

Absence of the father from the home due to death, divorce, employment, or military service may be interpreted by the child as a rejection. More frequently it leads to a treatment of the child by the mother as a substitute for the father and indirect or even overt seduction is likely to occur. In this respect West commented:

> So one might go on and on, but the point could hardly come out more clearly. Among Henry's cases it is sometimes difficult to categorize the parents with precision, but well over half conform to the pattern of absent or unsatisfactory father and a mother who dominates the child's life to an unusual degree. But the cases also show how other factors obtrude in even the most clear-cut instances of mother fixation. . . . In matters of sex, the boy normally identifies with his father and takes upon himself his father's manly, assertive approach to life.[20]

3. *Sexual immaturity* with a failure to develop an adequate adult capacity for love as a cause of homosexuality is in accord with the psychoanalytic concept of the development of adult sexuality. According to this hypothesis each individual goes through successive stages in his sexual development (see p. 35). Emotional traumata may cause an individual to become fixated at any of these levels. Fixation at the homosexual level may result in the development of adult homosexuality. As properly understood, in regard to normal development, the homosexual stage of sexual development means only that during this period boys are interested in boys and tend to play boys' games and girls play with girls at girls' games. There is no implication of latent or of overt sexual activity. In recent years parents have had a tendency to interfere with this phase of development by pushing their children too early into heterosexual associations. This cannot help but have detrimental effects.

4. *Mistreatment of one parent by the other.* Homosexuality may have its beginning in the home where the father is cruel to the mother, and for this reason the boy may hate the father. On the other hand, if the child is neglected, he may come to hate all women. Overprotectiveness on the part of one or the other parent may be a factor in the forming of homosexuality. For the child, heterosexual outlets would mean infidelity to the parent.

5. *Other situations* which various authors have considered significant in specific cases are the following:

a) A very important element of environment is the existence of societies of homosexuals in every large city; a young boy or girl through curiosity may be drawn into these circles.

b) Cruel or excessively strict punishment for sex play in childhood; i.e., a girl may come to believe that only sex activity with boys is taboo.

c) Excessive parental concern for imagined future sexual misdeeds is unwholesome for the child.[21]

d) Poor sexual information. The boy who is inadequately instructed may continue to picture the vagina as a bloody mouth as he pictured it in his early fantasy (castration fear).

e) Gratifying early homosexual experiences.

f) The parent who thinks that sex is "dirty" may transmit this attitude to a child.

g) Lack of effective males in the family. The example of a weak, henpecked father will certainly not inspire the boy with confidence in his relations with the other sex.[22]

h) Fear of loneliness.

i) Parents who want a boy and treat the girl that is born to them as if she were a boy, or want a girl and dress their boy in girlish fashion, letting his curls grow long and polishing his fingernails, and so on.[23]

j) A puritanical view of marital intercourse may be the occasion for the development of homosexuality.[24]

k) The very antithesis of puritanism may lead to homosexual practices, e.g., if the child is reared in a home where the parents are known to be sexually careless and promiscuous. The youngster follows the example of his parents whose affections he has enjoyed but seldom.[25]

l) Sibling jealousy is also worthy of mention; the boy may see his sister preferred (or the other way around) and, feeling rejected in his own sex, may adopt the attitudes and characteristics of the preferred sex in gait, gestures, and behavior to win favor.[26]

m) The rejected child who looks for a protecting being on whom to center affection, finds none such in his home, and finally meets with an adult seeking a homosexual outlet.[27]

n) Adolescent girls may acquire homosexual habits from fear and disgust at the rudeness of men in sexual matters.[28]

o) Both St. Paul and St. Augustine suggest that homosexual sins are the result of a wider sinfulness and an abandonment of moral standards. These views have been strikingly confirmed by contemporary research workers, for, in many, although not all, homosexual "case" histories, there is a background of parental divorce, separation, or estrangement. If homosexual practices are in fact increasing, may not the cause be traced further back to broken homes and the decline in standards of heterosexual morality?[29]

In specific cases it seems quite likely that other factors may play a part — certainly all possible factors have not been enumerated. There was, for example, Fred, who up to the age of fifteen years had his room plastered with pin-up girls and who masturbated frequently with heterosexual fantasies. About this age he heard that masturbation and sexual relations with girls were sinful. He turned to homosexuality for sexual relief because no one had told him that this was wrong. He became quite active as a homosexual.

Where the fusion of the sex instinct into the total personality of the individual is either long delayed or only partially, if ever, accomplished, or where the instinct remains fixed at an infantile level of development while its strength increases, there is a danger of the development of sexual perversions. By such sexual perversion, including homosexuality, is meant a deviation of the sex instinct from its natural goal. As the natural instinct becomes more mature, it is normally directed toward a person of the opposite sex. This is in contrast to its less specific activity during the time of childhood and early puberty. During this period of life the sex instinct is more or less undetermined, often turning toward the same sex or to objects not in keeping with its ultimate purpose. If the naturally inclined instinct is so misused in individual actions that it cannot attain its primary purpose of procreation, there may be perverse individual acts, caused through seduction or other lapses.

Homosexuality in the strict sense, the type with which we are primarily concerned in this study, refers only to those sexual deviations which are so deeply rooted in the general personality of the individual that they pervade his whole mental life in all its aspects, not merely those which pertain to sex.

ADDITIONAL MATERIAL ON ETIOLOGY

To encourage further research into the literature, I have prepared abstracts of one book and several important articles which I hope will provoke the reader into looking up the originals.

IRVING BIEBER, editor, *Homosexuality — A Psychoanalytic Study* (New York: Basic Books, Inc., 1962), pages 303 ff.

This book represents the findings of a recently completed nine-year study by the Society of Medical Psychoanalysts of 106 male homosexuals. In the opinion of the authors the role of the parents in relationship to each other and to the son is of prime importance. All parents of the homosexuals studied had severe emotional problems with each other which in turn created an abnormal environment in which to rear the child.

Here are some of Bieber's conclusions:

> The father played an essential and determining role in the homosexual outcome of his son. In the majority of instances the father was explicitly detached and hostile. In only a minority of cases was paternal destructiveness effected through indifference or default.

> A fatherless child is deprived of the important paternal contributions to normal development; however, only a few homosexuals in our sample had been fatherless children. Relative absence of the father, necessitated by occupational demands or unusual exigencies, is not in itself pathogenic.

> A good father-son relationship and a mother who is an affectionate, admiring wife, provide the son with the basis for a positive image of the father during periods of separation.

> We have come to the conclusion that a constructive, supportive, warmly-related father precludes the possibility of a homosexual son. . . . Most mothers of homosexual sons were possessive of them.

SANDOR RADO: "A Critical Examination of the Concept of Bisexuality," *Psychoanalytic Medicine*, II, October 4, 1960, pp. 459–467.

Rado insists at the outset that "There is no such biological entity as sex . . . sex of the gametes and sex in bodily structure or expression are two radically different things."

The whole reproductive system of a human being comprises more than his sexual organs. It is composed of a multitude of cellular structures, organic secretions, and functions. Each of these structures, secretions, and functions contributes to the total sexual activity of the individual. No one of these parts may be taken in itself as the sole criterion of sex. Therefore it is absurd to establish "maleness" and "femaleness" simply on the basis of the structure of genital organs or on the relative amounts of androgen or estrogen in the body.

The sex of an individual can only be determined by looking at the reproductive system as a whole. Sex is not merely a small bundle of cells within a larger bundle of cells. We should consider sex more as a group of factors which is part of a larger group of factors . . . a complex biological system which we call the human being.

When we study this human being in his totality we realize that he is more than cell tissue. Besides his cell structure he has drives and activities — all of which are tied into his pleasure system. When we look at human beings from this perspective, we are better able to understand why some become homosexuals. Homosexuality is simply an attempt on the part of some human beings to fulfill the tendencies of their pleasure system when it has been thrown out of line by some other factor in the total integration of the human being.

Human beings will perform acts of sexual intercourse without having any intention of reproduction, and with the sole intention of achieving pleasure. They may even perform acts of sexual intercourse without intending insemination. Their sole intention is to achieve pleasure. We can find this difference between the physical and emotional factors in any heterosexual act. We also observe that in any sexual act the male always achieves a distinctly male pleasure and the female always achieves a distinctly female pleasure.

When we look at the homosexual's activity we find that he has separated the reproductive function from the pleasure function. All sexual activities whether heterosexual or homosexual are eventually oriented toward one goal — the pleasure that results in the orgasm reflex. The homosexual simply is incorporating an abnormal means of stimulation to achieve his pleasure goal.

Besides the sexual pleasure system there are other pleasure systems — oral, anal, and tactile — which are parts of the total pleasure system of the total individual. These pleasure systems interact on one another and together they achieve an integration on a higher level. The integration of these subordinate pleasure systems undergoes a series of changes throughout the life span of the individual.

It would seem legitimate to conclude from what Rado has said that the pleasure system which is part of the larger entity called the human being is subject to other factors on a higher level of integration. If this is true, then the functioning of the pleasure system as a whole would be partially determined by other systems. We might speak about a logical system in the individual. This would be the whole system of activities by which a man reasons and orients himself to reality. If some block arose in the logical system — suppose that the person judged marriage to be at best a bad risk — then his pleasure system might be adapted in line with this conclusion. In this case, the individual would not derive pleasure from anything he saw as directly related toward marriage. This would block off sex pleasure so far as marriage was concerned — and the pleasure might seek some other outlet. In this case the compromise might be homosexuality.

LIONEL OVESEY: "The Homosexual Conflict," *Psychiatry,* Vol. XVII (1954), pp. 243–250.

Ovesey describes the origins of homosexuality in relation to the concepts of masculinity and femininity and the struggle for supremacy in our culture. One of the dominant factors in Western culture is the exaggerated emphasis put upon all kinds of success. The concept of success is involved with masculinity and femininity because in our culture masculinity is identified with strength, dominance, and superiority, whereas femininity is equated with weakness, submissiveness, and inferiority. In other words the traits of masculinity are associated with success, and the traits of femininity are associated with failure.

Ovesey then goes on to say that a male who fails in any field begins *unconsciously* to have doubts about his masculinity. He says, in fact, that the unconscious process of reasoning can be written out in the following steps:

1. I am a failure, therefore
2. I am castrated, therefore

3. I am not a man, therefore
4. I am a woman, therefore
5. I am a homosexual.

(Ovesey says that if there is any doubt about this unconscious thought process, it may be easily demonstrated with dream material.)

The homosexual conflict contains the aspects of sex, dependency, and power. Only the sexual aspect really has sex as a motivation behind it. The other two — dependency and power — are not truly sexual in motivation but they work with the sexual apparatus in order to achieve their own effects and they determine the kind of sexual activity a homosexual will adopt.

The homosexual who is extremely dependent on others for any feeling of achieving success tends to take a passive role. In each case he symbolically incorporates the masculinity of another male into himself. The active homosexual — that is, the one who assumes the male role in a homosexual relation — is homosexual because he is afraid of sex with women; but he still retains enough independence and power so that he is incapable of seeing himself in the feminine role. This active masculine type attempts a compromise by loving an individual of his own sex. But this loved individual must have feminine characteristics. The masculine type of homosexual may even practice fellatio and anal mount, but in each case is the one acting rather than the one acted upon.

M. BOSS: *Sinn und Gehalt Der Sexuellen Perversionen* (*The Meaning and Content of the Sexual Perversions*) (Berne: Medizinischer Verlag Hans Huber, 1947). Review in *Psychoanalytic Quarterly*, 17 (1948), p. 106.

Boss is of the opinion that homosexuality, like other sexual perversions, is an attempt at compromise between the urge to love and inhibiting environmental factors. The urge to love seeks to express itself but is unable to do so in a heterosexual manner. Factors in the environment (such as conditioning, learned attitudes, etc.) do not allow this heterosexual outlet.

The homosexual act is an attempt to bypass these barriers and establish some positive kind of emotional relationship with the world around us. This attempt is doomed at the outset. The homosexual tries to be satisfied with only half a loaf rather than with no loaf at all.

Clinic 5 — Notes

1. See O. Fenichel, *The Psychoanalytic Theory of Neurosis* (New York: Norton, 1945); Karen Horney, "The Problem of Female Masochism," *Psychoanalytic Review,* 22 (1935), p. 241.
2. Charles Berg, M.D., and Clifford Allen, M.D., *The Problem of Homosexuality* (New York: The Citadel Press, 1958), p. 143.
3. Harry Stack Sullivan, *The Interpersonal Theory of Psychiatry,* Helen Swick Perry and Mary Ladd Garvel (eds.) (New York: Norton, 1953). Quoted by Irving Bieber *et al., Homosexuality* (New York: Basic Books, Inc., 1962), p. 9.
4. Quoted by Bieber, *op. cit.,* p. 10.
5. *Ibid.,* p. 303.
6. Donald W. Cory, "Homosexuality," in *The Encyclopedia of Sexual Behavior,* Albert Ellis and Albert Abarbanel (eds.) (New York: Hawthorn Books, Inc., 1961), Vol. I, p. 491.
7. *Ibid.,* p. 492.
8. Quoted by William Stekel, M.D., *The Homosexual Neurosis* (New York: The Physicians and Surgeons Book Company, 1934), p. 15.
9. Stekel, *op. cit.,* p. 15.
10. Walter Bromberg, M.D., "Homosexuality," in the *Encyclopedia of Mental Health,* Albert Deutsch and Helen Fishman (eds.) (New York: Franklin Watts, Inc., 1963), Vol. III, pp. 751–752.
11. Dr. Howard Davidman, "What You Should Know About Homosexuality," *State of Mind* (published by CIBA, Summit, N. J.), Vol. II, No. 4 (April, 1958), (pp. not indicated.)
12. Albert Ellis, "The Effectiveness of Psychotherapy With Individuals Who Have Severe Homosexual Problems," *Journal of Consulting Psychology,* Vol. XX, No. 3 (1956), p. 191.
13. Clifford Allen, *A Textbook of Psychosexual Disorders* (London: Oxford University Press, 1962), p. 176.
14. *Ibid.,* p. 185.
15. William G. Cole, *Sex and Love in the Bible* (New York: Association Press, 1959), p. 358.
16. Anomaly, *The Invert* (Baltimore: The Williams and Wilkins Company, 1948), p. 130.
17. Paul Le Moal, "The Psychiatrist and the Homosexual," in *New Problems in Medical Ethics,* Dom Peter Flood (ed.) (Westminster, Md.: Newman Press, 1955), Vol. I, p. 82.
18. Adelaide M. Johnson, M.D., and David B. Robinson, M.D., "The Sexual Deviant," *Journal of the American Medical Association,* 164 (1957), pp. 1559–1565.
19. Donald J. West, M.B., *The Other Man* (New York: Whiteside, Inc., and William Morrow and Company, 1955), p. 152.
20. *Ibid.,* pp. 148–149.
21. Johnson and Robinson, *op. cit.*
22. "The Hidden Problems," *Time,* December 28, 1953, p. 29.
23. Dom Thomas V. Moore, O.S.B., "The Pathogenesis and Treatment of Homosexual Disorders," *Journal of Personality,* Vol. XIV, No. 1 (September, 1945), p. 79.
24. John F. Harvey, O.S.F.S., "Homosexuality as a Pastoral Problem," *Theological Studies,* Vol. XVI, No. 1 (March, 1955), p. 90.
25. *Ibid.*
26. James H. VanderVeldt, O.F.M., and Robert P. Odenwald, M.D., *Psychiatry and Catholicism* (New York: McGraw-Hill Book Company, 1957), p. 429.
27. Moore, *op. cit.,* p. 79.
28. VanderVeldt and Odenwald, *op. cit.,* p. 429.
29. Norman St. John-Stevas, *Life, Death and the Law* (Bloomington, Ind.: Indiana University Press, 1961), p. 215.

"A diagnosis of homosexuality based solely on physical evidence is not possible."[1]

The comment is frequently heard that an individual "looks" like a homosexual or that two men or two women who live together or are frequently seen together are "probably" homosexual. Such statements are not only uncharitable but, if based on such evidence alone, may result in grave injustice. It should be understood that there is no physical evidence in either the male or female homosexual which would lead to their recognition as sexual inverts. There are, of course, female impersonators who mimic the mannerisms of women for their own purposes, but many of these are not inverts; those who are are usually prostitutes who wish to "flaunt their charms" before other homosexuals. Some are transvestites, the majority of whom are not homosexuals (see p. 93). A few will be transsexualists (see p. 95). Some of these readily adopt feminine characteristics.

PHYSICAL CHARACTERISTICS

In the popular mind homosexuals have distinct physical characteristics. It is important to point out the falsity of this common belief.

In the following statement, Dr. Kinsey gives a good summary of what is "commonly believed" on this point:

> It is *commonly believed*, for instance, that homosexual males are rarely robust physically, are uncoordinated or delicate in their movements, or perhaps graceful but not strong and vigorous in their physical expression. Fine skins, high-pitched voices, obvious hand movements, a feminine carriage of the hips, and peculiarities of walking gaits are supposed accompaniments of a preference for a male as a sexual partner. It is *commonly believed* that the homosexual male is artistically sensitive, emotionally unbalanced, temperamental to the point of being unpredictable, difficult to get along with, and undependable in meeting specific obligations. In physical characters there have been attempts to show that the homosexual male has a considerable crop of hair and less often becomes bald, has teeth which are more like

those of a female, a broader pelvis, larger genitalia, and a tendency toward being fat, and that he lacks a linea alba. The homosexual male is supposed to be less interested in athletics, more often interested in music and the arts, more often engaged in such occupations as book-keeping, dress design, window display, hairdressing, acting, radio work, nursing, religious service, and social work. The converse to all of these is supposed to represent the typical heterosexual male. Many a clinician attaches considerable weight to these things in diagnosing the basic heterosexuality of his patients. The characterizations are so distinct that they seem to leave little room for doubt that homosexual and heterosexual represent two very distinct types of males.[2]

It should be emphasized that masculinity and maleness are related but are not synonyms. Size of body or genitalia has no relation, for example, to masculinity.

Dr. Berg is emphatic in regard to the absence of physical characteristics significant of homosexuality:

> In general, the statement I made ten years ago in my book *The Sexual Perversions and Abnormalities* still holds true and is unlikely to be disproved. This is that "we can state with confidence that there is no discernible difference between the physique of the homosexual and heterosexual by any tests, microscopical, macroscopical, biochemical, or endocrine of which we are aware at present."[3]

Cory also emphasizes this lack of specific characteristics in the invert: "The ordinary run of homosexuals are not to be distinguished from their fellow citizens by a casual observer."[4]

CHART I
Comparison of Effeminate and Noneffeminate Homosexuals*

	Effeminate	Noneffeminate
1. Aware of homosexuality by age 11	62%	8%
2. Knew about homosexuals by age 13	75	50
3. Knew about heterosexuality by age 13	71	92
4. First homosexual partner older by at least 6 years	48	33
5. Repetition of first act in one week	87	50
6. Repetition of first act with same person	78	50
7. Passive in first relationship	57	17
8. Passive relationship preferred in adult life	90	40
9. First ejaculation due to homosexual act	42	0
10. Frequency more than 4 acts a month	62	30
11. Frequency in prison more than 4 times a month	60	15

* Compiled from data contained in "Effeminate Homosexuality: A Disease of Childhood" (this investigation was supported, in part, by the U. S. Public Health Service Grants MH-7081 and MH-5804 from the National Institute of Mental Health), R. Eugene Holemon, M.D., and George Winokur, M.D., Department of Psychiatry, Washington University School of Medicine, St. Louis, Mo.

EFFEMINATE AND NONEFFEMINATE HOMOSEXUALS

Based on both personal observation and that of others, the author does not believe that there are any physical characteristics which distinguish homosexuals from heterosexuals. There are certain homosexual individuals who from habit or intention have developed traits which give them an effeminate appearance. Although this group is greatly in the minority, there apparently are differences between them which, however, are not physical but psychological. In a recent study by Holemon and Winokur these differences were described. Chart I, page 72, was compiled from data in their article.[5]

PSYCHOLOGICAL CHARACTERISTICS

Physical Attraction

The physical attraction between homosexuals has many characteristics in common with the erotic attraction of heterosexuals. There is the same yearning for the presence of the loved one, the same physical desires, and the same joy in his presence. In the homosexual relationship, however, there is more suspiciousness, less trust, more selfishness. Homosexual associations are usually full of strife and seldom persist. In such relationships there is usually one partner who assumes a more passive role. Such passivity may not continue into other homosexual relationships and the passive partner of one may be the aggressive member of another. The physical sexual activity of homosexual males is usually more active than that of female inverts and in this respect differs from the activities of Lesbians who are less concerned with overt sexuality and are more often concerned only with companionship. The true homosexual has a genuine aversion to heterosexual relations and although he may associate with members of the opposite sex at an intellectual level he has no interest in them as sexual partners.

The following statement volunteered by Patient II is enlightening on this point:

A homosexual love affair may have all the characteristics of a heterosexual love — the same anticipation, the same delight in the company of the beloved, the joy in receiving a letter, in telephone conversation, in doing things for the beloved or in having things done by the loved one.

The relationships possible are as varied as there are kinds of homosexuals, I might even say, as many as there are kinds of human beings. There are homosexuals who are completely faithful to one person throughout their whole life. [I have never known of a case. — AUTHOR] But these seldom are altogether smooth relationships. They are marked by possessiveness, jealousy, and a struggle for power. After all, the homosexual is never entirely sure of himself, and he is bound to be assailed by doubts when the partner goes away for two or three days — especially if they are living together. And if one of the partners is older, he may become self-conscious about his age. Or the younger man may pick up with someone else just to prove he is not dependent upon an older person. Insecurity is the plague of all homosexual relationships.

The relationship may break up from social pressure. The two homosexuals may attempt to conceal their affection for each other by acting out scenes of cold detachment in the company of other people. The exaggerated detachment is one of those instances in which "the lady doth protest too much." In enacting these scenes the inverts are likely to concretize this cold detachment. Homosexuals are always hypersensitive. It does not take very much to break a love situation.

Homosexual Marriages

Thompson says that homosexual "marriages" are frequently dominated by sadomasochistic feelings, by hate and fear, and sometimes by a child-mother relationship. She asserts that sometimes, however, a great deal of mutual help is afforded to homosexuals by these unions. A timid man, for example, may establish homosexual contact with a stronger man; or a homosexual who is afraid of the world may attach himself to some homosexual who will support him and protect him as a mother does a child. When Thompson speaks about mutual help in these unions she is probably not thinking of them in a long-term view. To merely leave a timid man in his timid condition and to bolster him with false props does not help the man himself.[6]

I have never heard of a homosexual "marriage" that was platonic. And it is no real help to the homosexual to be in the company of another homosexual who will engage him in unproductive sexual acts.

Hans Giese made a five-year study on the sexual relationships among two thousand homosexual men and among one hundred homosexual women. He found that the male relationship was usually an unstable one whereas the female relationship was more frequently permanent and firm. The male homosexual tends to recapitulate his youthful experiences. He plays certain roles and adopts mannerisms.[7]

One of the reasons for this may be found in another study made by Giese wherein he concluded that in the male relationship there was a greater tendency toward actual physical sexual satisfaction whereas in the female relationship there was a great display of tenderness, but not so much a need for physical expression. Giese also pointed out that where there is actual physical expression, it differs in the male and female homosexual relationships. Many homosexuals are content with expressing themselves physically by caressing the body of the one loved. The mere assurance of being loved is enough.[8]

Although male homosexuals often enjoy feminine company and women, in turn, enjoy the company of male homosexuals and may even be sexually attracted to them, it is a fallacy to believe that exposure of homosexuals to seduction by attractive women will favorably affect their condition or even arouse them sexually. Nothing is further from the truth. Homosexuals are as unaffected by feminine charms as a heterosexual would be by a fellow male. This must be stressed so as to quash the idea that marriage is a cure for homosexuality. On the contrary, the homosexual-heterosexual marriage is merely a prelude to tragedy (see p. 135).

Not all male homosexuals are attracted to all other males whether they are homosexual or heterosexual. In this respect they resemble the heterosexual individual who similarly is not physically attracted to all members of the other sex.

Some homosexuals are attracted only to adults; others, only to adolescents; still others, to children below the age of puberty; and there are even some who prefer their homosexual relations with old people. Even where an attraction exists they may not seek a physical outlet, but find sexual satisfaction in exhibitionism, transvestitism, voyeurism, fetishism, or in other perverse activity.

RACIAL CHARACTERISTICS

The experience of Patient I will be drawn upon for a description of sexual practice in other cultures. He comments:

I think some note should be made of racial background in sexual habits. Again I can only speak from personal experience and from information gained from others. In the Arab world where homosexuality is a common thing, it is usually in the form of pederasty, or anal relations. Fellatio is almost never indulged in, nor are caresses with the mouth in any form. I have never run into any form of perversion, as you term it, among the Arabs. [It is interesting to notice that Patient I apparently does not regard homosexuality as a form of perversion. — AUTHOR.]

The Latin world has also a very direct approach to homosexual acts — but here fellatio is indulged in, as well as anal forms. But again the thing is very natural, and not tied up with perversions of any kind. I have rarely in my many years in Latin countries found perversions among the homosexuals. The French indulge in more complicated forms of sex but, I feel, from viciousness, not because of the need to express themselves sexually in this way.

But it is when one gets into the Nordic countries that one rarely finds homosexuality without complete perversion, masochism, voyeurism, fetish-ism — the whole gamut is always a preliminary to the sex act, and one rarely finds an individual who wants the simple sex act without all the rest. This is the rule in Germany, and as one gets into Scandinavian coun-tries, it really gets wild — where the most complicated and recherche forms are indulged in, these often being more the end of the sex act than sex itself.

The English are in the above class, but then one gets into the Celtic elements where one finds that the mental side of sex, the stimulation of the imagination, not by acts, but by words is absolutely essential to a satisfactory sex act. This kind of lechery that the Celts indulge in as a part of sex is rather peculiar to them. I don't think I have ever run into it in other races than in the Scotch and Irish and Welsh groups.

The Americans, I find, are almost seconds to the Scandinavians in their approach to sex. Perversion is the rule among homosexuals. Sadism and masochism seem definitely to be increasing here. Very neurotic habits are prevalent. I recently met an Air Force officer — a man of forty odd, with no signs of homosexuality, who finally proposed relations with me, but stipulating that he could only indulge in fellatio if his partner smoked a pipe while he was doing the act. Unfortunately, a pipe is inclined to make me ill, so I had to decline his services. I don't know, but if I had a fetish of this sort I would feel some sort of embarrassment about proposing it, but he seemed to feel that this was his normal method of sex, which he could not have without the pipe smoking business.

One thing I have noted is that the rather flagrant homosexual is more normal in his sex act than the type that one would not suspect of homo-sexuality as there are no outward signs or physical characteristics that is more apt to indulge in these fantasies and perversions.

Then again I have noted that racial background in these habits tends to continue — the Italo-American, though three generations here, is more natural in his sex act, like his Latin family, than the German-American who follows his racial pattern.

DEPRESSIVE FEATURES

Many homosexuals are depressed and confused by their sexual relationships. The following autobiographical sketch contained in a letter directed to her therapist reveals quite frankly the emotional reaction of a Lesbian (Patient III) to repeated attempts to establish a homosexual union of some permanence. This is typical of the feelings of guilt, confusion, and suicidal depression which so frequently confront her:

Doubt that I'll have the nerve to mail this — I will have to take a couple more drinks to give me courage, I guess — shouldn't have started drinking the vodka — but I couldn't just keep on thinking — I wanted to just lay down and sleep and not remember — now it's worse than before — and I'm not drunk enough to blame anyone but myself — how can I think something and yet not think it — if I really did think nothing mattered and I didn't care what happened — why am I so disgusted now at both of us — mostly at myself — what kind of a person am I really — am I part of the thoughts and beliefs that I have or am I in two parts — what I do and what I feel — am I just a weak immoral person whose desires rule or am I someone with a sense of right and wrong?

All of this is as mixed up here on this paper as I feel — I know for sure I'd never get this told if I were talking to you — I can't even get it down in writing so it makes any sense at all — if I get this written and have the nerve to mail it — what will be your attitude — is a person beyond help who would openly do what I did tonite — I had a couple of drinks hoping to drown out my aching head and all my thoughts — and had reached the stage where I could say nothing is important — I don't care what happens any more — It was the wrong time to have a visitor — and especially one like Jim — anyway we had a drink together — what do I blame the rest on — the drinks — loneliness trying to make myself believe I didn't care what happened — or the thought that at least for a little while I wouldn't be all alone — any of those reasons — or is the truth in another reason — that if I ever did have any integrity or any decency, I'm losing it — I don't know any more how I feel — except confused — Why was I so suddenly sick — and not mentally — at that point — I was physically ill — nauseated — he had only pulled me down on the davenport — put his arms round me and kissed me — all I could think of was that his face was hard, not soft and smooth like a girl's — and then all I could feel was that I was sick — and that I hated him — Even now — after all these hours I still have that feeling of hate — and yet I don't actually hate him — maybe I hate the maleness of him — hate him because he wasn't Mary — he left shortly after that and that should end this sordid tale, but far from it — as the vodka wears off, the whole thing became more of a nightmare.

I wish so much I could put my arms around Mary — and that is a wish without any physical desire — a wish to hold on to something solid in the middle of what seems to be all confusion.

Am I becoming the kind of person I've always disliked — one whose values go no deeper than the first layer of skin — one whose desire today is all important — and tomorrow — a new fact — a new desire — still the ruling force — or have I always been that person — with a veneer — coated with what I thought was decency and self-respect — and now the veneer is wearing off — showing the person hiding under it — and not a pretty picture — the episode with the girl at the post office — no excuse or reason that it happened — reason maybe — my weakness of character — the nurse at the hospital — an unhappy episode that had no beginning and no ending — like something built and hanging in space — no start — no finish — just the middle — and Joan — I guess even the most despicable character would hesitate with a seventeen year old — and who could sort out all the phantoms in a million dreams — and most of all my wild phantasies about Mary — how much decency and self-respect can be left in anyone after all that?

Shocking — illegal — immoral — ridiculous — whatever adjectives may be used by anyone else — I know that the life Mary and I had together was the one nearly perfect thing in my life — and I know that I loved her as deeply as it's possible to love another person — and I also know that she was the one person who has ever loved me completely — and that love was based on something more than physical desire — Mixed up as this is, all I'm trying to say is a big *why* — why — I'm making a mental shambles of what we had because of the dreams I have of Mary — my desire has become the center of my whole mind — I think — From the dreams I have I wonder if our whole life together wasn't one long sex orgy — why — why should something that was a secondary matter — most of the time — now be so uncontrollable — am I turning into a sex maniac?

It took me so long to forget — or at least bury them below the surface — the things my mother said to me when she found out about Peggy and me — but I finally built up enough confidence — or conceit — to face most people — and even to feel that I was a decent human being with the rights that other people enjoy — but now I feel like all my carefully built fences have fallen — and I'm right back where I started — with all my doubts — maybe I am a "depraved, immoral thing."

If you've read all this, I suppose you think I should be in a mental hospital for sure — maybe you're right — I looked at this gun a long time tonight — and kicked myself for being so damn smart and throwing the box of bullets out — and you told me that anyone who tries that is definitely "ill" — so . . .

LATENT HOMOSEXUALITY

Latent homosexuality has only recently been recognized as an entity. As a consequence it is poorly understood and frequently not diagnosed. It is, however, a serious cause of unhappiness in marriage and frequently leads to its disruption. Since the concept is comparatively new and frequently unrecognized, its importance as a cause of unhappiness in marriage cannot be underestimated.

Definition

Overt homosexuality, as previously defined in Clinic 2, *is a persistent, postadolescent state in which the sexual object is a person of the same sex and in which there is a concomitant aversion or abhorrence, in varying degrees, to sexual relations with members of the opposite sex.*

Latent homosexuality refers to this same condition but, in this case, it exists outside the patient's consciousness. This condition may also be referred to as *unconscious* or *masked homosexuality.* The important element here is that the individual is not aware of his homosexuality as such. It does, however, produce certain conscious attitudes which although they may not appear to be related to homosexuality may puzzle or frighten him. In some cases the manifestation may be, for example, a preference for perverse forms of heterosexual intercourse such as fellatio or sodomy; in other cases, it may show in partial or complete impotence in heterosexual relations. In women it may cause dyspareunia or frigidity.

There has been extensive discussion as to the real meaning of the term "latent" as it refers to homosexuality. The term apparently has its origins in the writings of Freud. The discussion has revolved around the question as to whether *latent* means *dormant* or *potential.* Dormant would mean that fully developed and matured functions were present unconsciously in an inactive state, whereas *potential* would mean the presence of possible, but undeveloped, functions.[9] A lengthy discussion of this topic is not intended here, but experience leads to acceptance of the belief that the condition represents one which is dormant and not merely potential. This means that the homosexual tendency is repressed and, therefore, out of consciousness, but nevertheless it is dynamic and capable of affecting conscious behavior and attitudes.

Clinical Manifestation of Latent Homosexuality

Clinically, the affected individual may experience only periodic, transient, free-floating anxiety. To the diagnostician, however, the condition may manifest itself in a variety of symptoms which may reveal themselves in different degrees of frequency. The condition occurs in both sexes.

1. There may be a lack of sexual interest in the other sex. This may be manifested by a delayed interest in social dating which may continue until it is commented upon by associates. Even then, if manifested, the interest remains purely platonic. Due to a reaction formation the subject may on occasion display an antisexual puritanism.

2. There may be a lack of sexual arousal even when "petting" is undertaken. That is frequently done out of curiosity to see if sexual arousal will take place; at other times, merely because it seems to be expected.

3. A preference for the company of the same sex. This is obviously only significant when the other sex is available.

4. The occurrence of varying degrees of erotic fantasy in regard to the self-sex. This is likely to arouse some anxiety because, although its significance is not understood, it is regarded by its subject as "abnormal." Such fantasy may be associated with masturbation. There is a tendency for such imaginings to be masochistic in nature; if so, they may involve the other sex.

5. Erotic dreams of a homosexual nature, in both their manifest and latent content, occur with varying degrees of frequency. They may also be associated with anxiety.

6. There frequently occurs an obsessive curiosity concerning inversion, and in men there may be an excessive interest in physical culture as if there was a need to prove masculinity.

7. In addition to this curiosity such individuals may express a fear of being homosexual without being able to offer an explanation. This may not, however, seem unreasonable to them in view of their recurring thoughts and feelings. Such a preoccupation may be associated with an obsessive tendency to look at the genital area of the self-sex.

8. They may give a history of advances made to them by overt homosexuals. Their reactions to such advances may be quite violent. They may also report being uncomfortable or self-conscious in the presence of known or suspected inverts.

9. Childhood or adolescent experiences may have occurred. These, however, should not be regarded as significant *per se,* but only if related to other, and continuing, manifestations.

10. In some cases there may be present traits which would indi-

cate an identification with the other sex in thoughts or attitudes. Occasionally there may have been present a more or less conscious desire to be a member of the other sex.[10]

11. If such individuals get married, varying degrees of impotence may be manifested. This may reveal itself in an almost total lack of sexual interest; e.g., in one case there was only one act of intercourse in 36 years of marriage; in other cases there may be a gradual decrease in sexual interest until it is displayed only on the urging of the heterosexual partner.

12. This disorder is of much greater importance in men than in women. In the man the sex act requires active participation whereas the woman may be passive. The man must give; the woman receives. Impotence and frigidity are unitary in the male; they are not necessarily related in the female.

It must be emphasized that in such cases the individual is not consciously aware of his basic disorder and, except in adolescence, may never have overtly experienced homosexual arousal.

ADOLESCENT HOMOSEXUAL ACTIVITY

Special attention must be paid to adolescent homosexual activity, although it does not necessarily lead to adult inversion. Patient IV, who is 27 years old, describes his own adolescent experience as follows:

Before I entered the military service I performed a number of homosexual acts. When I was examined for a job, I told them about these, and they seem to think that I am probably a homosexual because of them. I had not given it a thought until they asked me about them. It had been completely out of my mind. I never discussed it with anyone. I wasn't very proud of what I had done, but I regarded it as past. At the time I didn't think anything about it.

I performed my first act when I was 14 or 15 years old — I can't actually remember the first act — I tried to forget it. Right now, I couldn't say exactly how it came about. The first act I can recall was with a boy about my own age. We used to go on camping trips. I probably made the suggestion, but I'm not certain. We performed 69. On other trips we kept this up. It probably went on for two or three years. He was not the only one. There were acts with others such as at summer scout camps. My last homosexual contact was about 8 years ago. That was the end of it. I went into the service and didn't perform any homosexual acts either in the service or since.

I was shy in high school with girls, but I did have some dates. I spent most of my time camping or hunting. I dated a couple of girls I worked with. In the service I didn't date much, but after the service I began to date a couple of girls, quite steady. Right now I'm engaged to get married. I do a fair share of petting which I enjoy, and have relations with other girls every time I have a chance. My sex dreams up to two or three years ago were jumbled up. In the last couple of years, they have been about "making out" with women. In the last six months I haven't had any sex dreams. Before the service I used to dream of men. I want to forget it so bad I don't talk about it and I don't like to hear others talk about it. It upsets me to talk about my early experiences.

I have been engaged to get married for about a year. I have dated this girl over two years. We have both petted and had relations which have been very satisfactory. I was in the service for two years. During this time I had no sexual problems and no temptations — I thought at first maybe I would have because I didn't know anybody. The first heterosexual relations I had were on a weekend pass with a prostitute. I couldn't get aroused — I didn't complete the act. I masturbate about once a week with fantasies of nude or part-way nude women. You get strange ideas of right and wrong — it seemed wrong to do it by rectum.

Discussion of the Case

This is not a clear-cut case of adolescent homosexual experimentation and is presented for that reason. It is only the cases which are not clear that promote discussion, and I hope that this case will do so. On the positive side, in favor of the purely adolescent nature of the sex play are the following:

1. It stopped at the age of 19 years. This is a little late, but there could well have been a delayed adolescence.

2. It occurred under circumstances of isolation in camps and on hikes. It might be argued that the camps and hikes were sought to make opportunities.

3. The subject was shy with girls through high school but did have some dates.

4. Present dreams are heterosexual.

5. He has had no homosexual contacts for eight years.

6. He is petting and having heterosexual relations regularly and plans to get married.

On the negative side are:

1. He states that he performed 69, although there were other acts. This is a type of relationship in which mutual simultaneous fellatio is performed. This is not a common practice in adolescence.

On the other hand, he may have read about it in a book and decided to try it.

2. He had sex dreams about men until he was 21 years of age, and his sex dreams for several years after this were "jumbled up." He was probably going through a period of sexual confusion.

3. It still upsets him to talk about these experiences.

To help evaluate this subject a series of psychological tests were performed. Most of these were not unusual. Those most suggestive of pathology were the Rorschach and the Thematic Apperception Test which were reported as follows:

Rorschach Personality Test

The out-of-the-ordinary and significant things about this patient's Rorschach test include:

1. Relatively meager number of responses for a person of his intellectual level (23 total).

2. Also, especially in relation to his intellectual level, slow responses, indicating a lack of breadth of interests and little evidence of resourcefulness.

3. Frequent inability to accept his responses without qualifications and reservations.

4. Basically introvertive type of personality; indications of inadequacies in handling human relationships.

5. Evidence of inner anxiety, frustrations, and struggle.

6. There are no sex content responses and the "sex-loaded" card (VI) shows nothing out of line with his dealing with the rest of the cards.

7. In general he had much more trouble dealing with the unstructured situation presented by this test than with the more structured situations. He was hesitant, unsure of himself, and seemed insecure in the situation.

8. His Rorschach test generally suggests a rather high degree of drive and ambition, with a somewhat inadequately developed personality to meet all the demands he sets himself.

Thematic Apperception Test

The stories produced by the patient were extremely brief, were generally on some type of human conflict or struggle for attainment situation. Despite instruction to include them, his stories generally lacked outcomes. Sex themes were not prominent.

Opinion

It was my final evaluation that this patient represented a delayed adolescence and that he was not a homosexual.

In the history of many individuals there will occur instances of sexual contacts during adolescence with members of the same sex. These have usually been in the nature of sexual exploration or mutual masturbation. As a rule these acts have not been frequent and have usually occurred before the age of sixteen. The individual giving the history may or may not have been the aggressor. If these experiences occurred over a relatively short period and did not recur as the individual grew older they may usually be disregarded as being significant of homosexuality. They are not usually significant as evidence of the individual's adult sexual orientation. Anomaly agrees with this:

> It is fairly evident that the homosexual acts of adolescence are not necessarily evidence of inversion, nor are they even an inevitable accompaniment of inversion.[11]

For this reason the counselor must be careful never to tell the boy who admits masturbation with his companions that he is a homosexual or in danger of becoming one.[12]

> A priest who in confessing an invert lad pictures in detail the sins and punishments of the Cities of the Plain may drive his penitent out of the Church, or even out of his mind; while a fair and honest facing of the peculiar difficulties of mind, body and conscience which envelop him may turn a potential sinner and criminal into a happy and useful member of society.[13]

These experiences are almost always the result of sexual curiosity which leads to experimentation. They may occur in both sexes. The significant factor is that they have occurred in a circumscribed period of time and have not persisted beyond adolescence.

Particular Friendships — Angelism

Certain types of adolescent love would seem to partake of the character of homosexuality, not because they necessarily result in an overt sex act, but rather because of the thinking behind them, or the emotional immaturity of the parties involved. Some authorities see in exclusive friendships of this sort a phase of homosexuality; but even when these friendships go so far as to manifest themselves in acts which are characteristic of physical love, one should not be too quick to call them homosexual. There are many factors which could be involved, e.g., unhealthy curiosity seeking to satisfy itself, or youthful sexual passion seeking satisfaction under conditions in which there are no persons of the opposite sex available, and so forth. In many cases such disorders are temporary.[14]

There is a danger, however, that true homosexuality may have its origin at this age and lead to the fixation and inversion of the normal sex instinct. The emotional reactions are very similar to those of the teen-age boy and girl who develop a "crush" on a member of the same sex. Even though the situation may begin with a spiritual bond, it is nonetheless a "particular" bond which may degenerate into physical expression. Such love would have the same characteristics as the personal sex attraction found in heterosexual love.[15] Such a degeneration in an adolescent friendship may come from a false conception of love. As Father Harvey says:

> The youth thinks that he can love with the soul alone another young man who loves him in the same way. This is "angelism," a most apt term coined by the French. For usually these individuals are inclined to regard their love as more noble than that between the sexes. They like to fancy themselves as Davids and Jonathans. They presuppose that there is something angelic about love between man and man, while love for women is simply a means of gratification for the carnal passions of men, and, accordingly, does not evoke from the human heart the noblest sentiments of friendship.[16]

Such individuals feel that only the intellectual is capable of such high-level friendship. They feel that their love for each other is with the soul only. These are, of course, rationalizations, probably unconscious, for a relationship that is outside the realm of natural emotional reaction. A love of man for man is natural, but when it takes on the characteristics of heterosexual love, e.g., exclusiveness, emotional reactions to the other party when separated, etc., the relationship has gone beyond the platonic stage, and entered the realm of angelism and homosexuality.

"The love of angelism does not seek God, but seeks self in neighbor. It is lacking in supernatural motivation which purifies and elevates human love to the level of divine charity."[17] It is a discovering of oneself in another being, and rejoicing in the recognition of one's reflection. "Thus, it is often accompanied by a smug feeling of false superiority."[18]

> Dr. Le Moal has underlined the sin of angelism which is found in all homosexuality, a sin so very well defined by Gide in his *Cahiers d'Andre Walter:* "To love with the soul alone a soul who loves you in the same way." And does not love, for the adolescent, ordinarily present itself above all as a union of affection?[19]

An excellent example of angelism which illustrates all of its characteristics is found in the novel *Compulsion* by Meyer Levin.[20] Although this book is fiction, it is alleged to be based on fact. It purports to illustrate the personalities of Leopold and Loeb, who were convicted of the murder of Bobby Frank in the 1920's. This murder was the direct result of the superiority these two boys felt, and this superiority was to a great measure caused by their angelism, which was also manifested in overt homosexual acts performed by them. A reading of this novel gives a good insight into the emotional and mental processes characteristic of misguided immature love.

Venereal Disease

Promiscuous homosexuals (almost to the same extent as heterosexual prostitutes) are a source of the spread of venereal disease. Syphilis accounts for the highest number of cases with gonorrhea being less frequent. Ketterer says that "the degree of promiscuity of some homosexual persons is significant (W. V. Bradshaw, 'Homosexual Syphilis Epidemic,' *Texas J. Med.,* 57:907–909 [Nov.], 1961). During the prediagnostic period promiscuous persons may have 10 to 20 contacts or more (J. D. F. Tarr and R. L. Lugar, 'Early Infectious Syphilis: Male Homosexual Relations as Mode of Spread,' *Calif. Med.,* 93:35–37 [July], 1960)."[21] Of the contacts named by such individuals venereal disease will develop in 20 to 50 percent.[22] In a letter to the *Journal of the American Medical Association,*[23] Dr. Herman Goodman stated that in a study reported in *Acta Dermato-Venereologica* and in other recent studies, the investigation

> . . . began with four male homosexual syphilitics and led to the discovery of 748 exposed persons (735 males and 13 females), plus 243 named by these as suspects (228 males and 15 females).

The chief of the District of Columbia's Venereal Disease Control Division referred to homosexual venereal disease as "a definite and serious problem in Washington."[24] Homosexual organizations apparently recognize the extent and seriousness of the problem as evidenced by the fact that the Mattachine Society of Washington is working with the Health Department in the District to distribute a pamphlet on "Homosexuality and Venereal Disease." This pamphlet stresses the confidential nature of the information given to the Health Department and stresses the fact that such information will not be handed over to the police. This is recognized as an important factor in epidemiological studies. Ketterer, for example, states:

> Indication of homosexuality on confidential reports (Public Health Service form No. PHS-2936) may create problems for patients. The venereal disease offices of the State of California and the USPHS both agree that the epidemiological report should not indicate information identifying the contact as having been exposed to venereal disease through homosexual practices. (Venereal Disease Informational Report, State of California, Department of Public Health, Oct 15, 1962) Even code symbols identifying the informant as homosexual have resulted in employment problems and other personal liabilities.[25]

An important role for the counselor is to urge the invert under his care to be aware of this problem. He should encourage him to seek frequent and adequate examination if he is continuing his homosexual activity, especially if he has many or new contacts.

CLINIC 6 — NOTES

1. John F. Oliven, M.D., *Sexual Hygiene and Pathology* (Philadelphia and Montreal: J. B. Lippincott Company, 1955), p. 435.
2. Alfred C. Kinsey *et al.*, *Sexual Behavior in the Human Male* (Philadelphia: Saunders, 1948), p. 637.
3. Charles Berg, M.D., and Clifford Allen, M.D., *The Problem of Homosexuality* (New York: The Citadel Press, 1958), p. 43.
4. Donald W. Cory, *Homosexuality: A Cross Cultural Approach* (New York: The Julian Press, Inc., 1956), p. 386.
5. R. Eugene Holemon, M.D., and George Winokur, M.D., "Effeminate Homosexuality: A Disease of Childhood," mimeographed notes distributed after the talk delivered at the annual meeting of the American Psychiatric Association, May, 1964, Los Angeles, Calif.
6. Clara Thompson, "Changing Concepts of Homosexuality in Psychoanalysis," *Psychiatry*, 10 (1947), p. 188.
7. Hans Giese, M.D., *Jahrbuch Psychol. Psychother.*, 1 (1953), pp. 223–225.
8. Hans Giese, M.D., "Differences in the Homosexual Relations of Man and Woman," *International Journal of Sexology*, May, 1954, pp. 225–227.
9. Leon Salzman, "The Concept of Latent Homosexuality," *American Journal of Psychoanalysis*, Vol. XVII, No. 2 (1957), pp. 161–169.

10. Irving Bieber (ed.), *Homosexuality — A Psychoanalytic Study* (New York: Basic Books, Inc., 1962), pp. 257–258.
11. Anomaly, *The Invert* (Baltimore: The Williams and Wilkins Company, 1948), p. 143.
12. Dom Peter Flood, O.S.B., ed., *New Problems in Medical Ethics* (Westminster, Md.: The Newman Press, 1955), p. 115.
13. Anomaly, *op. cit.*, p. 130.
14. John F. Harvey, "Homosexuality as a Pastoral Problem," *Theological Studies*, Vol. XVI, No. 1 (March, 1955), p. 87.
15. Gerald Kelly, *Modern Youth and Chastity* (St. Louis: The Queen's Work Publishing Company, 1941), p. 18.
16. Harvey, *op. cit.*, p. 88.
17. *Ibid.*
18. *Ibid.*
19. Rev. Charles Larere, "Passage of the Angel Through Sodom," in *New Problems in Medical Ethics*, Vol. I, p. 111.
20. Meyer Levin, *Compulsion* (New York: Simon and Schuster, 1956).
21. Warren A. Ketterer, M.D., "Venereal Disease and Homosexuality," special communication in the *Journal of the American Medical Association*, Vol. 188, No. 9 (June 1, 1964), pp. 811–812.
22. See W. J. Daugherty, "Epidemiological Treatment of Syphilis Contacts," *Journal of the Medical Society of New Jersey*, 59 (November, 1962), pp. 564–567. See also W. V. Bradshaw, "Homosexual Syphilis Epidemic," *Texas Journal of Medicine*, 57 (November, 1961), pp. 907–909.
23. *Journal of the American Medical Association*, Vol. 185, No. 5 (August 3, 1963), p. 415.
24. Reported in an article by Jean M. White in the *Washington Post*, Feb. 3, 1965, p. 1.
25. Ketterer, *op. cit.*, p. 812.

Differential Diagnosis of Homosexuality

In attempting to establish the presence of homosexuality in an individual there are two basic questions which need examination:

1. Does the individual find himself sexually stimulated by thoughts about members of his own sex?

2. Does he find himself sexually unmoved by thoughts about members of the opposite sex?

If both of these questions are answered "yes" and the individual is past adolescence there is reason to believe that he is a homosexual. In some cases, of course, these questions are easily answered and it is readily apparent that the individual is an invert. In other cases where the condition is less obvious or where it may exist in a latent form or where the individual for some reason wishes to conceal his condition the diagnosis can be less easily established.

RATING SCALE FOR HOMOSEXUALS

The late Dr. Alfred Kinsey devised a schema or scale which portrayed a heterosexual-homosexual continuum. His seven points for evaluating the degree of sexuality were:

0. Exclusively heterosexual, with no homosexual.
1. Predominantly heterosexual, only incidentally homosexual.
2. Predominantly heterosexual, but more than incidentally homosexual.
3. Equally heterosexual and homosexual.
4. Predominantly homosexual, but more than incidentally heterosexual.
5. Predominantly homosexual, but incidentally heterosexual.
6. Exclusively homosexual.[1]

This scale has several useful purposes: (1) it demonstrates the continuity of sexual feeling and indicates that the homosexual is not a separate sex; (2) it is helpful in establishing a prognosis; and (3) it helps in the evaluation of the results of treatment. Since it is relatively objective, it is even more useful.

DIAGNOSTIC CONSIDERATIONS

Although the diagnosis is obviously dependent in large measure upon the subjective statements of the patient, one is interested in much more than merely an answer to the question, "Is this individual a homosexual?" Other questions which must be answered would include:

a) Where does he stand on the Kinsey scale?

b) Is he sincerely interested in therapy?

c) Based on the background, is he prepared for the long process of therapy?

d) What vocation is most suitable for him?

Many other questions will occur. A psychogram (a complete psychological study) of the patient should be done of sufficient intensity to satisfy the need of the counselor or therapist to understand his patient and his needs. This examination should be systematic and be suited for the purpose for which it is intended. It should include the following:

1. *A careful and thorough history of the subject* which should go as far back into childhood as possible.

It is generally conceded that the homosexual tendency reaches far back into the life history of the individual, and that the critical fixation of the sex drive is usually an accomplished fact well before adolescence, probably even before what we would designate as the *use of reason*. Nevertheless, it is with the coming of adolescence and the first awakening of romantic love that the homosexual is confronted with the painful anomaly of attraction to the same sex. It is then that the self-probings and self-accusations begin, the disillusionments, the inability to comprehend "why God has made me a freak."[2]

Since the homosexual drive may make such an early appearance careful research in the early life is necessary. In some cases there is a clear-cut attraction to males as early as five years of age; in others the boy has tended to engage in "girlish" games or in some other way shown a feminine identification. In other cases there has been seduction by an older person or by older children. The relationship of the child with his parents should also be carefully explored, as should the many factors considered under the subject of etiology (see Clinics 3 and 4). Careful consideration should also be given to the possibility that the manifestations of the individual are not those of genuine homosexuality but may represent delusions of homosexuality, obsessions of homosexuality, the loss of sexual inhibition due to alcohol, or merely adolescent homosexual activity (see *infra*).

2. *A study of the client's dreams.* Most individuals, especially those who are not leading an active sex life, have sexual dreams periodically. In men these are associated with nocturnal emissions; in women they may be associated with physical orgiastic reactions which occur during sleep. The characteristic content of such dreams reveals the sexual orientation of the individual. Occasional dreams involving homosexuality should not be considered diagnostic but when most or all of the sexual dreams are indicative of a homosexual orientation, they are important indicators of inversion.

3. *Psychology tests* should be performed in many cases. These tests are especially valuable in those cases in which the dynamics are not clear and where the clinical picture may be confused. They may be helpful in the determination of the basic personality pattern. Projective tests are the most useful, such as the Rorschach Ink Blot Test and the Thematic Apperception Test. It must be realized that these tests are no more reliable than the individual administering them. The psychologist who is to perform them should be chosen with care. There are no right and wrong answers to such tests, so that each must be interpreted individually.

It would serve no useful purpose to go into detail on what these tests might show. For details, reference should be made to source material in the bibliography.

It should be remembered, of course, that psychological tests of all sorts are fallible.[3]

4. *The presence of homosexual fantasies,* either alone or associated with solitary masturbation, are quite diagnostic.

5. *Persistent jealousy of self-sex associates* when attention is paid to them by others is a very common manifestation of inversion.

6. Keep in mind that *perverse acts are not always evidence of true homosexuality.*

In spite of all the above considerations the diagnosis of homosexuality can be very difficult. Above all, the counselor must carefully distinguish between the sin and the sinner, between the act and the actor. The law at present condemns the deed without much understanding of the doer, nor is it always administered with compassion. There is here then a double role for moral education: toward a deeper comprehension of the psychological causes and a clearer condemnation of the evil acts.

DIFFERENTIAL DIAGNOSIS

There are a number of disorders in which the part played by homosexuality is not clear. In some of these disorders, e.g., transvestitism, some believe that inversion is related to its etiology. In others, e.g., the paranoid delusion of the schizophrenic, the part played by homosexuality is debated. Since these conditions sometimes confuse the diagnosis of homosexuality, they will be discussed briefly.

These conditions are:

1. Transvestitism
2. Transsexualism
3. Pedophilia
4. Paranoid schizophrenia
5. Obsessions of being a homosexual

Also to be considered is the subject of adolescent homosexual acts. These have been considered above on page 81.

Transvestitism

The term "transvestite" itself comes from *trans,* a "transference," and *vesta,* the "clothing." Many individuals are of the opinion that transvestites are all basically homosexual. For example, Allen[4] says, "This [homosexuality], I believe with Stekel, is the main or primary root of transvestism [*sic*]." Kinsey[5] states that only a small portion of transvestites are homosexual. Oliven[6] states that there is no connection between primary transvestitism and homosexuality. Brown comments that "it is unfortunate that transvestitism is often considered nothing more than a form of *homosexuality.* As a matter of fact, these two phenomena are separate and independent."[7]

From these statements it is clear that there is little agreement among the authors. I have changed my own mind over the years and now do not believe that homosexuality is basic. It would seem to me, rather, that the condition represents a sexual deviation in which satisfaction is derived from the wearing of the clothes of the other sex, or leading their kind of life, rather than through orgasm.

although this may also occur. There is no doubt that some transvestites are also inverts.

There is also some disagreement among authors as to definition. This definition of Kinsey seems quite satisfactory. I believe, however, that it should also include the comment that there is a certain degree of sexual satisfaction involved.

> An individual who prefers to wear the clothing of the opposite sex, and who desires to be accepted in the social organization as an individual of the opposite sex, is a transvestite.[8]

Since transvestitism is not basically homosexually oriented, it has no real place in our clinic. A few comments regarding its general nature, however, may be helpful.

It is more common in men, although its exact frequency is not known. The practice is usually indulged in by the male at home, since it is illegal for a man to wear a woman's clothing in public. The opposite is not true. Many male transvestites are married and frequently quite happily so, especially if the wife understands the condition. They frequently have children, and to all outward appearances, under most circumstances, seem to lead a normal life. The condition is, in most cases, quiescent for longer or shorter periods of time. Should the desire to transdress be frustrated the subject may be moody and not infrequently drinks too much. They are seldom vigorous in their sex life.

As to etiology, there are several suggestions. Probably there is no single etiology for all cases. Idiopathic transvestitism must, of course, be differentiated from the cross-dressing of male and female impersonators, of male prostitutes seeking to attract other males, mannish Lesbians, and other allied conditions.

Since this subject is so tangential to our main theme, little time will be spent on its psychopathology. It may be the result of *conditioning* by parents who raise their children as if they were of the other sex. Parents, for example, who were disappointed in the sex of the child may repeatedly tell the child so and, at least during early childhood, dress him in the clothes of the other sex. *Fetishism* has also been suggested as a basis for transvestitism with the clothes of the other sex serving as a fetish. *Exhibitionism* has also been suggested as a factor in etiology. In this case the male, at least, would be seeking affection by the assumption of the clothing of a woman,

or perhaps he has "accepted castration" and considers himself a
woman.

There is a rare form of transvestitism in which the individual
dresses in the clothes of an infant or small child. This is referred to as infantosexual transvestitism. It is obviously a regressive
phenomenon.

Such cases seldom come to the attention of the counselor or
psychiatrist except through the wife who may be startled and anxious
when she first discovers the condition. I saw one such patient who
was almost literally dragged in by his wife with the comment, "I
want him examined. I think he is a homosexual." When the story was
elicited it developed that the wife had found, on an upper shelf in
the closet, a complete set of woman's underclothing and several pairs
of high-heeled shoes. It also developed that the husband was impotent
under normal circumstances, although they had three children. Eventually it developed that he was potent only when he wore the
woman's underwear and shoes. Since he anticipated his wife's refusal,
he would put on the shoes and underwear and masturbate. No
attempt at insight therapy was made in this case, but the cooperation of the wife was enlisted, and he was allowed to wear the
female clothing during intercourse. This led to a successful sex life,
and when last heard from they were both doing well.

An interesting paper on this topic, called "The Disease of the
Scythians," or "Morbus Feminarum," was published by William A.
Hammond, M.D., in the *American Journal of Neurology and Psychiatry* in 1882 (Vol. I, p. 458). Dr. Hammond blamed the difficulty among the Scythians, which was earlier described by Herodotus,
upon excessive horseback riding. He also described a condition of
the *mujerados* (men who had changed to women) which be observed
among the Pueblo Indians of New Mexico. In both of these instances
he appeared to be describing transvestites who had adopted the way
of life of a woman.

He closed his article by describing the case of Lord Cornbury,
governor of New York during the reign of Queen Anne. He did not
seem to recognize the case as one of transvestitism, but he did
recognize its psychiatric nature. The case he described was reported
by Dr. Spitzka in the *Chicago Medical Review* for August 20, 1881,
under the title "Historical Case of Sexual Perversion":

This person was "a degraded, hypocritical and utterly immoral being, devoid of anything remotely resembling a conscience, and so thoroughly mean and contemptible that it required but a short period of his rule to array all classes of the population against him. . . . He was devoid of caution, a spendthrift, and altogether erratic in his behavior. Obtaining his position through nepotism, the Queen was compelled to remove him, although he was her own cousin and the son of Lord Clarendon. On losing his position, his creditors in New York locked him up in a debtor's prison, where he languished until his father died. Then money was sent over to liberate him and to enable him to represent the English people in the House of Lords!"

"Unfortunately," continues Dr. Spitzka, "only the most notable feature of his insanity has been preserved in the records. But that single feature demonstrated the character of his mental disease. His greatest pleasure was to dress himself as a woman; and New York frequently saw its governor, the commander of the colonial troops and a scion of the royal stock, promenading the walls of the little fort in female attire, with all the coquetry of a woman and all the gestures of a courtesan. His picture, which is extant, shows him to have had a narrow forehead, an unsymmetrical face, highly arched eyebrows, a very sensual mouth, and a very feminine expression. The painting, of which I have seen a copy, represents him in female dress, with his neck and part of his chest bare, and his hair done up in female fashion."

Transsexualism

In this condition there is a desire to change sex. Allen[9] includes in the definition the delusion that a change of sex is taking place. This would seem to be a manifestation of a schizophrenic delusion rather than transsexualism as usually understood. A few years ago a case of this type was seen in the clinic. This was a young man of about 25 years who began to feel that he was changing into a woman. This was his explanation of why he felt attracted to men. He sought psychiatric help but was unable to accept insight. After several months of this feeling, he developed hemorrhoids which began to bleed. He was then quite certain that he was a woman in that he had started to menstruate. He, therefore, went to a secluded spot where he "castrated himself." It must be remembered that in the psychiatric sense "castration" implies removal of the penis, not removal of the testicles as in the surgical sense.

"The term transsexualism has been applied to the person who hates his own sex organs and craves sexual metamorphosis."[10] The term refers to cases such as that of the former American soldier Christine Jorgenson. This case received much publicity as "a man who had been made into a woman." Actually what had happened was that the penis, the testicles, and the scrotum had been removed, followed by plastic surgery to construct a vulva. Following this, estrogenic substances were administered to cause the breasts to develop. Following the publicity given to this case, the surgeons who performed it, Hamberger, Sturup, Herstedvester, and Dahl-Iverson,[11] received 465 letters (40 percent from the United States) from transsexualists asking for similar operations. Three out of four of these letters were from males. According to Allen:

> Hamberger has published an analysis of the letters he received. These show that a desire for a change of sex is most apparent in patients suffering from transvestism. Roughly three times as many men as women wish for the operation. The average age of the men was 28½ and of the women 26 years old. He found that "a homosexual libido plays a considerable part if not a dominant role in the wish to change sex."[12]

The reasons given in the letters sent to Hamberger were:

No information   50
Always wanted to be a girl
Cannot live as a man
Life history like reported case   116
Feminine psyche in male body
Homosexual   75
Other causes (wants admission to a Buddhist nunnery!) . . .   1

Pedophilia

Pedophilia is a condition in which there is sexual activity which involves a sexually immature subject. Although the child may be of any age he is usually considered as being below the age of 14 years. This activity may occur in an individual of any sexual orientation and is not limited to homosexuals, although it is frequently said to be. The condition is sometimes confused with pederasty which refers only to erotic relations between adult males and young boys. Pedophilia refers to activity with either boys or girls. This is made clear in this definition of Oliven:

> Pedophilia is a collective term for any type of abnormal interest in a child on the part of an adult, whether in a nature of infatuation, molestation, abuse, or a pathologic desire to inflict pain. Much overlapping of motives and personality disorders can be found among the abusers of children.[13]

The male pedophile is frequently impotent, at least in his attempts with adult sexual objects. With children he is quite likely to masturbate or merely exhibit himself. Paul Friedman comments that the juvenile object is frequently a fully willing participant in these acts.[14]

Table I shows the frequency of pedophilia in relation to other offenses in 284 sexual psychopaths. Table II shows the variety and sex of the activity of the pedophile. The much higher incidence with girls would seem to rule out homosexuality as the only cause of this disorder.

Classification

Pedophilia may be classified as compulsive pedophilia (pedophilia erotica) and symptomatic pedophilia (pedophilia sexualis).

1. *Compulsive pedophilia* is a chronic disorder occurring most frequently in men. It manifests itself in a compulsive abnormal fondness for younger children. It may be divided further into two types: (*a*) tender and (*b*) aggressive.

The *tender type* of compulsive pedophilia is almost always directed toward young boys by an adult male who may be married although he frequently has difficulty in relating to women of whom, however, he is capable of being fond. His heterosexual drive may be quite deficient but he is usually not completely impotent. Masturbation in such individuals is frequent:

> In some of these deviates the impression prevails that they are vastly "attached to themselves" (narcissism) or rather to their own childhood image of themselves. For instance, they may shave repeatedly all their pubic hair, admire or even kiss their mirror image. Most of these men masturbate a great deal.[15]

The *aggressive type* of compulsive pedophilia is more frequently directed against children of the other sex. In this type, instead of showing tenderness, the subject is cruder, crueler, and more aggressive. He may physically harm the child and may occasionally panic and kill, although this is accidental rather than intentional. Not all the conduct of the aggressive pedophiliac is cruel. It may vary from intimate fondling and playful spanking to attempts to have the child masturbate him, masturbating against the child's body, or rape attempts.

TABLE I

Kinds of Offenses in Which 284 "Sexual Psychopaths" Were Involved*

	Number	Percent
Pedophilia (under age 14)	148	52
Sodomy	12	4
Other homosexuality (over 14)	35	12
Exhibitionism	40	14
Rape (forcible, attempted, and statutory)	14	5
Incest	4	1
Voyeurism, fetishism, bestiality	10	4
Obscene acts	14	5
Miscellaneous	7	3
Totals	284	100

TABLE II

Pedophiliac Activity (Limited to Children Under Age 14)*

	With Girls	With Boys	Total	Total Percent
Masturbation and/or fondling . . .	86	38	124	84
Oral-genital	7	7	14	10
Intercourse (including intercrural) . .	9	1	10	6
Totals	102	46	148	100

Both types are a serious danger to the community. Chronic alcoholics are frequent in this group. In such cases latent homosexuality may be activated. Neither type tends to change from one sex to the other in succeeding instances.

Both types must be distinguished from *Dorian Love* in which the aggressor is a homosexual who prefers relations with an adolescent male.

2. *Symptomatic pedophilia* may occur at any age past adolescence, and in about 10 percent of the cases it occurs in women. The condition differs from compulsive pedophilia in that it is symptomatic of some underlying condition such as mental deficiency or organic brain disease. These individuals are at least as much a danger to the community as the compulsive pedophiliac and less susceptible to treatment.

* Daniel Lieberman, M.D., and Benjamin A. Siegel, Ph.D., "A Program for 'Sexual Psychopaths' in a State Mental Hospital," *The American Journal of Psychiatry*, Vol. 113, No. 9 (March, 1957), p. 802.

Paranoid Schizophrenia

In the paranoid type of schizophrenia there is as a rule a poorly organized delusional system. These delusions are usually of persecution or grandeur but not infrequently are of a homosexual nature. Hallucinations also occur which are of the same nature. The "voices" not infrequently are accusatory and imply that the individual has been guilty of a variety of acts of a homosexual nature. They may respond with an emotional reaction of hostility because of the feeling of being persecuted.

Whether homosexuality is the cause of paranoid schizophrenia or paranoia has been discussed over the years. This discussion was initiated by Dr. Freud's analysis of Dr. Schreber's autobiography in which he suggested that paranoid psychotic symptoms develop as a defense against emerging unconscious homosexual desires. It is not my intention to discuss this subject at length, but Sakel and Winokur offer interesting new opinions on the relationship of homosexuality and schizophrenia.

Sakel doubts whether paranoia is a repressed form of homosexuality:

> The more recent evidence most aptly described and presented by psychoanalysts, of the symptoms of homosexuality and its reversal during the insulin treatment in schizophrenia, seem to obviate this concept and point to the fact that the sexual instincts in paranoia, which is a part of schizophrenia, are reversed (as when love becomes hate, etc.). In other words, it seems that the homosexual symptom so much stressed by Freud, far from being a cause of paranoia, is rather a symptom of a schizophrenia disease process.[16]

Winokur comes to this conclusion: "Sexual difficulties in schizophrenia are not proved, and any causal relationship between homosexuality and paranoid schizophrenia must be considered quite tenuous if not totally absent."[17]

The *differential diagnosis* in this case is usually not difficult. Other evidence of a schizophrenic reaction will be present. This is not the type of case for the counselor to handle; the patient should be referred to a psychiatrist.

Obsession of Being a Homosexual

An obsession is an overpowering, persistent, and irrational idea accompanied by feelings of tension and fear. From the conscious standpoint of the patient, the obsession is uninfluenced by logic and is distinctly unwanted.

Phobias and obsessions are closely related inasmuch as all obsessions are phobias and phobias are obsessive. The latter adds to the former a note of mental preoccupation with the object feared. The two states are practically inseparable; e.g., those who have a fear of cancer are in reality obsessed with the idea. The thought of cancer is constantly before their minds. The fear element is phobia, the thought element is obsession.

Types of obsessions: As in the case of phobias, almost anything can become the object of an obsession: (*a*) sexual obsession, i.e., the inability to eliminate thoughts of sex or sexual perversions; (*b*) irremovable thoughts of blasphemy, sacrilege, and loss of faith (commonly known as religious scruples); and (*c*) persistent thoughts of murder, suicide, and maltreatment of others or oneself.

In the situation with which we are concerned, the individual for some reason, e.g., seduction, curiosity, while under the influence of alcohol, perhaps even because of a latent homosexuality, or for other reasons, is involved in some way with homosexuality. There may not even have been a complete act. For whatever reason, he became obsessed with the idea that he is a homosexual and, as is typical in obsessions, cannot be dissuaded from this belief. The anxiety displayed by the obsessive individual over his condition is different from the apparent need that the true homosexual has to prove to those who question him the validity of his assertions. The obsessive person does, however, seek every possible reason of which he can think to prove that he is *really* a true invert.

With care and patience, such individuals are likely to respond to counseling. A careful differential diagnosis is important, because early stages of schizophrenia are often characterized by such obsessive symptoms.

SUMMARY

In summary it may be said that the diagnosis of homosexuality is usually not difficult. The determination of the prognosis may not be so easily arrived at. There is seldom an urgency for a definite diagnostic formulation. *Festina lente.*

CLINIC 7 — NOTES

1. Alfred C. Kinsey *et al.*, *Sexual Behavior in the Human Male* (Philadelphia: Saunders, 1948), p. 638.
2. Radcliffe Hall, *The Well of Loneliness* (New York: Covici, 1928).
3. D. Riccio and A. Petiziol, "Psychological Examinations in Homosexuality," *Sessuologia*, Vol. IV, No. 4 (October-December, 1963), pp. 215–218.
4. Clifford Allen, *A Textbook of Psychosexual Disorders* (London: Oxford University Press, 1962), p. 245.
5. Kinsey, *op. cit.*, p. 679.
6. John F. Oliven, M.D., *Sexual Hygiene and Pathology* (Philadelphia and Montreal: J. B. Lippincott Company, 1955), p. 397.
7. Daniel G. Brown, "Transvestism and Sex-Role Inversion," in *The Encyclopedia of Sexual Behavior*, Albert Ellis and Albert Abarbanel (eds.) (New York: Hawthorn Books, Inc., 1961), Vol. II, p. 1017.
8. Kinsey, *op. cit.*, p. 679.
9. Allen, *op. cit.*, p. 252.
10. Karl M. Bowman, M.D., and Bernice Engle, M.A., "Medicolegal Aspects of Transvestism," *The American Journal of Psychiatry*, Vol. CXIII, No. 7 (January, 1957), p. 583.
11. C. Hamberger, G. K. Sturup, and E. Dahl-Iverson, "Transvestism," *Journal of the American Medical Association*, Vol. 152 (1953), pp. 391–396.
12. Allen, *op. cit.*, p. 253.
13. Oliven, *op. cit.*, p. 409.
14. Paul Friedman, "Sexual Deviations," in *The American Handbook of Psychiatry*, Silvano Arieti (ed.) (New York: Basic Books, Inc., 1959), p. 605.
15. Oliven, *op. cit.*, p. 410.
16. Manfred Sakel, *Schizophrenia* (New York: Philosophical Library, 1958), p. 177.
17. George Winokur, "Sexual Behavior: Its Relationship to Certain Affects and Psychiatric Diseases," in *Determinants of Human Sexual Behavior*, George Winokur (ed.) (Springfield, Ill.: Charles C. Thomas, 1963), p. 98.

Female Homosexuality

Female homosexuality is a condition about which little is known. There is confusion even in regard to its incidence. It is certainly less noticeable and less disturbing socially than male homosexuality. "No doubt one reason for the ease with which we can conceal our attitude is that so few people are at all conscious of our existence."[1] The female homosexual is generally referred to as a Lesbian. This relationship between women is sometimes also called "sapphic love." The term "Lesbian" is derived from the Island of Lesbos where the renowned Greek poetess Sappho was born (circa 600 B.C.). The term "sapphic" refers to sensual indulgence associated with Sappho and her followers. St. Paul referred to such activity in his Epistle to the Romans when he condemned the pagan women who "changed the natural use into that which is against nature" (1:26–27).

In spite of the fact that male homosexuals are so involved with the law, there are practically no legal sanctions against Lesbianism.[2] There may be several reasons for this. Lesbians are more concerned with companionship than with sexual activity. Perhaps, also, because male homosexuality is frequently involved with sodomy which, in the popular mind, is disgusting and degrading. Such acts tended to lower the status of men in the public eye, whereas sex acts between women do not tend to lower either their personal or sexual status. Perhaps also, in the male, the "precious" seminal fluid is lost, whereas in the woman it is not.[3] Male homosexuality is more obvious, whereas women have traditionally shown affection for each other.

INCIDENCE

The incidence of Lesbianism is disputed. In my experience it has been twice as frequent as male homosexuality. This would mean that if there were approximately 4 percent of male homosexuals in the United States, there would be about 8 percent of female homosexuals. I realize that others disagree with these figures; in fact, reverse them.[4]

In a study of 1200 women by Katharine Davis 50 percent had shown evidence of some degree of homosexuality at some time in their lives. About one half of this number had engaged in overt activity.[5] Kinsey, in his report on the female,[6] stated that by age 45, 28 percent of women had had some type of homosexual response, but only 20 percent had had actual experience. It is interesting to note that many heterosexual prostitutes are Lesbians. Simone de Beauvoir[7] estimates that 20 percent of the prostitutes in Germany are homosexual.

THE DYNAMICS OF FEMALE HOMOSEXUALITY

According to Brody[8] the pre-Oedipal aggression in such cases is oral-sadistic and its intensification is considered as the central characteristic of homosexuality in women.

Brody also states that the unconscious attitude toward the parents is strongly ambivalent and has been described as a characteristic of homosexual women. In the sexual act, he states, the homosexual woman plays a double role. She is the one who suckles and who is, at the same time, suckled. Not only is the oral system highly charged but urethral eroticism plays a powerful part in the homosexual picture.

Homosexuality, Brody feels, is a syndrome, a mode of behavior. Homosexuals, male and female, are driven to self-degradation, expressed obviously or more subtly and to a more or less marked degree. Unable to tolerate the degraded self, they rationalize that they are so superior that there is no need for them to compete with others (healthy people). The rationalization then continues: Healthy people are so weak and degraded, so afraid of their position in life that they are driven to compete. Homosexual people never show their capabilities and at the same time are enraged that their talents are not recognized. Embittered that they have failed to receive due recognition (for traits they have never shown themselves to possess), they retaliate by refusing to show their capabilities. Homosexuals as seen by the psychiatrist are not individuals who present themselves for treatment because they and society differ as to what mode of sexuality is preferable, but they are neurotic with deep-rooted character disturbances. These people would not be healthy persons even if they lived in a society where sexuality with the same sex was socially acceptable.

As noted on page 50, both Deutsch and Horney held that difficulties in the Oedipal stage, rivalry with the mother, and predominance of castration feelings always lead to a more or less marked tendency toward homosexuality in women.[9]

CLINICAL FEATURES

Clinically, there is nothing clearly distinctive in the dress or mannerisms of the Lesbian. Traditionally, the active female homosexual is supposed to be dressed in a mannish-cut suit of somber color. This is occasionally, but rarely, true. Most of the Lesbians whom I have treated have not worn clothing which would distinguish them from other women.

One characteristic, while certainly not pathognomonic, is that Lesbians would often come to the office for consultation in pairs — one somewhat older, the younger one perhaps more feminine. Frequently the older woman (by perhaps ten to fifteen years) would have an air of proprietorship, as if to say, "I want you to take good care of this little girl."

Although there are fewer case reports on women than on men, there is little doubt about the type of sexual acts employed between them. To some extent the type of sexual contact depends on the ages of the women involved, although this is not an absolute rule. As a general rule the contacts will start with simple lip-kissing, general bodily contact, tribadism (rubbing the genital areas together),[10] mutual masturbation, manual stimulation of the breasts, oral stimulation of the breasts or genitals, deep tongue-kissing. Obviously, all of these contacts require a partner. Probably the most common sex act performed by the homosexual, whether male or female, is solitary masturbation with homosexual fantasy. In some cases an artificial phallus is employed.[11]

The life histories of Lesbians are remarkably alike, although obviously not identical.[12] Some one or all of the following facts are likely to be found in the clinical history:

1. The Lesbian is an only child.
2. She has a normal female appearance physically.
3. She behaves like a normal female in society.

4. She has wanted to play a dominant role with women.

5. She is sexually attracted to girls.

6. She preferred her father.

7. From early life her interests had been masculine; e.g., she liked boys' games, disliked dolls, etc.

8. She is disgusted with the thought of intercourse with a man.

ETIOLOGY

The factors concerned in etiology are the same as those which play a part in male homosexuality. Women, however, do not seem to have a tendency to seduce little girls, as frequently as the male pedophiliac does. Kinsey mentions seduction of young girls by older women.[13]

CASE REPORTS

As the following cases are read, reference should be made to the clinics on etiology. Clinically, as one would expect, all female homosexuals do not fall into one class. Some are "gay" and go from one partner to the other. Patient V (see below) was of this type. Two cases will be presented in this clinic. The first case is that of a young, married, psychopathic, "gay" type of Lesbian. This case is presented for three reasons: to demonstrate, with her own words: (1) The behavior and thinking of a gay Lesbian. (There may be some argument as to which type of homosexual she is. I would put her in the class of the true homosexual instead of the pseudo-homosexual group. I would do this principally because of her "total" pattern of behavior, without forming a judgment merely on her early behavior.) (2) The pattern of psychopathic (sociopathic) behavior which she demonstrated. (3) The type of patient who, in my opinion, would not be suitable for psychotherapy.

The second case (Patient VI) is quite different. She was young and unmarried, her sexual contacts were less frequent; there seems little doubt that her condition represented a neurotic disorder with true compulsive homosexuality. This case is presented as one which demonstrates many of the psychodynamics of the development of the disorder.

In both cases, the patient was instructed to freely associate, i.e., to say the thoughts merely as they came into her mind. This may account for some disconnection between thoughts; other lack of connection may be due to an editing of their productions to condense them and to eliminate duplication.

Patient V

I was born in 1932. . . . I had a very happy childhood. I was strictly Daddy's girl. It seems he and I had more in common, and were more alike than Mother and I. I guess I hurt my mother's feelings a lot. I can remember one time I got mad at Mama, and there was a picture of her and Daddy in my room — so, like the rotten brat I was, I drew a halo around Daddy's head and horns on my mother's head. That afternoon when I got home from the movies, Daddy told me Mother had been crying. I really felt awful about it, and yet sort of shocked. . . . Daddy is uppermost in memories of my childhood. It seems like he spent an awful lot of his time and energy on me. There was always a lot of yelling and contention in our house, even when I was very young, as I recall.

*   *   *

I was unquestionably a spoiled, rotten brat, very difficult and hard to manage. According to Mother, nobody could ever *make* me do anything. I guess that's the way I am now, too. I'm really a hard-headed Irishman.

I was a lousy student in school. I always got caught — never got away with a damn thing. Daddy used to say, "Mary, if you want to skip school, go ahead; but if you're dumb enough to get caught, I'll whip you." It seems like I was always standing in the hall for talking or throwing spitballs or humming, or just anything. I told one teacher to go to hell because he thought I was cheating on a test, and I wasn't, although I have cheated at times. I can remember there was one teacher I dearly loved in the fifth grade — Mrs. White. She was kind of fat, too, and she sort of understood my problem. I guess I was kind of her pet, which was pretty novel for me. I wasn't the type to be anyone's pet. I was pretty bad and uncooperative. When I was real young I used to boss all the kids around, and if they didn't like it, I beat them up; but half the time I was nice. I was a very generous kid and pretty much fun. I always had more nerve than anyone else. I really hated school because I was fat, and the kids always teased me. I did like science, though, when we studied the planets and stars and stuff. I liked music a lot, too, but I hated anything else. I took piano lessons for about a year. But I could hear the song and figure it out, so I had a hell of a time learning to read notes. Then I broke my arm, so that was the end of that. I just never went back to it. I guess I didn't think I could ever really learn to play well like my friends Alice and Jane. Alice and Jane were two little girls I grew up with . . . they lived next door. I was such a devil, though; I, like a lot of other kids, played doctor and patient with the little boys up the street. Alice and Jane never did anything like that. You know, you show me yours and I'll show you mine.

I was really pretty bad, I guess. Once I threw a rabbit down the basement steps in a fit of anger. And another time I was having a tantrum — Daddy was going to spank me and I was running around the dining room table. I always ran around the table when he tried to spank me, and I fell on one of my cat's kittens and broke its neck. It was pretty awful. I'll never forget how it ran around the room like a chicken with its head off. Maybe these two things left their mark on me — I don't know.

* * *

In Jr. High School I got suspended twice and also once in the first year of high school. I never went past the tenth grade. I got married and quit. Well, actually I quit before I even thought of getting married. I loved my husband very much. But I was married so young that I don't suppose that I really knew what love was. Jim and I lived with Mother and Daddy for a while after he was drafted. I moved from camp to camp with him, and we got an apartment off the post. I had a great deal of respect for Jim. He was very intelligent. He was a very thoughtful, considerate and affectionate person. He was also a very good lover. We lived there for about a year and then Jim was transferred to France. . . . We were in Germany for a week prior to our departure from Europe. When we got home we were fighting like the devil; and then Jim started working for a Senator during his campaign. He ran into a girl he had gone to high school with, Becky, and they had an affair and they eventually got an apartment together. And then I found out, and I also found out that Becky and I were both pregnant. It was a mess. So Jim and I broke up. Becky and I had our babies, and Jim left town a few months after the baby was born. I suffered a great deal over him and my situation, but I lived through it. After the baby was born, I went to business school for about a year and learned typing and shorthand. I also learned that there was another side of my personality, for that was where I met Jackie, my first "gay" lover. My affair with Jackie lasted approximately a year.

* * *

My first sexual experience was with a boy named Samuel Jones. I was about 14, and I thought I was madly in love with him. He was about 22 and a real bum. My mother forbade me to see him, so naturally I met him at the corner. He was only interested in one thing, but at my age I didn't realize, and I thought he loved me, I guess. I remember the first time we did it; we were in a big field. There was a big old deserted house that at one time had been a very well-kept mansion. I recall very vividly lying in the grass and Samuel trying to put it in, to no avail. It hurt like the devil and we just couldn't get it in. But the next time I'm afraid we succeeded.

* * *

Between the time I broke up with Jim and started to have sex with Jackie, the first girl, there was a period of dating and drinking. I met a

guy named Bob Brown and was pretty crazy about him. He was also a
bum. I had an affair with him, and his lack of character disgusted me so
thoroughly I wouldn't go to bed with him anymore. He was pretty rotten
to me. Then one night for no reason at all I had sex with his best friend.
I don't know why I did it. I had been out with an awful lot of guys and
said "no" before Bob. I guess I figured, what the hell.

Then I met Jackie in school. She was a bitch. I was really crazy about
her. It was almost as if I was drunk with her. I think she was the most
exciting thing in my whole life. She was mean as hell, though, and slapped
the hell out of me all the time. She was a real nut.

*   *   *

But I was just too crazy about her to get her in trouble. (After she
had more or less kidnapped me and taken me to Florida.) They would
have sent her back to a mental institution. Finally, after about a month,
she brought me back. I continued to see her for a few months, and then
I got fed up with her childishness and bully attitude and I left her. I tried
going to bed with her after we broke up once, but she just didn't move me.

By the way, I want to mention that I never touched her sexually. It was
always one way. She sort of made fun of my attempts to touch her.

After Jackie I met a very nice boy named Bill. We had a wonderful
time together. Our personalities really clicked and we laughed all the
time. He aroused me pretty much, and after we had gone together about
six months, we had sex. This was a mistake. It changed everything in my
eyes. Then I found out he went to bed with a girlfriend of mine named
Linda, and I called him up and told him off and wouldn't see him any
more.

One night Jackie called and asked me to meet her and lend her $5.00.
I did and she told me about a place in Baltimore where all the gay kids
went. I had never met anyone gay but Jackie. So I asked her to take me
there. She did, and I thought it was terribly exciting. So I started skipping
business school and going over in the afternoon, when I was supposed
to be in school. I would arrive about 10:30 in the morning and stay until
about 2:00 in the afternoon. In that way I could return home at approximately the same time I would have if I had been in school all day. I would
sit at the bar and watch all the gay girls, hoping like hell I could meet
someone I could be interested in. After a while I started staying until night
time; and then one night I met this adorable little singer named Pam. We
sort of just looked at each other for a couple of days, and then someone
introduced us. Then she took me to get something to eat after the club
closed, and then to a couple of parties. We went through the hand-holding
stage for about a month before we even kissed. It was a couple of months
before we had sex. She was a very nice person. She didn't sing for a living,
just for kicks. During the day she worked for a bank. She was, and is, one
of the most intelligent people I have ever known. She has a way of seeing
everything in the right light, in focus. She always makes me see sides of

things I couldn't see by myself. She is steady, reliable, faithful, honest, kind, gentle, affectionate, loving, a good lover, talented, considerate. Everything I can think of, Pam represents to me. I loved her very much. I'm no longer in love with her, but I have a deep respect and love for her, and I will until the day I die.

Pam and I lived in Baltimore for a while, and I could have my child on the weekends. Then I finally talked Pam into moving near my parents. We were very happy all the time. Then we bought a puppy and they didn't allow dogs in the apartment. So we moved into a lovely new apartment which we couldn't afford, even though we were both working at the time. We traded in my old Chevy and bought a new (almost new) white convertible. Then we bought new furniture. Needless to say, we were way over our heads. We had a few unexpected financial mishaps, and that was it. We started getting farther and farther behind in the rent, until we finally had to move out. We had planned to rent a house and me take the baby to live with us. So I felt I just couldn't move again and start over without him. I suggested we move in with Mama and Daddy for a couple of months until we got on our feet, but Pam wouldn't do it. Consequently I moved home and she moved in with some friends. This was supposed to be temporary, but one thing after another happened, and we were not getting along. So we never got back together.

I was pretty much of a wreck for a while. I cried all the time and was really miserable. I was alone for about a year after that. Then my sex urge got the best of me and I had an affair with a good-looking French girl named Larry. But she wasn't Pam, so I ended it after about three months, and I started drinking and going to parties and staying out all night and doing nothing. I got about ten traffic tickets and wrecked my car twice — the second time it was a total loss, and I got a few broken ribs and many bruises. I had a couple more affairs.

And then I met Sally. I met her in a bar also, but so what. Bear in mind that during all this, my home life was getting progressively worse. Daddy was thinking more than ever, and Mother was screaming more than ever, and I was withdrawing from my family more than ever, and neglecting the baby more than ever, and losing one job after another. One due to hangovers and insomnia, one due to the accident, one because I hated it, one because they went out of business. And the last because of a personality clash with my supervisor, plus the fact that I was getting more and more depressed, until I slashed my wrists and took off a week — during which I was either drunk or full of sleeping pills. Since then I have done nothing. I have been living partly at home and partly with Sally. Sally and I are so much alike that it is pitiful. I'm very much in love with her. She's a good little thing. She has a wonderful heart. She's overly sensitive and very emotional. She has a terrible temper and is very bossy and jealous and possessive. But she's kind and loving and affectionate and generous. She's steady and reliable in her job, and has many wonderful qualities. But she doesn't believe that I really love her, and I don't believe that she loves me enough to endure time. I think one day she'll leave me. I have to be constantly reassured of her love, and she has to be constantly reassured of mine.

Sexually, I have never met anyone with whom I was more compatible. She's really a wonderful lover. Sally and I fight a lot, I'm afraid, but three quarters of it is through misunderstanding. The other one quarter is mistrust. We both have to exercise a lot of patience with each other and twice as much self-control. I'm so wrapped up in her that I can't imagine life without her. Maybe if I can make my mind healthier, I can help her.

Patient VI

At the time this patient first came under treatment, she was single and twenty-two years of age; her father was a professional man. This case is presented for several reasons: (1) The patient was anxious about her condition and strongly motivated to overcome it. (2) The material is presented as it was produced in the free associations of the patient. (Obviously, not all the associations are presented, but those selected are complete within themselves. The selections were made to demonstrate etiological factors and emotional reactions. Reference should be made to the clinics on etiology before reading the case). (3) The patient had a good prognosis and represented a good case for therapy. Important factors in the good prognosis were her youth, her educational level which was postgraduate, her good family background, her good insight, and her feelings of guilt and anxiety. Ultimately she made a quite adequate heterosexual adjustment, and is today happily married with a family.

[Dream] — I was in a restaurant. There was a waitress — full-breasted — wearing a jersey sweater. As she leaned over to take my order, her breast touched my face. I immediately felt content and relaxed. She gave me her phone number. I refused to give my name and number. I wouldn't call because that would prove my perversion.

*   *   *

My thought about any boy is could I sleep with him, could I have sexual relations? I have never found one with whom I could. One night when I was drunk I went up to an apartment with a boy and slept with him. It was unsuccessful. At times I wondered how I could do it. I don't even feel that it is wrong now. I was brought up differently and yet did not feel any guilt. There was another boy who had lived abroad and seemed sophisticated. I deliberately tried to get him interested. Tried again in the back of a car — no pleasure? Why? Can I do it or not do it? Maybe I do feel a little guilty.

*   *   *

. . . I can't imagine spending the rest of my life with any man. I have felt socially insecure as long as I can remember, even as far back as the fifth grade. I can remember being hurt if I were left out of anything. If a friend is not loyal or sincere, I am terribly hurt. It seems that I want to be entirely sure of my women friends before I go out with a man. I was close to a male medical student. In giving myself to a man he must be intellectually above me and worthy of me. The medical student has been the only boy I have really admired. . . . I wish very much I were not an only child. I admired my grandfather a great deal. He was well-liked, did many considerate things, and on the other hand did many inconsiderate things, especially in regard to my grandmother. He kept a mistress whom he later married. She was a source of trouble in the family. My dad and I are not close. I admire him very much. I don't have his push. I take the easy way out. I get good grades, only because of the subjects.

. . . Once we were bathing at Ocean City. Mr. S. got fresh with Mother, and she said, "All men are disgusting. I'm not sure I can except your father." Men who are older always attract me. Intellectual women attract me. I have no attraction to younger, frivolous girls. . . .

. . . At the age of ten I had a boyfriend. It is amazing how close I was to him. I used to play "footsy" during assembly. I always wanted to kiss him, but I was afraid the other girls would see me. At 12–13 I went out with a large group of boys who were dirty and interested in girls. We went down to the railroad tracks and I let them look at me. I went through a whole period of being a nasty little kid. . . . There has always been a lot of talk about "the other woman" in our family. All the men seem to have other women as a matter of course. I have a great fear of a man dominating me. Yet, I don't want to dominate him; it is not right. Maybe that is the reason I turn to women, because I can dominate them. . . . Betty was in today. Every time I see her, even on the street at a distance, I have a terrific emotional upset. I think I am going to have to concentrate on getting her out of my mind. When Betty would come back for a week and tell me what she had done, I would make up stories because I wanted to do a lot of things, too. I have almost an obsession to be on the go. I don't want to sit still and read and think even for a minute. I have always made such a differentiation between acquaintance and friend. I get a big kick out of people asking my advice and needing me. I think I picked up this idea of being turned down from my mother. I get very afraid when I see these things in her, so I want to stay away. Dad and Mother believe I am not suited for nursing, like you did; they agreed that they would go along with me on social work. I know Mother feels badly about not going to college. Mother and I have always been a source of emotion to each other. If she cries, I cry. I have a great deal of contempt for myself, but also a conceit. Betty has always clung to me. I liked that very much, she depended on me for everything. When I saw her getting away I felt badly. She accepted my friends but I never seemed to accept hers as lightly as I wanted to. I was always embarrassed by our closeness, because I knew

it was not right. I don't think that she did. I don't know why it is when
I talk about it I have this great emotion. I wish there was someone to
take her place. I miss her depending on me.

* * *

We made it important that we be with other people. I used to beg her
not to leave. I have always had this terrific emotion over Betty. She felt
the same thing, I know. The attraction that we seem to have had is the
same attraction that a man feels for a woman. I didn't think of a perversion until after I had studied it. I like to have a man around because it
is a protection against the things I think of myself. I am weak and selfish.
I have really hoped that I could fall in love and marry him. . . . One girl
friend in New York said, "You don't seem to want me to have any
friends." I seem to recall other evidence of this overpossessiveness before
I met Betty. I don't seem to be possessive with men; one of them told me
I was not possessive enough. I've never been taught not to show my
emotions. . . . Until I met Betty, I was a "touch-me-not" sort of person.
After her I became more affectionate at home and with girls but not with
boys. In picking friends, I seem to pick those less attractive than myself,
always someone who has a problem and may become dependent on me.
. . . I was tired and lay down on the bed to go to sleep. Bad week because Betty was turned back to me in part (her father died last week).
Having her a little dependent and warmer than she has been has made it
rough. Every time I leave her I only live till the next time I can see her
and do something for her. I am afraid that when she gets over it she will
go away like she did before. I can't eat or sleep, I am jealous of everyone near her, especially boys. There is one boy who has been doing so
much for her. Seeing her dependent on him made me jealous. I don't
want to be with anyone but her. She has not been as dependent as I
would like her to be. I keep wanting to buy her things, to do things for
her, anything to bring her back. My friend is here from Maine but I haven't
wanted to be with her, even though she is my next best friend. The only
time I can have any free thoughts is when I am with her. I can't picture
anything in my thoughts without her. The thought popped into my head
at home (I had it before) of "this is fine, but wait till they get to know
you." I have felt before that first impressions were good, but I began to
. . . I think I am deliberately torturing myself, but I don't know how to
stop doing it.

The thought keeps going through my mind, would she come back if
I were ill. I think I am doing this to bring her back to me. . . . I associate
all upset emotions with my mother and yet Mother has always babied me,
we would give in to our emotions together. That is one reason I am so
afraid to be around her so much. . . . She turns to me now in her hour
of need but nothing compared to the way I would need her if the positions were reversed. . . . Do you pretend when you go to sleep at night?
I used to pretend I was a lover to my present crush. My crushes would

be of a type, young, tall, full-breasted. Greta Garbo through high school. I dated through high school, but was never much of a "necker." Mother used to say not to park. I can remember a couple of boys I used to like to neck with. There is only one time that I wanted him to kiss me. It became something you had to do. I sort of wished he wouldn't be so honorable. I felt more interested in men when I drank. It all stopped when I became interested in Betty. After that I couldn't wait for the date to be over so I could get home. I've tried to pretend that Betty was with me, but it doesn't work. . . .

Once we lived in a house near the woods where the rats came out on rainy days. I was not allowed to play in the woods because of the rats. At the age of 5–6 years, I was friendly with the boy next door, and we would take off our clothes and compare anatomy. I was never interested in dolls. I would rather have had a catcher's mitt or a train. Grandfather gave me a set of tools which I enjoyed. Grandfather called me Mike. He really wanted me to be a boy. He used to hold me on his lap and tell me the most delightful fairy tales. Those were really good days. . . .

Last night I saw a woman at the Statler. I liked her looks. I felt that I must know her. I began to plan. I decided that the first thing was to get rid of my friend, which I found an excuse for, and I waited around for her to finish her dinner, and my plan was to see if she was alone and then approach her. Fortunately, she and her friend remained together, got in a car and drove off. I even tried to get the number of the car. The idea of approaching people got into my head the other night when David told me about a homosexual approaching him. I don't see how I can be without principles like that. I told myself at the time that no matter how this turns out, I will not tell Dr. C. about it. My uncle and Mrs. B. were sort of neurotic, used to have nervous breakdowns; people used to criticize Grandmother for sympathizing with him. I don't want to be neurotic. I don't want Mother and Daddy to baby me too much. Things are getting better at home, the last few times I have been more relaxed. I can kid with Mother. I am not as strong in my religion as I should be either. There have never been any games or crafts that I could enjoy doing by myself. I never wanted to be alone. When we played house, I would always be the man and put on pants. Mrs. B. said, "you are more like a boy than a girl." Bob and I were real pals, and we are still very fond of each other. One thing you asked when I came with Mark stands out in my mind. "When Mark put his arms around you was there an erection?" I am overly conscious of it. Now when I am with David, I am constantly on my guard. I don't want him to get so worked up. . . . I went to a gynecologist at the age of fourteen and had an internal examination. I've had no dreams except vague recollection of shuffling $20.00 bills around. Just after leaving the office, it occurred to me why the word "erection" means so much to me. Last summer, I was sitting at a window at the university, looking out, and saw a man who had been sun bathing. He had a robe, but when he saw me, he took off the robe and began to masturbate. He kept it up for some time. This sort of thing seems to happen frequently in that neighborhood. I keep going back to sex because I am doing what I shouldn't do (directing her thoughts). It might not be that at all. I remember my uncle when he used to act improperly with me when I was 5 or 7. He would say, "doesn't that feel good." I would lie to him instead of telling my mother, but he really hurt. I would like to get my mind off sex, but when I talk to you, I seem to bring them out because they seem important.

*   *   *

[Dream] — Football game — girls playing — patient playing, caught pass and ran wrong way — one person cheered (girl from New York) — everyone else stood still — changed direction and made touchdown — no emotion. . . .

I enjoy David more the last ten days. I have fun with him. He really is a wonderful boy — everyone comments on what a good-looking fellow he is. He scared me one night — he asked me to marry him — I told him I wasn't ready. He said that I knew his intentions — he put me up on a pedestal. He even gave up smoking. He told me he had had other experiences with girls which he regretted now that he had met me. The fact that he's had experience sort of scared me and I froze up for a while, but I am getting over it. Every man I have ever met seems more affectionate than I am. I have the idea that all a man's mind is on is sex because all the men I've met have been like that.

. . . Girls always discuss the one who wasn't there. Now I have a great urge to find a friend, a woman, who will stick through hell and high water — I have had a lot of men friends who would, but not a woman — there again I think love is mostly sex. Men certainly go through an awfully lot to get what they want. . . . When I was in my teens and a girl would break a date with me to go with a boy, I always resented it very much. I remember one time. Ann called up to break a date. I felt badly about it. Aunt Mary said this is just the beginning, that a girl will always do that. So now as soon as a man enters the picture with any of my friends I don't trust them as much any more. I don't know whether I have ever done this myself or not — I guess I have and as I recall when I broke a date they took it all right. So now when choosing girl friends, the predominating thought is that they must have no connection with men. The one thing I would like to know is why I have always been closer to girls who are not very popular. Yet when I start going with them I try to build them up. It was the same with Betty and Pat. They turned out to be real cute "gals." Pat wrote recently and said that she was engaged and wanted to thank me. . . .

When I was 9 years old there was a kitten — he didn't belong to us — I was playing with him — I would mistreat him for crawling away. We had a housekeeper — Mother and Daddy were away — the housekeeper brought her daughter with her — I bullied her. . . .

. . . I don't know whether the role of a woman is completely submissive
or — .

Talking about a woman being passive — when I am with David I almost have to force him into taking the reins — If he thought I wanted to
go — he would go. Lately I have been letting him tell me what to do —
but it is like an act because I know I am letting him do it. I have been
trying to think if ever in my life I have been really dominated — I don't
think I have — ever. I think it would be a good thing if I were.

I know I have one or two friends whom I admire and they do sort
of dominate me — if they mention anything I give it lots of thought —
maybe I should be around people like that more. I don't know — David,
when I first went with him I don't think I admired him — now I do — as
a person. It is amazing the way he is handling me — you can see what
he is doing — but it is amazing how he does it. There aren't many men
who would have the patience with a woman — certainly not many his age.

There is an emptiness inside of me that I cannot seem to fill. What I
think it is, is someone — there is no one who talks my language. This
horrible thought occurred to me — whether I *was sexually attracted to
my own mother* (tears). It occurred to me that I am so much stronger
than she is. My mother is young — I remember thinking the same thing
before — even before I came to you. I am so afraid of my mother — any
sign of emotion scares me to death — I guess it is because I want her to
be strong. When mother shows signs of feeling inferior I just freeze up.
There is so much I could do for Mother — she has been through a great
deal and has no one to understand her. Even in friendly arguments Mother
takes my part against my father — when she does I begin to protect my
father.

When my father kisses me goodnight *I have the most horrible thoughts
— let it be a father and daughter kiss —* don't let it go any further —
such a horrible thought. I don't know why I have it. *I keep wondering
why it is that I don't want to live at home.* I wonder if it is because of
my thoughts — I wonder how much of it I put into my own mind. I want
to have a good, clean, healthy mind. I get the image of a male organ;
of David — all the time I am talking I am picturing it — I often think
of it — I can't get it out of my mind.

I told you I never masturbated — that was not true — up until a year
and a half ago I did. I told you about the man I saw masturbating. I used
to picture him doing it. When I was younger and masturbated I didn't
picture anything. I now look on masturbation as a sign of weakness —
you must exert your will.

. . . *When a woman belittles a man, all she does is make him not sure
of himself and thus deprives herself of something.*

I wish David would say more of what he is thinking — I have an idea
that I could trust his judgment more than my own. He is brighter than I
am and much more adult. I would be a pushover for him, he could wrap
me around his finger if he would assert himself. All I would need is an

assurance he would stay that way. I don't have the same attitude toward women I had when I came here at all — I don't know whether I will slip back or not. Maybe I feel that way because I want to — I couldn't imagine myself doing some of the things I once thought I could do. . . . There is one thing which David does when he kisses me (runs his tongue over my lips) which makes the whole thing repulsive — I've been kissed like that before, but I seem to expect more of David. There is no way to tell him, but I wish he wouldn't. . . .

Male organs always appear as a vivid fantasy. . . . The whole thing is just absolutely repulsive. If David stands too close in kissing me good-night, I want to push him away. I feel that I could sleep with a complete stranger rather than with David.

When I have been asked by boys to marry then I've often thought I could be their mistress rather than marry them. That is something you can get out of — you are more or less free to do as you please.

If you are really in love, you wouldn't mind being with them all the time. There are times when David is absolutely repulsive to me. He never knows what mood he is going to find me in. I have been trying to keep on an even keel. . . .

It's so strange that the slightest idea of passion on David's part is disgusting to me — why can't I understand it in him when I do in others?

When David kisses me he seems so vulnerable — seems completely in my hands. I feel like shoving him away and telling him not to be a fool — that is an awful attitude. I feel as though I am doing him a favor — it shouldn't be that way at all. I wish I could get over that feeling that any form of sexual relations have to be done because men are men. I know it isn't that way because when you love someone you want to be with him. This is the way I feel about Betty. . . .

Why can I think that the relations I had with Betty were practically spiritual whereas the same relation with a man is sensual. Maybe it is because I think that men look on it as merely physical — maybe they don't. I have no idea.

I can't imagine any man being in love with me for anything but physical reasons.

. . . Other people make changes and take them in their stride — why can't I?

It is horrible to think how close Betty and I were at one time and how the distance is growing and growing. If I just knew how to handle this fear. I seem to be afraid of everything. There are times when I still feel so bitter. I don't think at times like this that I am making any progress. I wasn't able to shake the depression or overcome the feelings. It just shows that when something hits me, I am back where I started from. It is at times like these that I feel so hurt about Betty. I still feel, however, that she has let me down. If I had only been aware a little sooner. I feel as though I was in the middle — too weak to give up but not strong enough to do anything about it.

Yesterday I felt as though I didn't want to do anything but wander around but I didn't want to wander alone — I feel as though I was back where I was 5–6 weeks ago. Maybe I'm not. It's at times like these that I wonder if I shouldn't find what I want in companionship and just stop coming to you at all.

A stranger in the street knows as much about how I am going to react to something as I do. I suppose eventually they won't. Why can't I just say to myself this is a down day and sit it out. I am not even strong enough to settle myself down to study, I have to keep going. . . .

. . . I've been brought up on the belief that men play around — I am going to hurt them before they hurt me.

Am I trying to recapture what I had with Betty? Crushes on movie stars — picture of Mae West in my room, Norma Shearer — attracted to their breasts — they were always in trouble, and I, in the masculine role, was going to get them out of trouble — they were aloof — I could approach them when no one else could — I would have intercourse with them later and that would be the end.

I can't figure out whether I like to dominate people or not. I think I do some people, but I can't figure out which ones — seems to be the weaker, more dependent people when I do. I don't do it at my work. You'd think I'd try to dominate other workers.

I had a desire to beat a horse or dominate a woman. When you ride a horse you are in complete control.

The women in fantasy have never been attractive and did not have much social opportunity — one who was lonely — and I made them happy. . . .

Tuesday night after dinner and cocktails with Dad, I had the sexual urge and the wish to dominate someone. I wanted to see Gerry, but I didn't.

. . . I was wondering tonight if my mother ever loved me — she makes me fill the gap that my father doesn't fill.

I was looking at my father the other night — he seemed so lonely — maybe he isn't at all [tears]. My mother is so cut off from him — I thought I should help him — then I thought of all the years he didn't help me — but the difference is that he wasn't aware of my loneliness, but I am of his. He has no realization at all, but Mother keeps smothering me with love.

. . . I was trying to think the other day about those fantasies I had when I was little — I was both the man and the woman — I was always like the woman — she depended on the man — was lonely — I was the woman, and the man was the way I wanted to be treated.

I don't see any of my mother in me — but I don't know what her expectations are — except to be dependent on someone.

Patient 1 (Commentary)

Because of a dearth of information on female homosexuality and the relations of Lesbians to male homosexuals, these comments of Patient I are included. They represent the observations of only one individual but, as pointed out before, he is an intelligent and perspicacious student of the topic. In spite of this, these comments must be regarded as particular statements and not necessarily uinversally applicable.

Having known a great many female prostitutes fairly well — I did have a lot to do with them during the war period, when we used them for information — I can confirm your statement that most of them are homosexual. I have talked this subject over with many of them, and feel that they have turned to Lesbian attachments, not from being basically homosexual, but from disgust and repugnance as a result of their experiences in the brothels. Being forced to repress any real pleasure with men clients, they seem to develop their own real and complete sexual orgasms with women.

I have known a few male prostitutes who rented themselves out to women. They were all homosexuals. I was intrigued enough to ask one of them, who had been a soldier of mine during the war, how he managed. He said he was capable of having a continuous erection and could operate as long as the client wanted, but he never had an ejaculation with them. He could only have an ejaculation with a man, orally. From his apparent success in the trade and opulence, he seemed to be very satisfactory and appreciated by women clients.

Another bit of brothel lore which I picked up during this time may interest you. A prostitute in Italy told me that the man who comes and pays feels free to ask the woman to do the things for him that he probably would never admit otherwise. Several of them commented to me on the very large percentage of men who wanted some kind of anal stimulus before they were capable of fornication.

I have known over the years fairly well a great many Lesbians and all I can say is that they are on the whole an unpleasant group of individuals, and I avoid them. The male homosexual, and I would say that this is true of at least 90 percent of them, has one redeeming feature. He does have a sense of humor about himself and his life — a quality that I found completely lacking in the Lesbian. The Lesbian by her inversion tends to be antisocial — the contrary of the male "homo" — with a nature turned completely inward — overly intense in everything, no humor, vindictive and generally unpleasant in all her contacts outside of her own friend.

The male "homo," even in his most involved moments, tends to see the whole business with a certain objectivity, and seeing it this way, there is something ludicrous about it, and he can laugh at it, and at himself — which is a saving grace for him and his contacts with the normal world.

I have noted that around the world people tend to exclude Lesbians from their normal social life, while they tend to include homosexuals in it, even though they may not approve, because the average male "homo" is by nature, gregarious, amusing, and really likes and enjoys life, so that he is in general a good companion and fun to have about.

A great many summers in my youth were spent with a cousin of my father's, who was a Lesbian, and the only really enjoyable one that I ever knew. She had been exiled by the family from Wales in the early years of the century, and turned into kind of a remittance woman by the family — paid to stay away, as a result of scandal in the village. She had drifted to Alaska during the Gold Rush, gone to the Pacific Islands, where she had met up with a most feminine creature with whom she had been for many years, at the time I stayed with her.

Jane spent her life with fast cars and boats, and knew every sailor that put into port, and could out-cuss any of them, and tell dirtier stories than they dared. I was taken around this world by Jane, and often wonder if this did not play a role in my own development, for my own sexual tastes have always run to these lower classes — for it introduced me to a world with which I would normally never have had any contact, and I look back on these summers and this strange environment with a certain nostalgia, a nostalgia that probably has played a role all my life.

MARRIAGE AND THE LESBIAN
(See Clinic 10)

In the case of the Lesbian the situation in regard to marriage is somewhat different from that of the male. Marriage for her is also not a cure, but women adjust better to family life, and because of the passive role she plays it is easier for the Lesbian to participate in the heterosexual act than it is for her male counterpart. There is some proof of this in the fact that many female prostitutes are homosexual and are able to participate in heterosexual relations without difficulty, although without pleasure. The security offered by marriage and the pleasure of raising a family may balance satisfactorily the loss of sexual pleasure which results from her frigidity in the marriage relationship. Motherhood does not have the same danger for the children as fatherhood, because the Lesbian is less aggressive and less active in sex than is the male, and the potential harm to the children and family relationships is less. In giving marital advice to the Lesbian the pattern which she has established concerning overt sexual activity must be carefully studied, as well as her adaptability, her ability to accept males socially and sexually, and her maternal capacity. If she knows herself to be a homosexual, she is, of course, morally bound to tell her partner about it before marriage.

SUMMARY

1. Little is known of female homosexuality.

2. Two cases of different types were presented for the sake of contrast and study.

3. Lesbians do not have the same problems in marriage as the male homosexual but they are advised against marriage.

4. In general the prognosis is better for adjustment and therapy.

CLINIC 8 — NOTES

1. Quoted from *The Homosexuals,* A. M. Kirch (ed.) (New York: The Citadel Press, 1954), p. 3.
2. Kinsey *et al., Sexual Behavior in the Human Female* (Philadelphia: Saunders, 1953), p. 484:
   "[34]There are specific statutes against female homosexuality only in Austria, Greece, Finland, and Switzerland."
   "[36]The states in which the statutes apparently do not apply to female homosexuality are: Conn., Ga., Ky., S.C., and Wis. Heterosexual cunnilingus has been held not 'the crime against nature' in Illinois, Mississippi, and Ohio, and the decisions would supposedly apply to homosexual cunnilingus. In Arkansas, Colorado, Iowa, and Nebraska there is also some doubt as to the status of female homosexuality."
3. See Derrick S. Bailey, *Homosexuality and the Western Christian Tradition* (London: Longmans, 1955), p. 164.
4. In Kinsey, *op. cit.,* pp. 475–476, footnotes 19 and 20 give these references:
   "[19]For instance, Clark (Clark, W. E., ed., *Two Lamaistic Pantheons,* Cambridge, Mass.: Harvard University Press, 1937, Vol. I, p. 70) and Bergler (Bergler, E., *Neurotic Counterfeit-Sex,* New York: Grune & Stratton, 1951, p. 317) feel that the incidence of homosexuality among females exceeds that among males. Others differentiate various types of homosexuality, and feel that incidental or temporary homosexuality is commoner in the female, as in: Bloch (Bloch, I., *The Sexual Life of Our Time in Its Relations to Modern Civilization,* trans. by M. E. Paul, London: Rebman, 1908, p. 525) and Hirschfeld (Hirschfeld, M., *Sexual Anomalies and Perversions,* London: Francis Aldor, 1944, p. 281). Others who estimate that homosexuality is equally common in both sexes include: Havelock Ellis (*Studies in the Psychology of Sex,* 3rd ed., Philadelphia: F. A. Davis Co., 1915, Vol. II, p. 195); Krafft-Ebing (*Psychopathia Sexualis,* trans. by F. J. Rebman, Brooklyn, New York: Physicians and Surgeons Book Co., 1922, p. 397); Freud (*Collected Papers,* trans. by J. Riviere and A. and J. Strachey, London: Hogarth Press and the Institute of Psychoanalysis, 1924, Vol. II, p. 202); Kelly (*Sexual Feeling in the Woman,* August, Ga.: Elkay Co., 1930, p. 143); and Sadler (Sadler, W. S. and L. K., *Living a Sane Sex Life,* Chicago and New York: Wilcox and Follett Co., 1944, p. 92).
   "[20]All specific studies have arrived at incidence figures for the male which exceed those for the female: Hamilton (Hamilton, G. V., *A Research in Marriage,* New York: Albert and Charles Boni, 1929, pp. 494–93) (57 per cent male, 37 per cent female); Bromley and Britten (Bromley, D. C., and Britten, F. H., *Youth and Sex,* New York and London: Harper & Brothers, 1938, pp. 117, 210) (13 per cent male, 4 per cent female); Gilbert Youth Research

('How Wild Are College Students?' [Unsigned article on a survey by Gilbert Youth Research], *Pageant*, November, 1951, pp. 10–21) (12 per cent male, 6 per cent female)."

5. Cited in *They Stand Apart*, His Honor Judge Tudor Rees and Harley V. Usill (eds.) (New York: The Macmillan Co., 1955), p. 69.

6. Kinsey, *op. cit.*, pp. 452–453.

7. Simone de Beauvoir, *The Second Sex* (New York: Alfred A. Knopf, 1953), p. 561.

8. Morris W. Brody, "An Analysis of the Psychosexual Development of a Female — With Special Reference to Homosexuality," *Psychoanalytic Review*, 30 (1943), pp. 47–58.

9. Helene Deutsch, "Homosexuality in Women," *Psychoanalytic Quarterly*, October, 1932, pp. 484–510; Karen Horney, "On the Genesis of the Castration Complex in Women," *International Journal of Psychoanalysis*, Vol. V (1924), p. 50.

10. Preuss (J. Preuss, *Sexuelles in Bibel und Talmud*, Allg. med. Zentral-Zeitung, 1906, p. 571 ff.) quotes a few passages from the Talmud which show that tribadism was known, but it is not mentioned in the Bible. The usual expression for it is *soledeth* (= "moving towards each other with a springing or hopping movement"). Only a few schools fancied that such women should be treated legally as prostitutes; the others declared such doings to be "unmoral," but attached no legal consequences to it.

11. The following is from Hermann Heinrich Ploss, Max Bartels, and Paul Bartels, *Woman* (London: William Heinemann, Ltd., 1935), pp. 74–76:

"In England the word *dildo* is usually employed. The O.E.D. states that it is 'a word of obscure origin, used in the refrains of ballads.' It was, however, used for other purposes, the word may be connected with the Italian *diletto*. Thomas Nash sang the praise of this object, 'attired in white velvet or in silk,' which indeed 'maie fill, but never can begett,' and for the pleasure it gives 'no tongue maie tell.' Such playthings were amongst the miscellaneous assortment of objects hawked by pedlars which trade Boucher has painted (see ('Bilder-Lexikon,' I, 245), and Shakespeare has mentioned when he speaks of the 'delicate burthen of dildos and fadings' ('Winter's Tale,' Act IV, sc. 4). . . .

"Here may also be mentioned the Madigo of the Hausa women, a contrivance made in imitation of the male organ, which women strap on in order to gratify other women, and which was employed especially in very large harems. Before England took possession of the country a woman found with such an instrument was severely punished: She was buried alive and her partner was sold into slavery. (For further details see Mischlich, 'Bilder-Lexikon,' I, p. 419; and for the same customs among the women of Lake Chad, see Bouillez). . . .

"In classical antiquity, especially in Greece, as Knapp illustrated with several examples, the use of an instrument called 'Olisbos,' knowledge of which apparently came from Asia Minor, was for a time very widely spread so that even the authorities took severe measures against it. Passages in Aristophanes, Herondas, Lucian, as well as certain pictorial representations, which Knapp discusses in greater detail, give full particulars."

12. Radcliffe Hall (pseudonym) in *The Well of Loneliness* gives a sensitive and artistic appraisal of the pathos of the homosexual conflict within a female homosexual, though the etiology suggested is oversimplified and perhaps naïve; furthermore, the solution suggested seems to be rather pessimistic acceptance of a *fait accompli*.

13. Seduction by older females: A. Moll, *The Sexual Life of the Child* (New York: The Macmillan Company, 1912), p. 314. H. Ellis, *Studies in the Psychology of Sex, op. cit.*, Vol. II, p. 322. M. F. Farnham, *The Adolescent* (New York: Harper & Brothers, 1951), p. 167.

CLINIC 9

The Homosexual Speaks

In this clinic the testimony of two patients is presented, one at length, and the other more briefly. The second patient is in the nature of a devil's advocate, but he is not a true *advocatus diaboli* because he states what he believes. In using the case method of teaching it is important for the student to realize that, even if a case is carefully presented, it represents actually only the experience and attitudes of one individual. It is also true that not all types and varieties of disturbance can be presented in this way. The cases presented should be used merely as exemplars and only the important facts should be abstracted from them. Patient VII, referred to as Mr. X, goes beyond the mere recitation of his history. He describes his reasoning and his attitudes. He is, as will be evident, a well-educated, obligatory homosexual. Patient I has been presented before, and, although he is also well educated, he has quite a different attitude toward morality than Patient VII. Both of these gentlemen have volunteered to discuss their cases here, for the benefit of counselors.

PATIENT VII

If there is one trait which follows in the wake of homosexuality it is probably a feeling of uneasiness. It reduces the spontaneity of a homosexual. He has to weigh his words twice to see that what he is saying is not something he is blurting out which will give him away. He must be constantly on his guard.

In my own case I think I was always afraid of revealing myself fully because I had been told that I possessed feminine characteristics. I can remember that it was not until I was thirteen years old and in the eighth grade that I ever adverted to the fact that I was engaged in sexual acts. That is, I never thought of them when at school until that time. Until then it was something recalled only when I was at home. But after that time, it would come to mind during school hours or at any time. But I had to keep it out of mind. When the subject of sex was mentioned I used to remain quiet. But I remember that I fully subscribed to the idea that sexual relations between an unmarried man and woman were unforgivable.

How, then, did I allow my own actions? I felt that normal men were not driven with the same force as I was, that normal sex acts were more easily controlled.

By the time I reached my fourth year in college I realized that I was accepted by men on my own merits. In high school I could not always be sure. But here I knew that I was accepted. And since that time I have always been able to hold my own in social relations with men — that is, with those who have some imagination, whether it be in matters of business or the arts. The people whom I find congenial are usually interested in history, literature, philosophy, finance, architecture, theology, government, and law. They have a broader view than their own particular field. They see it in relation to other fields. They need not share all the same interests. I have close friends who could not tell a tune from *South Pacific* from a Chopin *Fantasie Impromptu*.

Social and Business Relations With Other Men

There is something about a homosexual in relations with other men that makes him somewhat of a child. He sees other men growing up and building families. For him this is closed off. He cannot honestly say to himself that he has made the decision to remain single. But he sees his contemporaries taking over the role of parents. He feels like a high school student who is on the brink of maturity but who never arrives. And so, he decides that he will cultivate a different type of personality. He will be the quiet self-contained individual. He will be kind to the children of other people, he will try to see that these children do not fall into the difficulties which he has.

He is cut off from participation in the family interests of other men. He hears a man speak of his wife and tries to translate it into his own experience with a friend. He attempts to spread his affection around a large group of people. He does not expect to experience an intimacy with any one of them as deep as the intimacy which apparently exists between a man and his wife. On the other hand, he may expect to know a few people with whom he is free to discuss almost anything except the subject of homosexuality.

He will strive to be normal. In my own case, I asked my brother, once he had been told, if there was anything about my behavior that would lead anyone to suspect it. He said absolutely not. I asked him again later, and he repeated that this was true, there was no reason to suspect that I was a homosexual.

I think, however, that there may be some criteria which would make me suspect the existence of homosexuality in others. These are some of them:

1. A man with a taste for exquisite things and who had at the same time an affectionate attitude and who claimed to be a gourmet in food and drink. A bachelor who lived alone and gave way to his craving for other luxuries.

2. A man of the traveling salesman type who made jokes repeatedly on homosexuality, or who proposed to be an expert on Freud, and was otherwise unfamiliar with psychiatry.

3. A man who would adopt an exaggerated sensitivity on sexual moral problems but who indicated merely average sensibility on all other moral problems.

4. A man who professed to know nothing about sex.

The homosexual is always being gnawed by the awful truth that time is slipping by. He is painfully aware that he is not measuring up to the usual social standards. If he thinks on it long enough, it can cause him intense anxiety. It may make a pagan despair. The Christian will keep hoping, but he may put it off with the palliative, "This won't go on much longer. Everything will be all right!"

Coming to a Decision

There are two decisions which a homosexual has to face: one, to recognize his emotional condition for what it is; two, to decide what is to be done about it. The first one may come during puberty.

I had been "razzed" several times in my life for possessing feminine characteristics; once by an aunt who remarked, "It's a pity that he was not born a girl!" I don't remember the circumstances well enough to decide whether this was merely a remark which she made injudiciously in my presence or whether she was giving way to a fit of peevishness. But, in any case, the notion that I had a girlish temperament was left there. In the seventh grade I was once called a "sissy." I knew that my brother who is thirteen months older than I was considered one of the regular fellows in class. And as I best recall it was this reason which may account for my association with him. In other words, I assumed that if my brother accepted me, and if he was accepted by others, then they would accept me since they would feel that I must be O.K. to get along with my brother. This was a situation which continued through to the end of my high school career.

I was called "a girl" again in the eighth grade by a boy who had the highest grade in the class and who was considered a leader among the students. This merely increased my need for associating my activity with that of my brother.

In high school he did all the "approach" work toward other individuals. I could get along with people once I knew them, but I was extremely shy. I did not advert to this fact at the time. But I maintained consciously that I did not approach people because few people were to be trusted. This I had learned at home from my mother. She had learned it — and with reason — from the behavior of several relatives on both sides of the family. As I look at them now, what was once hostility is now pity for a number of these individuals. (The conversion from hostility to pity is not because hostility is socially unacceptable, but because I realized that they themselves were hopelessly entangled in neurotic conflicts and had no apparent place to turn.) Nevertheless, the result of this teaching that few people were to be trusted seemed to give me a feeling of sophistication — I knew more about "life" than these protected, well-to-do people did. Thus what was really a failing (shyness) was repressed and I clung to the notion that I knew more than the others. Moreover, I held on to the idea that I was working as "a power behind the throne" — I was the inner circle, people who knew my brother intimately enough would know that I was the source of many of his ideas.

He was the buffer between me and other people. I could not expose myself to the clear light of intimate scrutiny of other people. They might discover my feminine characteristics. I might get razzed or ignored by them. It was better to be the quiet type, inaccessible, somewhat of the mystery man about whom not too many had enough information.

In my senior year in high school I worked every evening from 3:30 P.M. until 10:00 P.M. (I knew that competition was stiff at school. The parents of most of my classmates were college graduates. They helped them with homework assignments. My own people were not college graduates. I could not get the help — and in addition I worked seven hours a day.) This work moved me further from whatever association I had with other students. Things somewhat struck rock bottom at the time of graduation. The night we were graduated a number of parties were given. My brother was invited to all of them. I was invited to none.

For the next two years my brother and I attended different colleges. He went to college away from home. The college I attended was near home. I lived at home. It was during these two years that I realized I could stand on my own two feet. I was asked to join a fraternity. I was a popular member of several clubs. I was still working at the place where I had worked during my last year of high school but I was working fewer hours. At this time I was working for an aunt for whom we had been taught tremendous respect. She was the epitome of my mother's teaching that in most cases it was the women who produced results and the men who were millstones around their necks.

This long digression came after I mentioned above that I was conscious of the fact that people both old and young had indicated that I possessed feminine traits. I was in my sophomore year in high school when I first noticed that physically I was attracted to men. There was an older boy (he's dead now) whom I used to pass every Friday noon. I used to look forward to that day. This appeared to me to be wrong. But I said to myself that this could not really be wrong. This was not homosexuality because "fairies" were degenerate men who wore red ties, put on make-up and indulged in penis-sucking and penetrated each other's anus. I was not doing anything like that; therefore, this was not homosexuality. For the same reason I felt that I was not committing masturbation because I believed that such consisted in fondling the penis with one's hands. I was not doing this, I was lying on my stomach. And for some reason (probably an inadequate explanation on my part) a priest had told me that lying in bed and having an orgasm was simply a nocturnal emission. Thus, I assumed the attitude that if what I was doing was not really masturbation, then I probably had an exaggeratedly fearful attitude toward this attraction to men; that it was merely "growing pains," a stage of emotional development.

The awareness of homosexuality was not something sudden. I realized for two years that my character possessed what could be called homosexual elements. Thus the knowledge of it did not come as a sudden shock but came gradually after a long debate with myself. The first decision was: I had it. What was I going to do with it?

Environmental conditions would not have allowed me to completely acquiesce to the situation. Religiously it was wrong. The natural law, as interpreted by those around me, showed that such an act was intolerable. To that extent I acquiesced. But I had also been told in early puberty that sex was uncontrollable. And the habit of masturbation seemed to be exactly that. It seemed as if there were no ways to overcome that. It was not until I began psychiatric treatment that I observed where the source of compulsion was — it was with my eyes. It had become so second-nature for me to look at male buttocks that I scarcely noticed myself doing it. Once the image of a man with a particularly desirable body frame was lodged in my imagination, it seemed that I could do nothing about it. The compulsive tendency toward masturbation never ceased until I broke myself of the habit of observing male physiques.

There was a moral situation here. It was quite obvious, even to myself. How could I even attempt to live with the problem? I reasoned that if this was so compulsive that nothing would stop it, then I was not fully responsible. Moreover, I was making novenas, going to confession, always repeating the same sin of masturbation. I always said to myself, "This is the last time!" It was this idea which saved me from an attitude of despair. I kept hoping and expecting that this would be the last time.

I remember that those months before the disaster when my homosexuality was discovered, I was constantly thinking of the Book of Job, especially the remark, "The Lord gives, and the Lord takes away. Blessed be God!" Somehow I had a premonition that the Book of Job would take on a deeper meaning. It certainly has since then.

I remember, too, that I used to pray that God use any means he wanted as long as I were rid of homosexuality and masturbation. Thus, when I was accused of it, while the situation produced a shock, at the same time there was a glimmer of hope.

This probably sounds like an animistic attitude, but I include it to show that while the situation was heartbreaking, it appeared also as the opportunity for making a break with the whole thing. In my own case, I decided to break with homosexuality. But this was because of my environment. If I had been brought up in an environment where religion and morality were less important I can see how, once established in homosexual habits, an individual would probably tend to keep them. But in order to do it he has to twist all concepts violently out of shape. For example, society as a whole will say that homosexual habits are to be condemned. The homosexual intellectual will say that there is nothing really wrong — that it is merely a convention for men to have relations with women. He will work his brain at white heat in order to devise reasons proving his point. This is the tragedy of a writer like André Gide. He did everything in the world to make morality look bourgeois, conventional, stuffy, and ridiculous. He tried to show that the truly great man was the one who had the courage to be an atheist. He tried to catch the unthinking with an emotional phrase which rocked them, and once he had them thrown off balance he tried to inject his own grotesque theories. He had an exquisite sensibility, a fine intellect poisoned at the very wellsprings.

The extenuating circumstance for Gide is that he probably never met a man whom he could take for an example. I know that in my own case I thought that all individuals were regularly obsessed with impure thoughts but that some (such as priests and nuns) overcame them because they probably possessed a relatively weak sexual drive. If you consider how many people there are today who assume extra-marital relations are normal, then it is not surprising that some take the further step and consider homosexual activities as normal. There is not enough definitive information submitted to the general public. The homosexual is told that his tendency is inherited, some say it is glandular, some say it is the direct outcome of childhood masturbation. Some say it can be cured in most cases, others despair of curing it. If the homosexual knew what the cause of it was and if the general public were told the medical background, and if it were taken off the stage in burlesque houses and treated openly, it could probably be stamped out in a short time. [Obviously an oversimplification. — AUTHOR.]

The homosexual, who has apparently yielded to it, knows deep in his soul that he is singing a false note. He has to build up all kinds of defenses:

1. He must limit his society to those who will accept him.
2. He must never think of death.
3. He must avoid any occasion which might make him think of the existence of God.
4. He must avoid any argument which would force him to prove or accept the existence of God and a moral order.
5. He must deny the moral order.
6. He must militantly oppose morality and set up a false system which will accommodate his belief. He is like the boy who walks through the graveyard whistling aloud to keep himself from being frightened. The existential psychiatrists have something when they say that deep down every man has a conscience.

I know that in my own case I had to accept my conscience and salve it with the opiates, "This will clear up eventually" and "I am not entirely responsible, since this is compulsive."

Death

When I was a child I always made a point of attending wakes. In fact, I remember that at one time I was told to stay out after I had attended Mrs. A's wake four times in the same afternoon and five times the day before. It did not matter to me whether or not I knew the deceased. All I had to do was see a wreath on the door and in I marched. I suppose the attraction they had for me was the abundance of flowers, the fact that everyone looked so special, almost like a party, with the folding chairs, candles, and potted palms. Since nobody died with whom I myself was intimately concerned, the sense of loss which one usually feels at death was absent from my view of funerals. A friend of mine in kindergarten died when we were in the first grade. I remember telling this to my great-aunt; I was standing by the table in her kitchen — a table which she always kept covered with a green fringed tablecloth. I was singing a song which I had learned in the first grade, "Angels ever watching guard me." I went to his wake only twice — once on Saturday and once on Sunday.

Among close relatives, members of my father's family were the first to die. Since I was never too closely allied with them, there was no particular sorrow. In fact, when my Aunt "A" died, I was given the piano which she would not let me practice on when she was alive. Since I felt no particularly close ties with her, I remember that the funeral almost was more of a celebration than a loss.

It was not until my Aunt "B" died that I felt the loss of a friend. But even then, I knew that my Aunt "C" would be more liberal to my mother than my Aunt "B" had been.

Thus I knew that until we ourselves would be able to do the same, my mother's hardships would be alleviated. It was how things turned out to be.

Apart from any relatives, I have always been disturbed for the past ten years by the sight of a funeral. I tried to take advantage of this discomfort by fixing my eyes on a hearse and remembering to myself, "All flesh will come to this." When three outstanding Catholics whom I knew were lying in state in the parish church, I went over and meditated on the thought: "These can probably account for their lives satisfactorily — will you be able to do the same?" I used to pray that I might be shocked out of my habits of sin.

PATIENT I

Comment on the Statement of Patient VII

It seems to me that Mr. X's criteria for judging who is homosexual are superficial — and a lack of very much experience in the broader fields of life. For example, a man with a taste for exquisite things — perhaps sometimes, may be homosexual, but my experience is that the homosexual is in general very superficial in this field. The real gourmets, the real connoisseurs of art are rarely "homos." Also among artists, the real artist, in almost any field, is rarely a "homo"; it is the second raters who are. I suppose that this stems from the fact that the existence of the same flaw in his character that originally made him a "homo," equally made him unable to be really first class. You find your homosexuals in the fields bordering on art — window dressing, interior decoration, where they are very successful, but as artists — well, the flaw comes out, and they never quite make it.

Homosexuals make a great point of the sexual status of Shakespeare — and undoubtedly one finds very strong evidence of homosexuality, both in his plays and in his sonnets, but I should say he was bi-sexual. No one could write Romeo and Juliet, if he had not been through a love affair with a woman. Most homosexuals who are writers show this inability to project themselves enough to write of heterosexual love, and one can spot them in a moment — but, strangely, some very normal men have written of homosexuality in novels with great understanding and insight. One should read Compton McKenzie's novels, such as "Vestal Fires," for this point of view, but then the man is a real artist.

The other three categories mentioned by Mr. X are not sure-fire methods of knowing — they only indicate some sort of sexual problem, but then the homosexual is inclined to interpret any sexual problem as being his problem.

I distrust this talk of making a break with homosexuality especially at the age of this man — I can only feel that the original drive would be changed into something that might in the end be more difficult and unpleasant to live with than his original problem. I see this all the time in teachers, boy counselors, etc. They probably never have any sexual relationship with the boys they have in their charge, but they tend more and more to create an emotional dependence of their boys on them which becomes a very unhealthy thing in the end. One is always hearing of men who devote their entire lives to helping others — and they do, but often at what cost — and I can only say that fornication might have been better than the emotional webs they weave and with which they try to entangle their subject. I have seen it so often in our own priests — who are always being pointed out to me as "wonderful with youth" — and they are, because the whole sex drive has been diverted to this, but I have never known one of them who approached the work from a disinterested (and by this I mean a fundamental sexual interest, though completely repressed) point of view, and inevitably the emotional element creeps in and I often feel that the normal boy would probably bear up to a seduction better than he bears up to this.

I find Mr. X's concern with death is very neurotic; probably the emotional side of going to wakes was for him only another sexual outlet. Most homosexuals I have known have too strong a sense of fatalism to be concerned about death in this way.

PATIENT VII (Further Testimony)

The homosexual is caged in a trap of unsurmountable social bars because of the stigma attached to his deviation. As long as the true nature of homosexuality remains unknown to the general public, the public will continue to persecute the homosexual whether it be by police action or making him the gaff of cheap jokes or merely ostracizing him as a leper from society. As long as this attitude is maintained a person possessing it will do everything in his power to conceal it, provided the milieu in which he dwells is a moral one. If the environment is one in which morality is flaunted, the homosexual will attempt to turn what he recognizes as a vice into a virtue [see *supra*, "Coming to a Decision"]. But in order to do it, he must do violence to his reason and he must accept the moral consequences which follow — though in most cases he will find means of repressing any guilt feelings. If society would recognize homosexuality for what it is, and if the homosexual could treat his trouble openly, a great deal of time and anxiety would be saved; the homosexual, once rid of his defect, would play a more forceful role in society.

I am convinced that at one stage or another, at least in the early stages, the homosexual sees his tendency to be in conflict with established morality. He must solve his dilemma. Either he will attempt to rid himself of the sexual deviation or he will attempt to show that what "ordinary unenlightened people" judge to be an absolute law is really only a social convention. Either his habit or morality will have to go. They both can't live in the same person. If morality is generally disregarded, he will hold on to his homosexuality — because it furnishes pleasure, it is more compulsive in his eyes. He will attempt to say that since he is out of the realm of the normal anyway, a new set of laws must apply for him which will not apply for ordinary people. He may spend his whole life trying to prove this to himself. If he is a genius he may draw many into the maelstrom. This I think was at the root of Nietzsche's writings. I have a feeling that he exaggerated his intercourse with women in order to drag a red herring across the path. (It seems to be one of the most common traits of a man who has no intercourse with women to boast of his accomplishments over women or to tell jokes derogatory to a homosexual. Nowadays I get suspicious when somebody tells homosexual jokes.)

When a homosexual goes to confession he finds the priest giving him advice to stop it, that it is "against nature." The priest will tell him that the homosexual should avoid occasions of the sin, and when he finds himself tempted he should take a cold shower or go for a walk.

The advice to avoid occasions of sin is an excellent one. But quite frequently the occasion of sin may be so ingrained that the advice seems useless to the penitent. For example, I was regularly confronted with the problem of compulsive masturbation. I found myself committing the act once a day for a period of two months. Part of it was, of course, motivated by the argument that I had already done it several times, once more would not be much. To a theologian such an argument would be incomprehensible. But the theologian has mind and body so integrated in his view that even one sin is enormous. The masturbator in such a situation is attempting to get an intellectual appreciation of its sinfulness and hopes that an emotional appreciation will soon follow. The trouble is that it usually doesn't. The masturbator may have read books on moral theology, the catechism, probably some treatises on purity. He may have made novenas. The compulsion still follows because he expects it to be taken away. In other words, he attacks it from another approach. Instead of attacking the habit of masturbation, he attempts to channel off the energy by substituting a virtue such as prayer, and the attempt at prayer will absorb the energy formerly spent in vice.

Ordinarily the masturbator is told in confession that he should take a cold shower or go for a walk. In my own case neither advice ever worked, because the source of my drive toward sex acts was in a vivid image in my imagination. I used to get up and read, I would speak to people, I would go for a walk, take a shower and the image would persist. The way I got rid of the image was in becoming aware of the fact that I had acquired the habit of sizing men up, and that I considered what I was doing to be an aesthetic practice.

Once in confession I was told to stop reading the kind of books I was reading. Of course, the priest had not even asked me what kind of books I was reading; he merely supposed that I was reading "scorchers." I wanted to tell him afterwards that the last two books I had read were "Introduction to a Devout Life" and "A Companion to the Summa."

Another priest told me (when I was in high school) that if I continued to practice masturbation (I had done it seven times in a week) he would have to refuse absolution. I mention this one because he apparently had no realization that I was undoubtedly a psychiatric case. At the time I did not realize it myself. And in any case I could not have afforded psychiatric treatment then.

In my experience priests are very tolerant to persons guilty of sexual sins. The masturbator or the homosexual does not fear an unpleasant situation resulting on the part of the priest, but there is a resistance on the part of the homosexual himself. If he is living a life where he is attempting to conceal the sin from other people, he makes it a universal rule never to bring this up to anybody at any time. When he plans to go to confession, he will find any number of excuses to put it off another week or another month.

No matter what his reason may be, the Catholic penitent will eventually come to confession mostly because his feelings of guilt are becoming intolerable to him and because his feelings of guilt exceed his fear of being censured for his behavior.

Since there is so little information available on homosexuality, the homosexual will ordinarily not approach just any priest, because he is afraid that if the priest possesses no information on the subject, nothing will be accomplished, and the homosexual has merely laid himself open. The present Christopher attempts at sex instruction for children should help solve some of the problems of masturbation and homosexuality. If a child knew that he could open himself up to a priest whom he knew would not condemn him and from whom he could expect to receive some understanding, that child would eventually ask questions either direct or oblique and the priest could give him the answers or work in conjunction with a psychiatrist.[1]

As a postscript I would like to add a résumé of my experience with homosexuality in confession.

At that time I knew that it was wrong for men to put their genitals into the genitals of women. But I never could see how this was done since I thought that women had the same genitals as men.

I understood masturbation to be the act of fondling one's penis with his hands. When I was a child of seven or eight I used to lie on my stomach and become somewhat sexually excited. Since I was not holding my penis in my hands, I did not believe it to be masturbation.

I continued lying on my stomach and exciting myself. It seemed to me that there was something wrong with this (a tribute to conscience). So when I was eighteen years old, I asked a priest about it. He told me it was masturbation. There was a tremendously deep habit by this time. I felt that I was not fully responsible, but used to confess it anyway. It was regularly occurring twice a week until the age of twenty-nine. Sometimes I might go for two weeks to a month without any trouble, but it always began again. At that age I met and lived near another man who was sexually attractive and who became a close friend. He mentioned sexual experiences he had had in Europe during the war. I began to envy the women who could do this with him. Fantasies crowded themselves into my imagination. But I rationalized myself and saw I would fight it on its own ground. At this time I was going to confession once every two weeks.

Masturbation increased to three or four times a week and for a period of three months it was daily. I did not go to confession at this time because I felt the priest would not believe that I was attempting to do anything about it.

Several months later I noticed while watching a wrestling match on T.V. with a friend that my friend was getting into positions which could be interpreted as sexual. I moved into similar positions. He lay on me and I realized that I could have homosexual relations with him. The first week we had them three times. The next week none. The next week twice. The next week once. I finally went to confession. I was surprised to find that the priest did not "bawl me out," that he merely told me to be careful about it.

I was still living near this friend. We had sexual relations once every two weeks. Eventually we gave it up. I had not gone to confession for ten months because I felt I had done nothing to show the priest that I was overcoming this temptation.

Now I go to confession weekly and attempt to go to Communion daily. The only thing which stops daily Communion now is when I commit an act which a year ago I would not have thought as sinful — touching the body of my friend when I would wake him up, going near the room of my friend (which is an occasion of sin for me), sins against charity, scandal — previously I thought of these sexual sins as my own sins; now I have to acknowledge them as sins against charity, etc.

As far as prayers are concerned, I think I made one novena at least five times. I made another novena twice. I used to say night prayers (though not as many as I should have). I remember once when my mother was speaking about syphilis to my older brother, I went into the bathroom and knelt down beside the tub and prayed; I even forced tears just to show that I was penitent. (I was about ten at the time.) It may be illustrative of an early guilt complex that at the age of eight I used to read in my mother's prayer book a prayer for the gift of tears.

I remember that several months before the disaster which caused me to take psychiatric treatment, I had been making a private prayer in which I had told God that I would undergo anything He wanted as long as I would become rid of these habits of sin. At the time of the disaster I almost welcomed it as the thing which I had hoped for. Someone may remark "He'll do anything for it but give up the sin" like they say about the Irish, that they will do anything for Ireland but live in it. I can see today that I can never go back to the past life.

Everything I have said is after my third year of treatment. There are still relapses into homosexual activity, but even these seem to be stopping as the result of another discovery, namely, the recognition that in human love relations there are two very distinct factors which never should be confused with each other. These two factors are acceptance and the sexual appetite. Certainly, in my own case (and I have found the same in conversation with other homosexuals), there had been a feeling of not really belonging to anybody except my mother. Granted, everybody does want their mother to think well of them, but there are other ways of being liked — and these I knew I lacked.

This confusion of acceptance with the actual sex appetite could account not only for homosexual activity, but is equally applicable to a lot of heterosexual promiscuity. When anybody makes the discovery that a person can be fully accepted by his peers without exercise of sexual appetites, he can maintain a more firm relation because it is not dependent on a sexual ebb and flow. It is also a free relation because there is no guilt involved.

Dr. Edmund Bergler published a book in November, 1959, "One Thousand Homosexuals" (New York: Pageant Books), in which he mentions curing patients when they have realized this fact. There is no doubt in my own mind that a realization of this fact will go far toward putting anyone in the right direction.

PATIENT I (Reply)

I must take exception to the first sentence used by Mr. X. This I can only feel comes from a strong guilt complex on his part, which I never, personally, seemed to have had. I have been fortunate in having other qualities so that I have never felt this way about my sex life. Then, too, I always seemed to have had the feeling that nobody's sex life would really bear being examined too deeply, and that mine was no worse than the general run of men, either homosexuals or heterosexuals, and that I should feel no shame about it. Then, too, I was fortunate in spending so many of those formative years in Europe where the subject is looked at in a quite different way. Actually, I felt that flaunting homosexuality was wrong, but I think the few times that I have been faced with it by some-one, I admitted it. Once, as a teenager, a girl fell quite hopelessly in love with me, and I could not respond. I simply told her it was this way, and fond as I was of her, I wanted nothing more.

I believe with Mr. X, that at one time or another, any thinking homo-sexual feels that he comes into conflict with established morality — or the Church. In any case, it came in my teens and religion went out of the window completely, and it was not till later in life that I came back into the Church, but, I am afraid, on my own terms, and with this you cannot agree, I know.

Another point which seems to strike me in what has been said by Mr. X, is that he must have a very low sexual drive, which simplifies his prob-lem considerably. In his account of his relations with his friend, I feel that this is important. It is a hell of a lot easier to give up something which is not very strong or forceful, as I feel it is in his case.

Naturally, solid human relationships are not built on sex, either homo-sexual or otherwise, and in looking back over the friendships that have survived over a great many years in my life, most of them were with people with whom there was no sexual interest, and if they were homo-sexuals themselves there had never been any sex interest between us. I can, however, point out that relationship that still exists between myself and the two people mentioned elsewhere, with whom I have been emo-tionally and sexually involved in what I will call, though you may disagree, a love affair. Here the old emotional tie probably still exists and will exist forever.

CLINIC 9 — NOTES

1. Mr. X apparently is not familiar with the Christopher Records. These records are designed for parents and not for children. They deal with the reproduction process. Tangentially they may be useful by giving parents a vocabulary with which to discuss sex with their children (*Christopher Dramatized Recordings on Sex Instruction,* The Christophers, 18 East 49th Street, New York, New York 10017).

Marriage and the Homosexual

True homosexuals, whether overt or latent, should not get married. A genuine, obligatory homosexual is personally incapable of entering a valid marriage. Ritty[1] and Oesterle[2] agree with this opinion and give excellent canonical reasons. Excepting the occasional marriage that would work because of an unusual circumstance of personalities, the vast majority of such marriages would fail. In spite of this fact, many such individuals are told by poorly informed counselors to "Go ahead and get married. After your marriage it will all work out." This is not so.[3] Marriage should never be a treatment for anything, much less homosexuality. It will not "work out." This statement brings up two questions which require answers:

1. Why will it not work out?
2. What can be done to prevent such marriages?

1. WHY WILL THE HOMOSEXUAL-HETEROSEXUAL MARRIAGE NOT WORK?

One thing is evident from all that has been said in previous clinics: there cannot be a satisfactory operational psychosexual relationship between an obligatory homosexual and a heterosexual person. Whatever physical sexual relationship does occur will be accidental, infrequent, and a counterfeit of the real thing. There is practically no disagreement among psychiatrists with the fact that homosexuality, when present, has existed from early childhood. The reference here is to true homosexuality, not the homosexual acts of the pseudo-homosexual, sometimes referred to as a bisexual.[4] Such an individual is not actually a homosexual at all, but is one who has a poor sexual identification and will utilize any handy sexual object to satisfy what he considers his needs. There would probably also be agreement that a homosexual individual could perform a sex act with a heterosexual partner if he were to indulge in homosexual fantasies while doing so. One other point of importance about homosexuality is that, except in a small number of strongly motivated cases, complete recovery from the condition is not likely to occur.[5] It is a condition, therefore, which is antecedent and permanent and opposes the very essence of marriage, the conjugal act.

I recognize that marriage enjoys the favor of the law and that the validity of a marriage is to be upheld until the contrary is proved (Canon 1014). This is the way it should be. But speaking as a psychiatrist, with an incomplete knowledge of the law and of theology, I would like to present a brief discussion of those aspects of homosexuality which, in my opinion, render the marriage of such persons a mockery of that sacramental state. Emphasis in the past has been on the physical aspects of the sex act with little accent on its psychological components.[6] For example, Harrington states the presently accepted criteria for the consummation of marriage in these words:

> In order that a man be considered potent and be apt for contracting a valid marriage, he must have a penis that is capable of erection and of penetrating the female vagina and he must be able to produce, emit and deposit *verum semen* within the vagina. The erection must be maintained and sustained until the vagina has been penetrated and until semination has occurred within it.[7]

Reasons for the Invalidity of Marriage

It would appear that the homosexual-heterosexual marriage is invalid because:

  a) The homosexual cannot give valid consent.
  b) The homosexual is incapable of genuine love.
  c) The homosexual is psychologically impotent.

a) The homosexual cannot give the consent necessary for a valid marriage contract.

Marriage is a contract which requires certain qualifications on the part of those about to enter the married state. Since the essential matter of marriage is the right to the other person's body for complete conjugal relations, it seems only logical that each partner should expect that his mate be capable not only of performing, but also of desiring in its true meaning, the marriage act. Such an ability would seem to be, at least from the psychological standpoint, an essential condition of marriage.

It would appear that under Canon Law, a restriction of consent involving what the law itself calls a *conditio sine qua non* will invalidate a marriage if the condition be not fulfilled. Certainly heterosexuality is, by the very nature of the marriage contract, a *conditio sine qua non* for a fruitful, happy, and valid marriage. Whether this condition be explicit or implicit would have no particular bearing, except that the explicit condition would be easier to prove. *Nihil volitum nisi cognitum.*[8]

If one partner reveals his homosexuality and the spouse persists in a desire to get married even after such a revelation, the marriage should be actively discouraged.[9] It seems clear that the matrimonial consent (which brings into existence the marriage bond) must be directed toward the giving and receiving of the right to act which are truly expressive of conjugal love and which lead to acts which are *per se* apt for the procreation of children. This is the real essence of marriage which cannot be complete and free in an invert. It will always be conditional. There must be a "meeting of the minds."[10] According to Canon Law, if "any essential property of marriage" be positively excluded, the marriage contract is invalid.[11] And according to Bouscaren and Ellis:

> Mere external expression of consent cannot constitute marriage; genuine internal consent on both sides is so necessary that no human power can supply it, and much less can the Church presume it in a case where it is known not to exist (C. 1081, 1).[12]

I do not believe that a homosexual person can give such consent.[13]

b) *The homosexual is incapable of the genuine love required for a proper marriage.*

As is being more frequently stressed today, since procreation is not the only end of marriage, the mutual love and happiness of the partners is also of the greatest importance. The spiritual and disinterested love of the spouses for each other must animate the marriage.[14] According to Pope Pius XII: "The child is the fruit of the conjugal union, involving not only organic functions and tender feelings, but also the spiritual and disinterested love that animates them. . . ."

The passage in Genesis relating the creation of man and woman first gives procreation as the only end: "Man and woman both he created them" and He said to them, "Increase and multiply and fill the earth" (1:28). But immediately afterward there follows a more detailed account. God made woman because "it is not well that man should be without companionship; I will give him a mate of his own kind" (Gn 2:18). Surely God did not intend a human mate merely for purposes of procreation, but one psychologically, emotionally, and sexually compatible.

If homosexual love is properly understood, it is soon apparent that such love is not love as it is usually understood between a man and woman, but a perverse, sensual love. It is certainly not the love meant by St. Paul when he stated: "You who are husbands must show love to your wives as Christ showed love to the Church when he gave himself up on its behalf" (Eph 5:25).[15]

It is also clear, as Dom Massabki has well said, that married love "is the love of a whole person for the whole of another person."[16] The fulfillment of the specifically human sexual act occurs by a union of the whole persons of both husband and wife. It is far more than a merely physical act. It is a mutual compenetration of two human beings who are united body and soul with each other. The sexual act is an incomplete act unless this physical compenetration of persons is effected with its psychical counterpart. Thus it is not permissible for the partners in a marital act to separate the psychical component of the act from the physical, nor the physical from the psychical. Such separation would be the rule rather than the exception in the case of a homosexual.

According to Jean de Fabregues:

> It is true and certain that the kernel of sacramental marriage must be a call of love. And neither the Church nor Christian wisdom has ever refused to recognize in the profound attraction of one being for another, to another, one of the greatest realities in the lives of men, one of those moments when a creature rises almost to the level of his supernatural destiny. Therefore, the Church desires with all her heart that the sacrament should confirm the consent of two beings who are drawn to each other by love, if it really is love.[17]

Such statements could certainly not refer to the narcissistic love of the homosexual.[18] In the absence of true heterosexual love there is a continuous threat to the permanency of the marital relationship.[19]

c) The homosexual is psychologically impotent.

Homosexuality is a form of impotency, although at times it may not evidence itself anatomically or completely.[20] Quinn, discussing the impediment of impotence, is one of the few clerical writers on the subject who mention homosexuality as a cause of impotency.

He divides the subject into two classes: (a) organic and (b) functional. The *functional type* occurs, he states, in those individuals who have intact organs which function defectively. He subdivides functional into: (a) nervous type, (b) neurasthenic type, and (c) psychic type.[21]

Under the psychic type he includes sexual perversion, especially homosexuality. He adds that perversion is defined by the Rota as any manifestation of the sexual instinct which does not correspond to the end of nature, which is procreation (for the psychiatric definition see p. 25). He further states that one cannot say without qualification that homosexuality always produces impotence, and, consequently, the Rota insists that each case be judged on its own merits. As a psychiatrist, however, I must insist that the homosexual is psychologically impotent in heterosexual relations. Both the stimulus and the desire for such relations are absent, and there is a positive aversion (in varying degrees) for the act itself. The homosexual lacks capacity for that unselfish love which is necessary for marriage.

We should also remember in evaluating the psychic factor in impotence that man is not a creature composed of a body and a soul, but a body-soul composite. He is neither body nor soul, but a human person. It is true, however, that philosophically considered, the body was made for the soul, not the soul for the body. We could also say that in the hierarchy of values the body occupies a lower level of function than the soul. Psychic values are recognized by common consent as having a high human value. It would seem, therefore, that the exclusively physical, technical requirements as set down by canonists need to be reconsidered in that they ignore a most important aspect of the marriage act.[22]

Proof of Preexistence of Homosexuality

In regard to the preexistence of the homosexual state with its coexistent psychological impotence, there is the interesting possibility that the heterosexual partner could insist on a written statement of

the homosexual partner before marriage and before witnesses that
he did consider himself a true homosexual.

Would the court accept such a statement or would it require
further proof from the spouses? This would raise the question of
what are the minimal diagnostic criteria of true homosexuality.
These are certainly important but, unfortunately, largely subjective.
They were discussed in Clinic 7. From the legal standpoint witnesses
could probably be produced to homosexual acts performed by one
or the other spouse, but then how many witnesses and how many acts
would be necessary to be acceptable as proof?

The Lesbian

Father John F. Harvey, O.S.F.S., is of the opinion that the true
female invert should be advised against marriage. He points out some
interesting differences between the male and female homosexual:

> The female differs from the male in such matters as the greater depth
> of her attachments, her avoidance of erotic transvestism, her ability to
> keep her anomaly secret, and the alleged deeper sensitivity of her
> conscience to the guilt of homosexual desires and acts. Perhaps this
> more sensitive conscience in female homosexuals induces them more
> readily to seek moral guidance than their male counterparts.

> While all sorts of consciences are found among male and female inverts
> it is noted in pastoral practice that the female is more docile than the
> male. She is not as likely as he is to defend her way of life by involved
> arguments of a pseudo-intellectual stripe, and she is more ready to
> admit the obviously emotional character of her homosexual attachments,
> to which she may continue to cling, not as a rebellion against moral
> principles, but really out of fear of the vacuum which she imagines
> will follow her renunciation of her beloved. In general, in the female
> there is more weakness and less pride.[23]

I am not sure that I quite agree with Father Harvey in regard
to the marriage of Lesbians. I would certainly agree that if they know
of this condition, if they are leading an active homosexual life, and
wish to get married only for the sake of appearance, then the marriage
should be discouraged. On the other hand, the sexual attitude of a
woman is different from that of a man, her drive is not as imperative,
many married women are frigid in any case; there is no reason to
believe that she could not be a good mother, and that she could show
proper interest in and affection toward her husband and children.
Father Harvey, in his paper, quotes Henry[24] and Karpman[25] on this

subject, both of whom dealt largely with "hard-core" obligatory homosexuals. I do not wish to be misunderstood. I would advise the Lesbian against marriage, but I do not feel that her marriage to a heterosexual male, especially if he had a low sexual drive, would be the catastrophe that is the marriage of a heterosexual woman to a homosexual male.

2. WHAT CAN BE DONE TO PREVENT SUCH MARRIAGES?

Serious thought should be given to the prevention and/or relief of the heterosexual partner of such a mixed marriage. Many homosexual individuals do marry, for one reason or other, without informing their prospective spouse of their condition. One of the most flagrant cases with which I have had personal contact was a young man who took his boy friend on the honeymoon with him. He thoughtfully arranged a lower berth on the train for his bride and got a compartment for himself and his male companion. This couple performed one sex act on their honeymoon, enough to consummate the marriage, and have not lived together since. The young Catholic girl, although normally sexed, is thus condemned to a state of celibacy for the rest of her life, or until the death of her homosexual spouse, or until she renounces her religion. The latter result is unfortunately frequent in this type of case. My purpose in this presentation is to explore the possibility of relief for such tragic situations.

Prevention of the Heterosexual-Homosexual Marriage

We must recognize the right of all individuals to enter the vocation of their choice. We must, however, also recognize that there are qualifications required for each state of life in those who wish to enter it. The canonical impediments to marriage are well known and need not be repeated here. I hope that I have shown that homosexuality is included in these already recognized impediments.[26] If homosexuality is a legitimate impediment, we need not feel guilty for discouraging the marriage of homosexuals.

More knowledge of homosexuality on the part of those giving premarital counsel would be helpful in the prevention of such marriages. This is especially important in view of prevalent erroneous opinion that marriage is a cure for homosexuality. Canon 1020, par. 2, requires the pastor to make certain inquiries concerning the state of mind of the individuals.[27] If he were well informed on this subject, he could judiciously inquire into the possibility of homosexuality in either partner. He could also point to danger inherent in the situation when the partners wish to proceed with the marriage even though aware of the deviant sexuality of the partner.[28]

CONCLUSION

In conclusion I wish to emphasize:

1. Those concerned professionally with marriage should become increasingly aware of the clinical syndrome of *homosexuality,* both overt and latent.

2. When this condition is present in its true form, the couple should be urged not to get married.

3. Ecclesiastical authorities should give thought to making homosexuality, whether overt or latent, an impediment to marriage because of:

   a) The personal incapacity of the genuine homosexual for the married state — for a union that is both valid and happy;

   b) His incapacity to give true marriage consent;

   c) The existence of psychological impotency in heterosexual relations.

CLINIC 10 — NOTES

1. Charles J. Ritty, J.C.L., "Possible Invalidity of Marriage by Reason of Sexual Anomalies," *The Jurist,* Vol. XXIV, No. 4 (October, 1963), pp. 394–422.

2. Gerard Oesterle, "Welchen Einfluss hat die Homosexualitat auf die Ehen," *Oesterreichesches Archiv für Kirchenrecht,* Vol. XII (1961), pp. 305–334. See also Monsignor Vincent P. Coburn, "Homosexuality and the Invalidation of Marriage," *The Jurist,* Vol. XX, No. 4 (October, 1960), pp. 441–459.

3. John F. Oliven, M.D., *Sexual Hygiene and Pathology* (Philadelphia and Montreal: J. B. Lippincott Company, 1955), p. 450:
   "The exclusive homosexual, as a rule, should be strongly advised against marriage, no matter how greatly he seems to long for the comforts of a conventional home or for a child. The belief that marriage can cure true homosexuality in any way is a fallacy. It matters little if the prospective bride is aware of his abnormal tendencies; such marriages almost always lead to sorry complications for all parties. Permissible exceptions are marriages of convenience with a woman who is totally anhedonic or a Lesbian herself, or considerably older than the patient. In these cases he may obtain some of the companionship and ordered life of marriage without its sexual obligations."
   Rev. James H. VanderVeldt and Robert Odenwald, M.D., *Psychiatry and Catholicism* (New York: McGraw-Hill, 1957), p. 434:
   "Is marriage indicated as a solution in cases of homosexuality? For pseudo-

homosexuals, as we have defined them, marriage or a return to regular marital life will often be the best and only solution. But it would be disastrous to advise marriage to a genuine homosexual as long as he has not been changed into a heterosexual by some method of therapy, regardless of whether his condition is supposed to be organogenic or psychogenic. Marriage does not cure the genuine homosexual of his deviant inclinations, and because he does not feel any real psychic attraction toward the other sex, his condition will cause his partner untold grief. Should a homosexual, before being cured, insist upon marriage, he is morally bound to reveal his condition to his partner."

4. John F. Harvey, O.S.F.S., "Homosexuality and Marriage," *Homiletic and Pastoral Review*, December, 1961, pp. 227–234; "Counseling the Homosexual," *Homiletic and Pastoral Review*, January, 1962, pp. 328–335. It would seem to me that Father Harvey does not clearly state the nature of the "bisexual" individual. In my opinion, as stated in the text, the individual usually referred to as "bisexual" is one who will accept relations with either sex. He is not really a homosexual but merely an "opportunist" (see p. 20 of this text).

5. See also John F. Harvey, "Homosexuality as a Pastoral Problem," *Theological Studies*, Vol. 16, No. 1 (1955), p. 98.

6. A great deal of emphasis has been put on the psychological components of marriage, other than the sex act, for quite some time. Every effort is made to safeguard the freedom of the parties from force and fear, simulated consent, mental disorders, psychic impotency, etc. However, the law by its very nature tends to stress the licitness and validity of acts. It leaves other aspects of marriage to dogmatic and pastoral literature.

7. Rev. Paul V. Harrington and Charles J. E. Kickham, M.D., "The Impediment of Impotency and the Condition of the Male Impotence," *The Linacre Quarterly*, Vol. XXV, No. 3 (August, 1958), p. 108.

8. See T. Lincoln Bouscaren, S.J., and Adam C. Ellis, S.J., *Canon Law*, 3 ed. (Milwaukee: The Bruce Publishing Company, 1957), p. 545: "Since marriage is a contract whose essential object (matter) is the conjugal right, it seems evident that matrimonial consent is impossible without some knowledge concerning the right which the contract purports to transfer. *Nil volitum nisi cognitum.*"

9. In the case of a person desiring to marry a confessed homosexual, the law does give the Ordinary the power of forbidding the marriage (C. 1039, 1).

10. "Marriage is always by its very nature a contract, even when it is not a sacrament. Now, a contract can be effected in no other way than by the consent of the parties, or, as the English law is fond of saying, by 'the meeting of the minds.' Consent is thus necessary to marriage according to its very nature and it follows that neither the state nor the Church, nor any human power, can supply it" (Bouscaren and Ellis, *op. cit.*, p. 543).

"An impediment which directly affects only one of the parties nevertheless renders the marriage illicit or invalid as the case may be, because the contract is indivisible; it cannot be invalid or illicit for one party by reason of an impediment and at the same time valid or licit for the other" (*ibid.*, p. 477).

"Although marriage exists by nature as well as by divine institution," wrote Pius XI, "human will also has a part, and a very noble part, to play, for each particular marriage, in that it constitutes the union in marriage of a particular man and woman and has no other origin than the free consent of the couple. This act of free will, by which each of two people give and receive the right which is proper to marriage, is so essential for a true marriage that no human power could possibly substitute anything for it" (*Casti Connubii*, quoted in Jean de Fabregues, *Christian Marriage* [New York: Hawthorn Books, 1959], p. 79).

11. Canon 1086, 2: "But if either party or both parties by a positive act of the will exclude marriage itself, or all right to the conjugal act, *or any essential property of marriage,* the marriage contract is invalid."

12. Bouscaren and Ellis, *op. cit.*, p. 551.
13. Ritty, *op. cit.*, p. 409: "Here there is no question of a diriment impediment, there is no question of insanity; but there is a basic incapacity of the subject to give full and free consent to the substance of the contract of marriage. Is it not conceivable, therefore, that one who is afflicted with one of the sexual anomalies, by reason of an obsessive compulsion to perform unnatural and perverted acts, could also be considered in the same category as the nymphomaniac, who has an invincible sexual instinct contrary to the substance of marriage?"
14. In the opinion of Dom Boissard the immediate end, that is, the one first achieved, "is to give the couple through the close, complete and final union of the lover's person with that of the beloved, that completion which is his natural desire: a deeply valued support — material, bodily, sensual, emotional and spiritual all at the same time — which is for the majority of human beings the providential means to their moral progress and of their sanctification" (*Questions theologique sur le mariage*, p. 17).

    This passage from Pius XI's encyclical *Casti Connubii* carries this same meaning: "In the community of the home love is not expressed by mutual support only: it must aim higher, in fact its principal objective must be to strive every day to form and perfect the interior life each in the other. Their day-to-day relationship will help them to make daily progress in virtue, above all to grow in true charity towards God and their neighbor, that charity in which all the Law and the Prophets are finally summed up. . . . This growth of the interior life of the couple, this continual effort to help each other towards perfection, can even, and truly, be called the cause and primary reason of marriage as strictly as the Roman catechism teaches, at least if we do not look at marriage as strictly an institution intended for the procreation and education of children, but take a wider view of it as the sharing of life as a whole, an habitual intimacy — a society."
15. De Fabregues, *op. cit.*, p. 23: "Can we conclude from a text such as this that an absolute parallel exists between the relation of the husband and wife and the relation of Christ and the Church? There is no question of this, and the reasons are obvious, the first one being in the very nature of a relationship between creatures and the fact that it is realized through the senses, physically, even though it is rooted deeper and grows higher. Yet St. Paul himself goes further, saying that the bride is the completion of the bridgroom as Christ is completed by the Church which 'is His body, the completion of Him who in all things is complete' (Ephes. 1:23). And again: 'You who are husbands must show love to your wives, as Christ showed love to the Church when He gave Himself up on its behalf' (Ephes. 5:25). We can see more clearly here the meaning that we should learn from this symbol. It is the greatness of an absolute giving which is here envisaged."

    Ibid., p. 54: "The Church measures love by the fullness of the meaning given to that 'yes,' by the completeness of that consent which is a promise quite different in standard from those that are exterior and purely emotional. Marriage is a 'society of love, that is, one in which its members are required to love each other,' writes Dom Massabki, who among recent defenders of Christian love has given it the highest place."
16. *Ibid.*, p. 54.
17. *Ibid.*, p. 53.
18. See footnote 14.
19. A sampling of the literature in reference to "homosexual love" shows a universality of opinion that he cannot experience true love: "In contrast to them stands another 'love' which is *sui generis* — a love between man and woman which seeks fulfillment in the establishment of a 'one flesh' *henosis*, the creation of an unique common life in marriage and the building of a family. This, too,

has its chastity, but of a different order for it is a love in which the sexual organs have their proper and necessary uses, both in its consummation and in the furtherance of its relational and conceptional ends; chastity here, therefore, relates to the due employment of the sexual faculties for their appointed purposes.

"It will be evident *ex hypothesi* that such a love as that last described and the union in which it results cannot possibly have any parallel in homosexual relationship. While, therefore, we may not deny that homosexual love can be a true and elevated experience, we must insist that it is one to which expression may not be given in sexual acts — a limitation which it shares with all forms of heterosexual relationships except one" (J. Tudor Rees and Harley V. Usill, *They Stand Apart* [New York: The Macmillan Company, 1955], pp. 51–52).

"Male homosexuals often enjoy feminine company and are liked by women, but it is a common fallacy to believe that if they are introduced to sufficiently seductive members of the opposite sex, they will arouse them. Nothing is further from the truth. They are as unaffected by the charms of a bevy of chorus girls as the normal man would be by a platoon of guardsmen. It is most important to stress this, and to contradict the common belief that marriage will cure homosexuality. On the contrary, it is merely a recipe for tragedy" (*ibid.*).

" 'All the world loves a lover' — but he must be a normal lover and a natural lover. This the invert cannot be" (Anomaly, *The Invert* [Baltimore: The Williams and Wilkins Company, 1948], p. 31).

"There is also a question as to whether it is ethically justifiable to ask any woman to give herself into the keeping of a man who is, and who will probably remain, incapable of giving her his full affection, and who will be tempted, at least, to seek expression for his radical passion in the society of his own sex. The idea is hideous" (*ibid.*, p. 97).

"The honest invert will admit — perhaps with regret — that he does not know what it means to experience normal desire and that, while he may, or may not, be peculiarly passionate, he feels that whatever potential romances lie sleeping in his heart, they will never be awakened by a woman" (*ibid.*, p. 53).

"There are inverts for whom feminine society has platonic attractions and who go sometimes even so far as to practice a little lovemaking for convention's sake. On the other hand, many inverts brought to frank admission will tell you that women bore them, while some regretfully admit that in the presence of women they are physically distressed" (*ibid.*, p. 103).

"These men are attracted exclusively toward men. Erotic situations involving an attractive woman leave them indifferent or even fill them with repugnance or vague fear" (Oliven, *op. cit.*, p. 431).

"The essential feature of this strange manifestation of the sexual life is the want of sexual sensibility for the opposite sex, even to the extent of horror, while sexual inclination and impulse toward the same sex are present" (R. v. Krafft-Ebing, *Psychopathia Sexualis* [New York: Physicians and Surgeons Book Company, 1934], p. 335).

"I am now speaking not of actual homosexuals who, as pathological figures are *incapable of a real friendship* and, therefore, find no particular sympathy among normal individuals, but of more or less young people who feel such an enthusiastic friendship for each other that they express their feeling also in a sexual form" (C. G. Jung, *Contributions to Analytical Psychology* [London: Routledge & Kegan Paul Ltd., 1948], p. 274).

"More common than this automonosexualism are the cases of homosexuality, in which persons of the opposite sex can cause no sort of desire or erection at all" (Magnus Hirschfeld, *Sexual Pathology* [New York: Emerson Books, Inc., 1940], p. 274).

20. Canon Law does not define impotence, though Canon 1068 refers to it:
    "1. Impotence, antecedent and perpetual, whether on the part of the woman,

or on the part of the man, whether known to the other party or not, whether absolute or relative, invalidates marriage by the law of nature itself.

"2. If the impediment of impotence is doubtful either in law or in fact, the marriage is not to be hindered.

"3. Sterility neither invalidates marriage nor renders it unlawful" (cf. James E. Risk, *The Law of Catholic Marriage* [Chicago: Callaghan & Company, 1957], p. 60).

21. Rev. Joseph J. Quinn, *Rotal Jurisprudence With Regard to Functional Impotence in the Male* (Washington, D. C.: The Catholic University of America, 1956), p. 11.

22. Oesterle argues that a marriage with a homosexual can be annulled on three grounds: (1) *exclusio matrimonii ipsius:* there is no intention of entering a real marriage; (2) *exclusio fidelitatis;* (3) *exclusio iuris ad coniugalem actum.* He attempts to prove the invalidity of marriage on homosexual grounds by stating that homosexuality is in its essence incompatible with marriage. Even though homosexuals may have the wish to break off their prior relationships, they often are unable to do so, because they lack the will to make such a break, or they are unable energetically to fight against their inclinations and, consequently, at the time of the marriage they are lacking in good faith (*op. cit.,* p. 305).

Oesterle has written extensively on this topic, e.g., see "Animadversiones in Sententiam S.R.R., die 23 feb., 1951, coram Staffa," *Il Diritto Ecclesiastico,* LXII (1951), 730–750; "De Relatione Homosexualitatis ad Matrimonium," *Revista Espanola de Derecho Canonico,* X (1955), No. 28; "Voluntas se obligandi et voluntas non adimplendi ad tempus vel in perpetuum in ordine ad prolis generationem," *Perfice Munus,* XXXIV (1960), 45; "Von der psychischen Impotens," *Ephemerides Iuris Canonici* (1955).

23. *Op. cit.,* pp. 231–232.

24. George W. Henry, *All the Sexes* (New York: Rinehart and Company, Inc., 1955), pp. 333–336.

25. Benjamin Karpman, *The Sexual Offender and His Offense* (New York: Julian, 1954), pp. 314–315.

26. See Ritty, *loc. cit.,* and Oesterle, *loc. cit.*

27. "Canon 1020. 2. He must ask the man and woman even separately and cautiously, whether they are under any impediment, whether they are giving their consent freely, especially the woman, and whether they are sufficiently instructed in Christian Doctrine, unless in view of the quality of the persons this last question should seem unnecessary."

28. Ritty, *op. cit.,* p. 417: "The arguments that homosexuality is incompatible with marriage may be summed up as follows:

"1. According to canons 1081 and 1086, the homosexual could not have the will to enter a true marriage; under the outward appearance of marriage he desires to continue his homosexual relationships.

"2. On the basis of canons 1081 and 1086, the person before the marriage proposes to sin against matrimonial fidelity, and this can sometimes be established by evidence before and after the marriage.

"3. On the basis of canon 1081, matrimonial consent is not had in the sense that the man and the woman reciprocally hand over and receive forever the exclusive right (*ius in corpus*).

"For these reasons the marriage is invalid: (1) because the homosexual is incapable, as a result of the homosexual relation, even if he had the intention of giving true matrimonial consent, of restraining himself from the homosexual relationship (often there results a true impossibility of normal intercourse with the spouse); (2) because the homosexual not only does not permit the exclusive right to marital intercourse, but often excludes it entirely. The conclusion is that homosexuality is incompatible with the essence of marriage."

Homosexuality and the Religious Life

Why after 2000 years, you might ask, does there recently come about this need for the psychiatric screening of candidates for the religious life? There are many who still object to such methods of selection. To require such an examination, they feel, is to naturalize a supernatural vocation. Such individuals feel that the older methods of examination were adequate and that the methods of the spiritual director provided sufficient screening. But those methods did not provide the best results in spite of their use for 2000 years. Especially in regard to sexual deviation were many spiritual directors inadequately informed and consequently likely to fail in their screening procedures.

Should the presence of perverse sexual conditions be a bar to the acceptance of a candidate for the religious life? There are some who believe they should be. Dr. Biot is one of these:

> At the time of admission, the orientation of the subject's sexuality must have been definitely established for several years. Any persistent deviation of the libido constitutes an absolute counter-indication. We must be inflexible regarding this, else we shall be responsible for a life of unhappiness for the future priest or monk, and greatly imperil the honor of the clergy.[1]

There are others like Father Connery who state: "It seems a little incongruous to demand an attraction for the opposite sex as a requisite for a life of celibacy." Father Connery concludes, however, that "if there have been lapses, a vocation is either out of the question, or should not be considered until a very long trial gives clear proof of control."[2] There seems to be no uniformity of opinion among those who discuss this subject. This may be due in large part to incomplete understanding of the subject and a failure to differentiate between degrees of homosexuality. It is wrong to adopt an "either-or" attitude, a black-and-white concept, in which anyone with any evidence of deviation would be thereby barred from the religious life.

As for the individual concerned, if he contemplates entering the *religious* life, he must give serious thought beforehand to whether he feels that he is able to meet all the obligations of the life. He should in addition consider his ability to cope with situations which will undoubtedly arise in an environment constituted entirely of members of the same sex. The aggressive homosexual should realize that such a step may be inviting serious conflict and possibly immorality. The passive homosexual should realize that under such circumstances he is likely to be a temptation to more aggressive homosexuals if such be present. In the case of pronounced feminine characteristics, he might be a source of temptation to heterosexual members of a community, particularly if it is cloistered. If he is recognized as homosexual he may be faced with the conscious or unconscious aversion or ridicule which may exist, even if in a small degree, in religious communities.

These objections are, of course, purely speculative; as one approaches more proximately to the forming of the final practical judgment, the circumstances of the individual case may overcome the anticipated danger. In an active religious community the individual might find just that proper balance of religious idealism, awareness and stimulation, charity and compassion, satisfying work, etc., which he will perhaps nowhere else encounter, and wherein he can most blamelessly increase in sanctity.

To help clarify misunderstanding, a more complete knowledge of homosexuality in all its aspects should be part of the training of all religious superiors, spiritual advisors, and confessors.

HOMOSEXUALITY AND THE RELIGIOUS LIFE

Our authority for discussing this matter, which will be limited to homosexuality, comes from many sources of which I shall mention only two. No less an authority than Pope Pius XII directed the exclusion of the homosexual from the religious life:

> . . . whoever has a special tendency to sensuality, and after long trial has not proved he can conquer it; whoever has no aptitude for study and who will be unable to follow the prescribed courses with due satisfaction; all such cases show that they are not intended for the priesthood.[3]

A private letter of the Sacred Congregation of the Sacraments of December 27, 1955, demands full proof before a given case should receive lenient treatment. And an element of that proof would be thorough examination by a doctor "who is a real expert in psychiatry, known for his skill, morality and practice of religion, advanced in years, free of the tenets of materialism. The doctor, after prolonged examination, should decide whether, having examined the psychic and physical condition of the student, he is fit to carry with honor to the clerical state the burdens of sacred ordination, especially celibacy." The letter goes on to advise the doctor: "If he finds him physically and psychically so disposed as to be considered not qualified for Orders, his other qualities, even though outstanding, must be set aside, and he must be counseled in a fatherly but firm manner that he should withdraw from embracing the priesthood."[4]

A LONG TRIAL

How long is a "long trial" as recommended by Pope Pius XII in his encyclical on *The Catholic Priesthood?* Experience would indicate that this should be a period of at least three years or the duration of the individual's stay in the seminary, whichever is longer.

SPECIFIC FORMS OF HOMOSEXUAL ACTIVITY IN RELATION TO THE RELIGIOUS LIFE

The screening examination should investigate at least the following types of homosexual activity when there is reason to believe that the candidate has perverse sexual tendencies:

1. *Adolescent Homosexual Activity* (see also p. 81). In the history of many individuals there will be noted instances of sexual contracts during adolescence with members of the same sex. These will usually have been in the nature of sexual exploration or mutual masturbation. As a rule these acts will not have been frequent and will have occurred before the age of sixteen. The individual giving the history may or may not have been the aggressor. If these experiences occurred over a relatively short period and did not recur as the individual grew older they may be disregarded as evidence of homosexuality. They are not significant as evidence of the individual's adult sexual orientation:

> It is fairly evident that the homosexual acts of adolescence are not necessarily evidence of inversion, nor are they even an inevitable accompaniment of inversion.[5]

The counselor must be careful never to tell the boy who admits such acts with his companions that he is a homosexual or in danger of becoming one.[6]

These experiences are almost always the result of sexual curiosity which leads to experimentation. They may occur in either sex. The significant factor is that they have occurred in a circumscribed period of time and have not persisted beyond adolescence. In general it may be said that if such activity does not persist beyond adolescence it should not in itself be a bar to entering the religious life.

2. *"Surprise" Experiences.* Father John F. Harvey in an unpublished manuscript speaks of homosexual acts, frequently the first, which are "committed more by surprise than by deliberation." If any such act was the first act it is conceivable that through ignorance the passive recipient might have innocently submitted. Such naïveté would, however, be quite rare in these days of sexual enlightenment. If the "surprise" is accompanied by violence or serious threats it would certainly involve no responsibility on the part of the innocent party. If one can accept the statement that the individual was innocently enticed by surprise into an act and this was his only act it should certainly not be a bar to the religious life. His remaining in the religious life should, however, be dependent on a probationary period. Such cases must be quite rare.

> When this innocence has been conserved by virtue — I mean through effort, with a struggle on occasion, without ignorance of evil or absolute calm of the senses — evidently we must bless God, and every director has experienced this joy. . . . It is different when innocence does not stem from virtue. Doubtless it remains quite estimable, since it is ordinarily a sign of a suitable temperament. But a certain doubt should arise in the face of this ignorance and this sluggishness of nature; in these cases, it would be necessary, besides enlightening the person, to impose a trial before sub-deaconship.[7]

3. *Sexual Arousal During "Contact" Games.* Sexual arousal during physical contact play such as wrestling and rough and tumble games may be an indication of homosexuality, although this is not universally true. Such behavior should definitely be avoided by erotically sensitive individuals of whatever sexual orientation. Repeated arousal or rough play sought merely for the purpose of sexual arousal should be carefully evaluated and if there is deliberativeness in it the individual should be accepted only after a period of observation. In cases of premeditated acts the candidate should be dismissed.

4. *Homosexual Experience Under the Influence of Alcohol.* In general homosexual acts committed while under the influence of alcohol have little prognostic significance in the evaluation of sexual inversion. However, when one is evaluating a vocation to the religious life any sexual act or any overindulgence in alcohol assumes a serious significance. How would we view a heterosexual act in the prospective seminarian even under the influence of alcohol? How are we to regard drunkenness in the candidate? If the act occurred before entry into the major seminary and it was not repeated, a sexual act under the influence of alcohol should not be considered as a bar to ordination. If the act is repeated the candidate should be carefully evaluated from the standpoint of both alcoholism and homosexuality. Dismissal or a prolonged period of observation would then be indicated.

5. *Homosexual Dreams.* Everyone from time to time has sexual dreams. In the male these are accompanied frequently by nocturnal emissions. Some individuals who appear to be heterosexually oriented have occasional dreams which seem to have a homosexual connotation. These should be disregarded. If, however, the majority of the sexual dreams are frankly homosexual in nature and are associated with emissions they are most likely evidence of homosexuality. If this is the only evidence of homosexuality and the individual has led an otherwise chaste life the dreams should not be considered a bar to the religious life but should be an indication for an intensive examination of the individual.

6. *Homosexual Attraction Without Homosexual Acts.* This condition is the one that gives rise to the most difficult decisions in regard to the acceptability of the candidate. Homosexuality, of itself, is neither moral nor immoral. If the decision in regard to vocation is based purely on moral considerations then there should be no question of the acceptability of the candidate for the religious life. Many have said that the chaste homosexual should be approved for Orders. If, on the other hand, we consider homosexuality as symptomatic of an underlying personality disorder, then we must evaluate the severity of the condition. Very often homosexuality implies the deification of the ego. "One invert said that God was his ego."[8] There is no doubt that sexual inversion reaches the depths of the personality. The attitude of the individual toward his condition is an important consideration. For instance he must, to be considered

acceptable, believe he can overcome his habit, or at least control the tendency. There are other questions which should be answered; e.g., Does the individual have real insight into his condition? Is he aggressive? Does he resent his condition? Does he feel able to control his impulses? When did he last masturbate? Was this associated with homosexual fantasies? Does he have a fatalistic attitude toward his condition? Is he anxious about the condition or his ability to control it? There may be individuals in this group who are suitable for the religious life.

7. *Masturbation With Homosexual Fantasy.* Masturbation in addition to its moral aspect is evidence of sexual and emotional immaturity. In compulsive masturbation there is some diminution of moral responsibility, but since the condition represents a severe disorder it would in itself be a bar to entering the religious life. Chronic masturbation with its associated moral responsibility when combined with homosexual fantasy would be evidence of a psychiatric disorder plus immaturity plus a lack of proper will and motivation. All of these added together would render the individual unsuitable for the religious life. Treatment may be of value in such cases to relieve the masturbatory tendency even though it is ineffective for the homosexual disorder. If such a habit persists into the major seminary the candidate should be advised not to continue with his studies. There may be some individuals who, after therapy, may be allowed to proceed but they should be carefully counseled. Masturbation with heterosexual fantasies is another problem, which does not concern us here. It should be understood, nevertheless, that regardless of the sexual orientation of the individual, persistence of masturbation into adult life is evidence of severe emotional and moral immaturity:

> Regarding masturbation, some persons advocate a trial period, since the candidate has a long road ahead of him; but the present writers would be inclined to be severe on this matter. Once relatives and friends have seen a young man wearing the cassock, postponing the decision will make it more painful for all concerned, and prolong the candidate's own suffering.[9]

8. *Homosexual Attraction With Acts in the Minor Seminary.* Some individuals in this category may fall into the class of those who perform adolescent homosexual acts or acts through ignorance. When such acts persist, however, they can hardly be regarded as

innocent. The homosexual attraction in some of these young men comes so close to bisexuality that one might be tempted to feel that such a condition was present. A boy going from grammar school into the minor seminary is achieving adolescence and is in a stage of developing sexuality. When sexual arousal takes place in an exclusively male environment as in play or games or even spontaneously from fantasy it is likely to be attributed by the individual to homosexuality, since he knows no other stimulus. Such a fear may lead to scrupulosity associated with a conviction that he is indeed a homosexual. In more susceptible individuals the homosexual conviction may be accepted without anxiety. Such persons are more likely to yield to seduction by more aggressive students or attempts to seduce others. In spite of these homosexual feelings many students will have strong heterosexual inclinations. In such cases a clear and frank discussion of why they feel as they do is needed — that their sexual arousal under certain circumstances is normal, that they are deceived into believing that they are homosexuals by their exclusively male environment. They should be told that one cannot be a homosexual and have strong positive feelings for the opposite sex. With such an explanation many of these boys straighten out and develop proper control. If the condition persists, i.e., if homosexual acts persist in spite of warning and advice, it is probable evidence of a lack of desire to change or a more deeply seated state of inversion. Such individuals should be advised to leave.

9. *Sexual Attraction With Acts in the Major Seminary*. When the condition described in the past section persists into the major seminary a more serious situation exists. This is especially true if it is associated with particular friendships. Homosexual acts occurring in the major seminary are sufficient evidence of a lack of proper will to conduct oneself in a manner suitable for the religious life and should be cause for asking the individual to leave.[10]

10. *Seduction of Other Individuals to Perform Homosexual Acts*. There may be differences of opinion in regard to certain aspects of homosexuality but not many would doubt that an individual with a moral attitude which permits the enticement of others to serious sin would be unsuitable for the religious life. Anyone who has been exposed to a proper Christian education knows that sexual acts outside of marriage are seriously sinful. He also knows that it is equally sinful to encourage others to commit sin. Add to this knowledge

the fact that the individual who seduces others has a homosexual personality disorder and any doubt of his suitability will vanish.

11. *Sociopathic Personality With Pathologic Sexuality.* There are several varieties of sociopathic personalities which are described in the "Diagnostic and Statistical Manual — Mental Disorders." These were defined on page 33. No one would question that such individuals are unsuitable for the religious life, so no further discussion is necessary.

12. *Obsession of Being a Homosexual.* Whether such an obsession is based on latent homosexuality or is an obsessional neurosis is not pertinent to our present discussion. In such a case the individual is most unlikely to perform homosexual acts. He is, however, seriously neurotic and would for that reason be psychiatrically unsuitable for the religious life (see p. 100).

13. Recidivists, psychotic individuals with delusions of homosexuality, voyeurists, exhibitionists, transvestites, fetishists, masochists, sadists, pedophilists are mentioned only for the sake of completeness. They are obviously not suited for the religious life.

WHY IS A HOMOSEXUAL UNSUITABLE FOR THE RELIGIOUS LIFE?

Father Connery has asked, "Why should heterosexuality be made a prerequisite for the religious life?"[11] This sounds like a good argument when one first reads it, but a little reflection leads one to believe differently. A vocation requires spiritual, physical, psychological, and moral fitness for the life which the subject is about to embrace. The homosexual is not psychologically fit for these reasons, among others:

1. Homosexuality is a personality disorder often associated with other psychiatric disorders (see Clinic 3). Heterosexuality is normal.

2. Homosexuals because of their condition are:
    a) Narcissistic;
    b) Fatalistic;
    c) Likely to submerge reason to emotional forces;
    d) Deeply affected in their personality.

3. Although the state of homosexuality in itself is not sinful, the homosexual individual because of his fatalistic attitude frequently yields to the tendency. This is usually due to his "sick will" which

is unable or unwilling to rule out such acts. If he is unable he is too sick for the religious life; if he is unwilling he is unsuitable.

4. Scandal is an ever present possibility with the homosexual clergyman. Homosexual conduct reflects discredit on all members of the clergy. It would be rash for a homosexual to venture being responsible for such a danger.

5. For the homosexual to live in a religious community where he is constantly exposed to other males is quite likely to make his sexual problems too difficult for him to handle.

6. If any difficulty does occur, there is no return after ordination. There is the possibility that a homosexual with help may make an adjustment to marriage, but this outlet is closed to a priest. If his resistance fails then he is likely to escape into sin or alcohol or both.

7. The pastor sets the whole moral tone of his parish, church, and school. The lapse of a homosexual priest could disrupt the whole religious community.

8. The homosexual cannot or can only vaguely understand heterosexual moral and marriage problems. There may be exceptions to this in individuals who make a special effort to understand.

9. If the clergyman slips or his condition becomes known, he may be subject to blackmail.

CONCLUSION

There are no hard and fast rules concerning the entry of the homosexually oriented individual into the religious life. Those concerned with selection should make reference to the suggestions made in this clinic. The homosexual who is giving consideration to the religious life should evaluate himself in this frame of reference. The effect of the grace of the sacrament of Holy Orders in such cases is not determinable. We cannot expect grace to work like magic. *Gratia perficit naturam.*

CLINIC 11 — NOTES

1. Rene Biot, M.D., and Pierre Galimard, M.D., *Medical Guide to Vocations* (London: Burns & Oates, 1955), p. 135.
2. John R. Connery, S.J., "Notes on Moral Theology," *Theological Studies,* Vol. XVI, No. 4 (December, 1955), p. 586.
3. Pope Pius XII, *The Catholic Priesthood* (Washington, D. C.: National Catholic Welfare Conference), p. 47.
4. "Thorough Examination of Candidates for Orders Strongly Emphasized" (S. C. Sacr., December 27, 1955); Bouscaren-O'Connor, *Canon Law Digest* (Milwaukee: The Bruce Publishing Company, 1958), Vol. IV, p. 312.

5. Anomaly, *The Invert* (Baltimore: The Williams and Wilkins Company, 1948),
   p. 143.
6. Dom Peter Flood, O.S.B. (ed.), *New Problems in Medical Ethics* (Westminster,
   Md.: The Newman Press, 1955), p. 115.
7. Biot and Galimard, *op. cit.*, p. 144.
8. Rev. John F. Harvey, O.S.F.S., private communication.
9. Biot and Galimard, *op. cit.*, p. 135.
10. *Canon Law Digest*, p. 312, Section 11.
11. Connery, *op. cit.*, p. 586.

Homosexuality and Governmental Agencies

Should homosexuality be a bar to service with the U. S. government or in the armed services? The homosexual's answer is "no." The "Interim Report" submitted to the Committee on Investigations states "yes" in emphatic terms.

Homosexuality is not of itself a condition which would be psychiatrically disabling for employment in the government or elsewhere, unless it is associated with some other disabling psychiatric disorder. The question concerning the employment of homosexuals in the government arises because of their susceptibility to blackmail which renders them security risks. Each case, however, should be evaluated on its own merits. A psychiatrist is often called upon to assist in the evaluation and diagnosis of the individual's sexual status. In the presence of sexual deviation the psychiatrist may be expected to give an opinion as to the specific traits of the individual such as his aggressivity, overtness, and so forth.

Experience or special training may qualify the psychiatrist to give information as to whether an individual is a security risk in regard to a particular job. If the question arises, for example, whether this specific individual with his particular set of emotional problems is, or will be, a security risk *under certain circumstances,* the psychiatrist may be expected to answer. It should be clear that not all homosexuals are security risks at all times merely *because* they are inverts. This is quite different from the situation noted in a recent newspaper article where it was reported that an agency had hired a psychiatrist to review its security regulations. The implication here was that only psychiatrically ill individuals are security risks. This is not true. The individual who needs money or has a grudge to work out is more likely to be a security risk than is the neurotic or even the psychotic individual.

HOMOSEXUALITY AND GOVERNMENT EMPLOYMENT

In regard to government employment there are a number of facts which should be borne in mind:

1. Sexual disturbance does not *per se* make an individual a security risk, or likely to be. This is especially true if his condition is known and is recorded in his personnel file. I have known professionally many homosexuals who served long and faithfully in government service.

If the condition is known and on file, such an individual is not subject to blackmail or coercion, nor would it be possible for him to form cliques.

2. Many government investigators regard as diagnostically significant adolescent homosexual experiences which are frequently only experimental and investigative. Such experiences have little, if any, significance from the standpoint of adult homosexuality and should usually be discounted. It is only when homosexual tendencies persist into adult life that they become diagnostically significant. Recently some agencies have taken a more realistic view of these experiences and do not give them the significance they once did. This topic was discussed at greater length on page 81.

3. Personnel and security officers should bear in mind that homosexuality is a way of thinking and feeling, as well as a way of acting. Many individuals who perform homosexual acts are not homosexuals. They may prefer the acts for variety or a thrill.

4. Individual sexual acts performed while drunk are frequently of little significance. There is one trait of homosexuals which seems unusual to the inexperienced. This is the characteristic of being self-accusatory; even when the condition is latent, they may act as if they were anxious to prove that they were genuine deviates. Information is offered which is frequently asserted against their own best interest. What has been said of homosexuality is equally true of other sexual deviations — bestiality, sadism, masochism, fornication, and so forth.

Each case must be decided on its own merits. The psychiatrist should not be expected to make moral judgments.

In the government setting, as well as in civilian life, homosexuals have functioned with distinction, and without disruption of morale or efficiency. Problems of social maladaptive behavior, such as homosexuality, therefore, need to be examined on an individual basis, considering the place and circumstances, rather than from inflexible rules.[1]

ATTITUDE OF GOVERNMENT TO HOMOSEXUALITY

The Interim Report previously mentioned states the government's attitude quite completely.[2] Although this report goes back several years, it is the latest on the subject of homosexuality issued by any governmental agency. It represents what would still appear to be the official attitude of the government toward the employment of inverts.

The Interim Report stated the purpose of its investigation as follows:

> The primary objective of the subcommittee in this inquiry was to determine the extent of the employment of homosexuals and other sex perverts in Government; to consider reasons why their employment by the Government is undesirable; and to examine into the efficacy of the methods used in dealing with the problem.[3]

The investigation by the committee was apparently precipitated by concern over the number of homosexuals in the State Department. No information is available on the number of such individuals who may have actually been security risks. Table III shows the number who were discharged from the government service for reasons of homosexuality. Interest in the matter was further stimulated by the defection of two alleged homosexuals from the British Foreign Service in 1951[4] and two employees of the U. S. National Security Agency in 1960. The report of the Interim Committee then continued (the italicized portions are so marked by the author):[5]

> Those charged with the responsibility of operating the agencies of Government must insist that Government employees meet acceptable standards of personal conduct. In the opinion of this subcommittee homosexuals and other sex perverts are not proper persons to be employed in Government for two reasons; first, they are *generally unsuitable,* and second, *they constitute security risks.*[6]

General Unsuitability of Sex Perverts

> Overt acts of sex perversion, including acts of homosexuality, constitute a crime under our Federal, State, and municipal statutes and persons who commit such acts are law violators. Aside from the criminality and immorality involved in sex perversion such behavior is so contrary to the normal accepted standards of social behavior that persons who engage in such activity are looked upon as outcasts by society generally.

Cases of Sex Perversion

TABLE III

Sex Perversion Statistics, Civilian Agencies of Government

Department or Agency	Jan. 1, 1947, to April 1, 1950	April 1, 1950, to Nov. 1, 1950	Total, Jan. 1, 1947, to Nov. 1, 1950	Resigned	Dismissed	Pending	Cleared
Agriculture	10	22	32	24	7	1	0
American Battle Monument Commission	0	0	0	0	0	0	0
Atomic Energy Commission	5	3	8	4	1	3	0
Bureau of the Budget	0	2	2	2	0	0	0
Civil Aeronautics Board	0	2	2	1*	0	0	1
Commerce	0	49	49	25	16	4	4
Displaced Persons Commission	1	1	2	2	0	0	0
District of Columbia	7	0	7	2	5	0	0
Economic Cooperation Administration	27	0	27	0	19	2	6
Export-Import Bank	0	0	0	0	0	0	0
Federal Communications Commission	0	3	3	1	0	2	0
Federal Deposit Insurance Corporation	0	0	0	0	0	0	0
Federal Mediation and Conciliation Service	0	0	0	0	0	0	0
Federal Power Commission	0	2	2	2	0	0	0
Federal Reserve System	0	0	0	0	0	0	0
Federal Security Agency	0	22	22	11	2	4	5
Federal Trade Commission	1	0	1	0	1	0	0
General Accounting Office	3	10	13	8	4	1	0
General Services Administration	0	19	19	8	0	9	2
Government Printing Office	0	2	2	2	0	0	0
Housing and Home Finance Agency	0	10	10	7	1	0	2
Indian Claims Commission	0	0	0	0	0	0	0
Interior	7	24	31	4	12	5	10
Interstate Commerce Commission	0	2	2	2	0	0	0
Justice	1	6	7	5	0	1	1
Labor	2	4	6	2	3	1	0
Legislative Branch:							
Botanical Gardens	0	0	0	0	0	0	0
Congressional employees	0	4	4	1	1	2	0
Library of Congress	0	15	15	9	1	5	0
National Advisory Committee for Aeronautics	0	0	0	0	0	0	0
National Capitol Housing Authority	0	0	0	0	0	0	0
National Labor Relations Board	1	1	2	1	1	0	0
National Mediation Board	0	0	0	0	0	0	0
National Security Council	0	0	0	0	0	0	0
National Security Resources Board	1	0	1	1	0	0	0
Office of Housing Expediter	0	1	1	0	1	0	0
Panama Canal	0	0	0	0	0	0	0
Philippine War Damage Commission	0	0	0	0	0	0	0
Post Office	2	6	8**	3	2	3	0
Railroad Retirement Board	2	1	3	2	1	0	0
Reconstruction Finance Corporation	0	3	3	0	2	0	1
Securities Exchange Commission	0	1	1	1	0	0	0
Selective Service System	0	0	0	0	0	0	0
Smithsonian Institute	0	2	2	1	0	1	0
State Department	106	37	143	15	106	12	10
Tennessee Valley Authority	1	0	1	0	1	0	0
Treasury	3	20	23	16*	4	3	0
U. S. Civil Service Commission	8	10	18	12	6	0	0
U. S. Motor Carriers Commission	0	0	0	0	0	0	0
U. S. Tariff Commission	0	0	0	0	0	0	0
Veterans' Administration	4	97	101	39*	9	10	43
War Claims Commission	0	1	1	0	1	0	0
White House Office	0	0	0	0	0	0	0
Total	192	382	574	213	207	69	85

* Allowed to retire.
** Covers only employees in the Department at Washington, D. C.; other figures not available.

The social stigma attached to sex perversion is so great that many perverts go to great lengths to conceal their perverted tendencies. This situation is evidenced by the fact that perverts are frequently victimized by blackmailers who threaten to expose their sexual deviations.

Law enforcement officers have informed the subcommittee that there are gangs of blackmailers who make a regular practice of preying upon the homosexual. The *modus operandi* in these homosexual blackmail cases usually follows the same general pattern. The victim, who is a homosexual, has managed to conceal his perverted activities and usually enjoys a good reputation in his community. The blackmailers, by one means or another, discover that the victim is addicted to homosexuality and under the threat of disclosure they extort money from him. These blackmailers often impersonate police officers in carrying out their blackmail schemes. Many cases have come to the attention of the police where highly respected individuals have paid out substantial sums of money to blackmailers over a long period of time rather than risk the disclosure of their homosexual activities. The police believe that this type of blackmail racket is much more extensive than is generally known, because they have found that most of the victims are very hesitant to bring the matter to the attention of the authorities.

In further considering the general suitability of perverts as Government employees, it is *generally believed* that those who engage in overt acts of perversion *lack the emotional stability of normal persons*. In addition there is an abundance of evidence to sustain the conclusion that indulgence in acts of sex perversion *weakens the moral fiber of an individual* to a degree that he is not suitable for a position of responsibility.

Most of the authorities agree and our investigation has shown that the presence of a sex pervert in a Government agency tends to have a corrosive influence upon his fellow employees. These perverts will frequently attempt to entice normal individuals to engage in perverted practices. This is particularly true in the case of young and impressionable people who might come under the influence of a pervert. Government officials have the responsibility of keeping this type of corrosive influence out of agencies under their control. It is particularly important that the thousands of young men and women who are brought into Federal jobs not be subjected to that type of influence while in the service of the Government. *One homosexual can pollute a Government office.*

Another point to be considered in determining whether a sex pervert is suitable for government employment is his tendency to gather other perverts about him. Eminent psychiatrists have informed the subcommittee that the homosexual is likely to seek his own kind because the pressures of society are such that he feels uncomfortable unless he is with his own kind. Due to this situation the homosexual tends to surround himself with other homosexuals, not only in his social, but in his business life. Under these circumstances if a homosexual attains a position in Government where he can influence the hiring of personnel, it is *almost inevitable* that he will attempt to place other homosexuals in Government jobs.[7]

Sex Perverts as Security Risks

The conclusion of the subcommittee that a homosexual or other pervert is a security risk is not based upon mere conjecture. The conclusion is predicated upon a careful review of the opinions of those best qualified to consider matters of security in Government, namely, the intelligence agencies of the Government. Testimony on this phase of the inquiry was taken from representatives of the Federal Bureau of Investigation, the Central Intelligence Agency, and the intelligence services of th Army, Navy, and Air Force. All of these agencies are in complete agreement that sex perverts in Government constitute security risks.[8]

The Rules of Government Regarding the Employment of Sex Perverts

The regulations of the Civil Service Commission for many years have provided that criminal, infamous, dishonest, immoral, or notoriously disgraceful conduct, which includes homosexuality or other types of sex perversion, are sufficient grounds for denying appointment to a Government position or for the removal of a person from the Federal Service. Furthermore, under the civil service regulation (Ch. S1–21, Federal Personnel Manual), specific procedures have been set up under which unsuitable Federal employees who are subject to the civil service regulations which are applicable to over 90 percent of the civilians employed in Federal Government and the remaining civilian employees who are not subject to the rules of the Civil Service Commission are covered by agency regulations which are similar to those of the Commission. In addition to the rules and regulations of the Civil Service Commission, the armed services have promulgated and adopted their own regulations for the handling of this problem among military personnel. As was previously pointed out in this report, the armed services have traditionally taken a firm and aggressive attitude toward the problem, but until early this year, each service was handling the problem in its own way. In December, 1949, the Department of Defense effected standard procedures for the handling and disposition of homosexual cases among military personnel. Since that time each of the services has issued regulations based upon these procedures and the problem is now being handled uniformly in all of the military services.[9]

Conclusion

There is no place in the United States Government for persons who violate the laws or the accepted standards of morality, or who otherwise bring disrepute to the Federal service by infamous or scandalous personal conduct. Such persons are not suitable for Government positions and in the case of doubt the American people are entitled to have errors of judgment on the part of their officials, if there must be errors, resolved on the side of caution. It is the opinion of this subcommittee *that those who engage in acts of homosexuality and other perverted sex activities are unsuitable for employment in the Federal Government. This conclusion is based upon the fact that persons who indulge in such degraded activity are committing not only illegal and immoral acts, but they also constitute security risks in positions of public trust.*[10]

The portions of the report in italics would seem to be purely gratuitous and unproven statements. The attitude of the Committee toward blackmail is particularly hard to understand. The homosexual is described as one who "usually enjoys a good reputation in his community"; "many cases . . . were highly respected individuals"; "the blackmailers often impersonate police officers." The Committee makes no suggestions for the relief of the besieged homosexual, but seems to accept the fact that this is his lot. It would seem that all citizens are entitled to the protection of the law even though they are homosexuals who "were highly respected individuals." The Committee by its own statements makes such blackmail more likely and more effective.

Much of the possibility of blackmail and of the Committee's attitude toward lawbreakers would be eliminated if homosexual acts between mutually consenting adults were made legal and the fact of their homosexuality made known in their personnel record.

A further argument for changing the law is that it is a fertile source of blackmail. The Wolfenden Committee gave some figures for 1950, when thirty-two of the seventy-one cases reported to the police for blackmail were connected with homosexual offenses. Some years earlier, speaking in the House of Lords, Lord Jowitt, a former Lord Chancellor, disclosed that when he was Attorney General, 95 percent of the blackmail cases coming to his attention arose from homosexuality. In the United States the law has also lent itself to blackmail. Judge Ploscowe, in his book *Sex and the Law,* reported that in 1940 the New York District Attorney broke up a blackmailing ring that had been operating for twenty years in and around New York City. Twenty-three members of the ring were sent to prison.[11]

Lest it be thought that the author is the only one not fully in accord with the Committee's findings, the following comments from authoritative sources are offered:

1. *The GAP Report:* This report was prepared by the Committee on Cooperation with Governmental (Federal) Agencies of the Group for the Advancement of Psychiatry,[12] under the title: "Report on Homosexuality with Particular Emphasis on This Problem in Governmental Agencies." The following comments were extracted from this

report. They would appear to be at variance with some of the conclusions of the Interim Committee:

> Perversion and homosexuality are not synonymous terms. Perversion
> is a general term which includes any clear deviation from usual sexual
> behavior, be it homosexual or heterosexual. Homosexuality is therefore
> a form of sexual perversion.

> Overt homosexuality stated simply may be an expression of fear of the
> opposite sex, of inability to accept adult responsibility, and an attempt
> to deal with competitive attitudes towards members of the same sex.

> In any governmental agency the implementation of established policies
> and directives pertaining to homosexuality may lead to undesirable
> complications. For example, in an endeavor to eliminate homosexuals
> from the service, innocent individuals may become involved; overzealous
> investigators may resort to "witch-hunting"; seventeen- and eighteen-
> year-olds who have engaged in isolated homosexual acts out of curi-
> osity may not be distinguished from homosexuals.

> . . . Some intelligence experts report that homosexuals are usually vul-
> nerable to breakdown under interrogation by the skilled questioner.
> This Committee, however, is not aware of any such material from a
> scientific study of this problem.[13]

2. *Karl M. Bowman, M.D.:*

It is of interest that some of our officials in Washington have the naïve
idea that excluding homosexuals from government service will do away
with the problem of foreign spies securing secret information. Homosexuals are no more open to seduction than are heterosexuals, and history is full of accounts of beautiful female spies who have secured important secrets from other governments by their heterosexual seduc-
tions. We find that some rulers in the past have tried to make their
positions safe by surrounding themselves with eunuchs, but even this
device did not prevent the rulers from betrayal at times. In view of the
high incidence of some type of homosexual indulgence in American
males as reported by Kinsey, there would seem to be little or no chance
of keeping our government offices free of overt homosexuals. If one
wishes to add the group of latent homosexuals, it is obvious that we
are witnessing some of the wish-fulfillment thinking, dissociated from
reality, that we see in our schizophrenic patients.[14]

3. *John F. Oliven, M.D.:*

The merit of these contentions remains in dispute, but available experience does not seem to confirm that homosexuals, in the majority
of cases, constitute a disruptive element in a government — or business, or industrial, or professional — organization. The most valuable
elements among these patients are capable of rendering outstanding
service, for instance as they "sublimate" much of their instinctual drive

into dedicated, perhaps ambitious furtherance of the business at hand (often the *res politica,* on a non-factional level), while leading a life of personal asceticism. A very few may "displace" rather than "sublimate" their deviate urges and display a highly undesirable, morbid combination of ambition, ascetic zeal, and, perhaps, cruelty in the service of a rigid, ruthless campaign of suppression of pleasurable impulses and institutions among those under their authority, whether subalterns or those they govern by authority of office. Of no merit is the contention that homosexual inclinations are by that fact indication of moral turpitude or depravity, or of "lack of moral fiber." The greatest source of error and personal injustice with regard to homosexuals in government is that a "diagnosis" often is based on police reports of unlawful or sometimes merely "suspicious" sexual contacts, without benefit of medico-psychiatric assessment of the individual.[15]

INTELLIGENCE SERVICES

There are many homosexuals who have commented on how exceptionally well the invert adapts himself to intelligence work, how successful he is in the work, and how secure he is. One confirmed homosexual states: "I have found a large percentage of agents of all countries having homosexual tendencies, and I think they naturally gravitate to this form of work."

There are certain characteristics of the homosexual which adapt him for this work:

1. The invert by the nature of his condition leads a double life, that of his sexual life, which must be kept under cover, and that of his normal relations with the world. The normal person valuing his own dignity and integrity has difficulty in leading a double life — unless he is a criminal — but for the homosexual to develop a third, fourth, or fifth personality and a life connected with it is not unusual. He frequently enjoys it, and the necessity of being all things to all men is usually easy for him. As one homosexual said:

Of course, the danger here lies, as it did with me, that I spread myself out so thin, was so many different people — with a different story for each, that I began to lose touch with reality, losing the core of my own being, and hence conflicting stories, attitudes, and so forth resulted. After this experience, in any new assignment I was obliged to keep to one or two targets, and not be a half dozen different people, for in that way lies trouble for me, for I had and could lose myself in my own different personalities, till I no longer knew where truth lay.

2. Much of the intelligence work appeals to the juvenile in the homosexual and may involve activity which the average individual

would not really enjoy. But because the homosexual maintains certain adolescent attitudes throughout life, he can enter into this type of work fully and enjoy it. "We like the cloak and dagger element, the continuous childhood game of cops and robbers." See the Ishmael theory, p. 50.

3. The homosexual has by necessity been forced to develop a kind of sixth sense about people — are they, or are they not? He develops a kind of intuitive sense which comes into full play in this type of work. He will go to endless lengths to find out secrets about people, for the power it gives him — this is always an element in the homosexual makeup; since by his nature he feels he cannot meet the world on its own values, he must triumph by this indirect way. The desire for power, channeled into this kind of work, can be of great value.

4. By the nature of his condition the practicing homosexual lives outside the law, and he may thus become a kindred soul with the many others who live outside the law — "the spy," the criminal, the deviate, the pervert.

I remember how well I found myself attuned to these people, murderers, thieves, etc., that I found during the war. It was always the feeling — I am one of you, and I understand you. My own homosexuality not only gave me entry to this group, but sympathy with them, which was of most valuable service during this period. I was one of them, rather than on the other side, and I continuously had the impression during this period that though they may not have known about me, they instinctively felt that I was one of them.

5. As has been pointed out, "fatalism" is one of the characteristics of homosexuality, and in intelligence work this is important. Most homosexuals have it very strongly.

I found myself taking chances during the war period, rather wild ones, because of it, knowing the odds were against me, yet one went through it with a kind of fatalism that usually led one to success. I found my so-called "normal associates" not able to do this — they wanted too many assurances.

6. The work itself demands a kind of lone-wolf attitude, which the homosexual has already, but which for normal people is sometimes very hard to accept. The agent must be able to accept social ostracism, lack of normal social life, lack of close friends, to carry out difficult assignments. Most men with families do not want this,

but to the homosexual it is already second nature. Things such as this which are a problem to many normal agents never seem to be for the homosexual.

7. Because of his adolescent attitude toward life in general, the homosexual likes constant change, shifting environments, new people, new problems, which the normal person tends to want to avoid as he grows older.

THE ARMED FORCES

The armed forces have always made efforts to keep homosexual individuals out of their ranks. The reason in the past was to prevent the discord which might arise in troops away from female company due to the presence of such individuals. This was particularly true in the Navy where the presence of a homosexual in a small crew at sea for a long time might result in sex acts or even in physical harm to the invert. The ultimate result would depend on the mood of the crew. It is only recently that the concept of danger to the national security has arisen as a bar to the presence of homosexuals in the military service. Table IV shows that 4380 individuals were

TABLE IV

Sex Perversion Cases, Armed Services (Military Personnel)*

	Number of Sex Perversion Cases Handled			Method of Separation	
	Jan. 1, 1947, through Mar. 31, 1950	Apr. 1, 1950, through Oct. 31, 1950	Total	General court martial	Other than general court martial
Army . . .	1,104	301	1,405	272	1,133**
Navy . . .	1,665	399	2,064	174	1,890
Air Force . .	476†	435	911	24	887
Total . . .	3,245	1,135	4,380	470	3,910

* Statistics on civilian personnel of the armed services are not included in this study. Due to the system of maintaining civilian personnel files in the armed services, prohibitive costs would be incurred in obtaining data concerning the number of civilian employees dismissed for sex perversion. Procedures are now being worked out whereby such information will be available in future cases. However, an incomplete examination of the civilian employee files indicates that at least 42 civilians are known to have been separated from the armed services on charges of sex perversion at various times since January 1, 1950.

** Includes a few separations resulting from rape charges.

† Air Force figures included with Army until separation of records of these two services in January, 1948.

discharged from the armed forces from January 1, 1947, through October 31, 1950. During this same period, 207 civilians were discharged (see Table III, p. 159).

The latest revision of the regulations dealing with the deposition of homosexuals from the armed services was made in 1959. Since the regulations in all the services are more or less the same, I shall describe only those of the Air Force. *Mutatis mutandis,* what is said of the Air Force will apply with minor changes to the Army and the Navy.

DISCHARGE OF HOMOSEXUALS FROM THE AIR FORCE

Air Force Regulation No. 35–66 is entitled: "Military Personnel: Discharge Processing Where Homosexual Acts or Tendencies Are Involved (Effective 14 April 1959)":[16]

> 3. *What the Air Force Policy Is Regarding Homosexuality:*
> a. Homosexuality will not be tolerated in the Air Force and prompt separation of known homosexuals is mandatory. Participation in a homosexual act, or proposing or attempting to do so, is considered a very serious misbehavior regardless of whether the role of a person in a particular act was active or passive. Members of the Air Force serving in the active military service represent the military establishment 24 hours a day. There is no distinction between duty time and off-duty time as the high moral standards of the service must be maintained at all times. All members of the Reserve Components not serving on extended active duty are required to maintain the same high standards as active duty personnel throughout the entire period of their military service.

Although Paragraph 3 mentions only acts or attempted acts, Paragraph 6 mentions *tendencies:*

> 6. *Who Will Report Acts of Homosexuality:* It is the duty of every member to report to his commander any facts concerning overt acts of homosexuality or association or tendency by any member which may come to his attention. Any member who makes a false official statement for the purpose of initiating action to obtain a discharge pursuant to the provisions of this regulation or for any other purpose is subject to action under the appropriate articles of the Uniform Code of Military Justice (UCMJ).

West *et al.* point to a serious difficulty for professional people handling such individuals. Under this regulation the medical officer and even the chaplain to whom the invert may have gone in confidence is required to inform; if he does not, he violates the regulations:

> Any physician or psychologist who learns of the existence in a patient of homosexual tendencies, or a history of a homosexual act at any time in the past, is duty-bound to report it to administrative officials. Needless to say, this requirement is a source of great distress to psychiatrists, and leads to considerable soul-searching.[17]

I cannot imagine either the medical officer or the chaplain making such a revelation, but their failure to do so makes them subject to disciplinary action.

Paragraph 12 of AFR 35–66 describes the classification of cases:

> 12. *Classification of Cases.* Cases are generally classified as follows:
>
> a. *Class I.* Those cases where a member of the Air Force has engaged in one or more homosexual acts accompanied by assault or coercion, as characterized by an act in or to which the other person involved did not willingly cooperate or consent, or where consent was obtained through force, fraud, or actual intimidation or where the homosexual act was committed with a minor, regardless of whether the minor cooperated.
>
> b. *Class II.* Those cases where a member of the Air Force has engaged in one or more homosexual acts, or has proposed or attempted to perform an act which does not fall into the Class I category. It is emphasized that no distinction is made in the administrative handling of cases of alleged participation in homosexual acts based upon whether the role of the person in any particular act was active or passive.
>
> c. *Class III.*
> (1) Those cases where a member of the Air Force exhibits, professes, or admits to homosexual tendencies, or habitually associates with persons known to him to be homosexuals, but there is no evidence that he has, *while a member of the Air Force,* engaged in one or more homosexual acts, or has proposed or attempted to perform an act of homosexuality.
> (2) Those cases where a member, *prior to becoming a member of the Air Force,* exhibited, professed or admitted to homosexual tendencies, or habitually associated with persons known to him to be homosexuals, or who engaged in one or more homosexual acts, or proposed or attempted to perform an act of homosexuality, but *there is no evidence that he has, while a member of the Air Force,* engaged in or proposed or attempted to perform an act of homosexuality.

The Class I cases are those generally recognized as criminal acts and which deserve punishment. Any revision of the law would undoubtedly, and should, single out this type of offense as criminal. Class II and Class III involve the danger of including the type of case described on page 171 and create the danger of a gross injustice. In the case of military personnel arrested by civilian authorities, great care must be exercised that their arrest did not come about by a form of entrapment (see p. 201 and Case X). It would seem that in Class II and Class III, if the individual is not to be retained in the service, his discharge could be handled at a local level (see p. 171).

4. *Character of Discharge Furnished Members Processed for Discharge Under This Regulation.* The character of discharge for all classes defined in paragraph 12 will be similar, without distinction as to sex or status.

a. *Class I.* Since trial by general court-martial is usually appropriate for cases in this class, the character of discharge will be that imposed by court-martial action.

b. *Class II.* Discharge Under Conditions Other Than Honorable (undesirable) for airmen or Discharge Under Other Than Honorable Conditions for officers, unless the particular circumstances in a given case warrant a General or Honorable Discharge.

c. *Class III.* Discharge with an Honorable or General Discharge, as appropriate to the particular circumstances of a given case.

I would like to make my own position clear. I do not intend to convey the impression that I believe that the homosexual should usually be retained in the Armed Forces. This is no place for a homosexual, male or female. My objection is that in so many instances the homosexual is penalized only for *being* a homosexual, not necessarily for *acting* like one. I also feel he should not be penalized by the Armed Forces for acts which he committed prior to entry into the military service, as happened in Case X (see p. 171).

Drs. West, Doidge, and Williams discuss revision in the present regulations designed to eliminate these injustices. Bowman and Engle have also stated

that the most reasonable view is that in which homosexual disturbances are seen as problems of individual morality and psychology, and that mutually consenting adults engaging privately in any non-dangerous sexual act should not be considered criminal.[18]

The revisions suggested by West *et al.* are:

1. *Punitive official attitudes should be modified.* Military law is sufficient to punish acts which might threaten the community; therefore, there is no reason why the individual should be punished because he has homosexual feelings.

2. *Extensive routine investigations should be eliminated.* The lengthy investigation of the O.S.I. (Office of Special Investigations) required by the present regulations (see Section B., Par. 11a) is in most cases unnecessary. It is expensive and keeps the airmen much longer than necessary in the service. This is especially true of self-confessed homosexuals and of those whose acts occurred before they entered the service. In these cases

> a man who is unsuitable because of his immaturity (marked only in part by homosexual impulses) can be sent home with a General Discharge soon after his condition is brought to light, just as though he were unsuitable because of enuresis, or stuttering, or lack of physical stamina.[19]

3. *Separations should be on the basis of the primary disorder.*

> Certainly within the first 60 days of service General Discharges could efficiently be utilized to separate those immature, passive-aggressive, or inadequate persons who happen to have homosexual symptoms as well as those who haven't.[20]

4. *The special stigma should be eliminated.* There is no reason for the specification on an individual's discharge that the reason was homosexuality, unless this occurred as a result of a general court-martial.

5. *Investigation should be a benign procedure.* "Great care should be exercised to guard the dignity and person of the individual being investigated."[21]

6. *Present retention policies should be given a fair trial.* These policies are not given a fair trial if the retention is decided upon after a long period of investigation during which the individual is removed from his job and kept in detention — AFR 35–66, Par. 15d (a); also Par. 20d (4). By this time the man is likely to be disgusted and discouraged and returns to his outfit with the stigma of having been under investigation for inversion. The local commander could very expeditiously handle most Class II and Class III cases while the individual was in a duty status.

CASE X

The subject of this clinic is twenty-three years of age and is a white male. He is unmarried. His case is presented, among other reasons, to show the element of entrapment (see p. 201).

WE ARE ALL INTERESTED IN YOUR CASE AND ARE ALL STUDENTS
OF THE TYPE OF PROBLEM WHICH YOU PRESENT. WOULD YOU, THERE-
FORE, TELL US AS COMPLETELY AND FRANKLY AS YOU CAN WHY YOU
ARE SEEKING HELP?

I will try to answer your questions. I am here because I was arrested.
For this, I was given an undesirable discharge from the military service,
and I would like to have that changed.

TELL US WHAT HAPPENED.

About 4 months ago I met a man in the recreation room of a large
club. It turned out later that this man was a police officer, but at that
time it seemed to me, by his actions and facial expressions, that he was a
homosexual. There was no bodily contact between us. The man seemed
to be trying by his conversation to get me to make a sexual proposition,
but since I thought he had a room in the club, when he asked, "What do
you want to do?" I merely said, "Let's go up to your room and find out."
Anyway, we took an elevator to the fourth floor. In the corridor he kept
asking questions which I now realize were intended to get me to incrimi-
nate myself. He finally said, "If you take it in the rear, I'll blow you"
(sodomy). After more such remarks were made by the officer I finally
said, "Yes, I will." I said "yes" not because I was really intent on doing
anything, but because I was lonely and wanted to talk to someone. As
soon as I said "yes," the man identified himself as a police officer and
"took me into custody." I wasn't sure whether this was the same thing
as being arrested, but in any case I went along with him and was brought
to a police station and put into a cell. I was quite upset by the whole
thing; it was the first time I had ever been "taken into custody" and I
wasn't at all sure what was going to happen to me. Confused as I was,
I remember that a few hours later, I was questioned by the same officer
who was still in plain clothes. I admitted to him that I had had homosexual relations before. I remember that there was at least one other officer
in the room at the time I was questioned. I believe that at this time I was
finger-printed and an FBI record was made.

THEN WHAT HAPPENED?

I spent that night in the police station and the next day I was turned
over to the armed forces police who took me to an Army stockade. Here
I was questioned by a man whose name I don't remember. He told me
that as a homosexual I was a security risk and, therefore, would probably
be released from the service. He also told me that I ought to admit to
being one now, because it would be easier on me since the psychiatrist
would find out anyway. I seem to remember that he also told me that I
might stand a chance of being cured of my homosexual tendencies and
be allowed to remain in the service. With this promise of a cure, I remember dictating a list of ten or fifteen of my previous homosexual contacts.
Of these only two were while I was in the service; these were with civilians,

however, and not with military personnel. I remember signing this dictation which, at the time, I did not know was a confession. I remember signing a waiver or some sort of statement which I understood to be my rights under the Fifth Amendment. To the best of my understanding, the story I dictated and signed was not a confession but something which was necessary before I could be referred to a psychiatrist who would cure me so that I could stay in the military. I never saw this man again.

The next day, while still under military arrest, I remember being taken to a military hospital for a psychiatric interview. I remember that no one in the Psychiatric Division seemed to know what to do with me — at least it seemed that way. No one questioned me or counseled me in any way. Later they took me to the M.P. post at the hospital where I was given a tongue-lashing by an officer. At this point I realized that there was to be no attempt at cure and that I had been tricked into signing a confession. Someone at the M.P. post gave me an emergency pass to return to my station, since I was already technically AWOL.

About a month later I was called in by my commanding officer, who told me that he had received notification of my "confession" and that as a homosexual I would be separated from the service. He asked me if I would agree to see the base psychiatrist. He said that this was the procedure in cases like mine. I agreed. I remember repeating the whole story of my homosexual life to two doctors and an enlisted man social worker. I remember being given a Rorschach test by an enlisted man and being interviewed very briefly by a psychiatrist who offered no solution to my problem.

Shortly after this I remember signing a paper whereby I would receive an undesirable discharge and would not have to face a court-martial. Two months later I was released from the service with an undesirable discharge.

This is all I remember. I don't want sympathy — I just feel that what was done was unfair and, since I most probably was mentally unbalanced at the time I signed the confession, that it was illegal. I am willing to return to the service or finish out my two years in the reserves. I do not feel that being a homosexual is moral, but, on the other hand, I do not feel that I ever was or will be a security risk to my country.

THE PURPOSE OF THIS EXAMINATION, THEN, IS TO HELP YOU GET A BETTER DISCHARGE FROM THE SERVICE OR TO RETURN TO ACTIVE DUTY?

That is true.

YOU HAVE GIVEN A GOOD DESCRIPTION OF THE CIRCUMSTANCES OF YOUR ARREST AND DISCHARGE; NOW TELL US MORE ABOUT YOURSELF. FIRST TELL US — DO YOU CONSIDER YOURSELF A HOMOSEXUAL?

Well, frankly I must admit that I have had homosexual experiences, if that makes me a homosexual, but I have liked girls, too.

TELL US ABOUT YOUR EARLY HABITS IN REGARD TO SEX.

I masturbated for about two years — that is, from fifteen to seventeen years of age. At first it gave me a sense of physical pleasure, but around seventeen it stopped having any attraction for me. I started to date girls about this time.

DID YOU EVER HAVE INTERCOURSE WITH A GIRL?

No, I never did. It seemed wrong to destroy the girl's morals by committing such acts. I went steady with a girl in college — she was about my age. We petted some — I wanted to see what it was like — but I never felt any excitement or pleasure as far as sex was concerned.

WHEN DID YOU PERFORM YOUR FIRST HOMOSEXUAL ACT?

My first homosexual act was the summer after I finished high school. I met a man in the restroom of a railroad station. I don't remember who made the suggestion. We performed an act of mutual masturbation. I don't recall the next incident exactly, but it consisted only of fondling the genitals of another man. During my first one and one-half years in college, I met some very fine people, and I hoped that I was normal again. However, later in the second year I met a man with whom I performed another sexual act and since that time, I have been both the active and passive partner in quite a few homosexual acts. I don't remember how many.

TELL US MORE.

When I was ten or twelve years of age, while I was masturbating, I would have fantasies of sex with both men and women. At that time, while I generally thought I would prefer homosexual activity, I hoped I would become heterosexual. My first actual homosexual experience was at the age of seventeen or eighteen. At that time the acts were mostly mutual masturbation with other fellows I happened to meet. I never did have any long affair with any one person. I also had "occasional" experiences of oral-genital (fellatio) and anal-genital (sodomy) contact in which I was both the active and the passive partner, but I found these experiences revolting.

IF YOU FOUND THESE CONTACTS SO REPULSIVE, WHY DID YOU CONTINUE?

I really don't know, but in spite of the distaste, it seemed that I had a strong tendency in that direction. It never happened before, but since I was in the service I have been teased by the other fellows because of my mannerisms; but none of them knew that I was a homosexual. I never did have any relations with other soldiers, only with civilians.

THINKING BACK TO YOUR EARLY LIFE, CAN YOU RECALL ANY OLDER MAN WHO MIGHT HAVE TOUCHED YOUR GENITALS?

When I was very small I can remember being very strongly attached to some man, but I don't recall who it was. It could have been an uncle or someone else in the family. I have always tried to be masculine, but those other "urges" got the better of me at times.

WERE THERE OTHER CHILDREN?

There were six of us, I was the fourth child. I have three older brothers who are all married. I came next, then I have a fourteen year old brother and an eleven year old sister who both live with my parents. We got along as well as most families, I suppose; I stayed a bit to myself, but they didn't seem to mind. My family was healthy, except that my mother has a brother who is in a mental hospital. I used to be his favorite before he got sick. I haven't seen him for two or three years now. As far as I know, none of my older brothers had any homosexual experiences.

HOW OLD WERE YOU WHEN YOU WENT TO SCHOOL?

I was five years old when I started in kindergarten. After a year I went to grade school. I got along well with my teachers and classmates and made good grades all through school. In high school I started to realize that there was something twisted inside me, because I was not attracted to girls, but I seemed to be to boys like I thought I should be to girls. Out of curiosity I got some books to find out about homosexuals. These feelings persisted all through college.

WHEN DID YOU ENTER THE SERVICE?

I was drafted into the military service in March, 1956, at the age of twenty-one. While in basic I got along very well because I felt that if I could get along in the service, it would prove that I was as much of a man as the next person. On several occasions I withstood more harassment and physical strain than some of the other fellows could. However, because of my effeminate characteristics, particularly my talk and my body, I was constantly teased by the fellows in the barracks. It was all friendly, however. While in the service I made no advances toward any of the men — in fact I had no desire to do so. Since this incident when I was arrested, I don't think the fellows kid me as much. I don't know why they don't, because no one knows what happened.

IS THERE ANYTHING ELSE YOU WOULD LIKE TO TELL US?

No. Do you think I can be helped?

Discussion of the Case

Many of the clinical features of this case are fairly typical. No case is really completely typical. It shows the features of early seduction, adolescent puzzlement concerning the direction of the sex drive, heterosexual experimentation, and a military handling of a case of homosexuality. One wonders what would have happened in this case if counseling or therapy had been attempted in adolescence when he "was reading the books on homosexuality." His heterosexual experimentation brings to mind the words of the fictional psychiatrist who commented: "I enjoyed sex with them [girls], I was proud of this, but they couldn't stimulate my mind, nor was I capable of loving them."[22]

The arrest features of this case are in my mind rather typical of entrapment (see p. 201). In this case the police officer does not "catch" the individual in the performance of an illegal act, but by his own actions traps him into an illegal act and then arrests him.

One wonders also if an undesirable discharge was indicated for a man who had performed no acts with military personnel. It seems, rather, that he was being punished for being a homosexual. As I have indicated before, the military establishment is no place for inverts, no more than is a boys' camp, a Turkish bath, or similar all-male establishment. My only point is that too frequently the homosexual seems to be penalized only because he is a homosexual.

In this case the condition seems well established and the motivation of the individual is such that the prognosis for therapy would be quite poor.

SUMMARY

There is no evidence to show that homosexuals are always security risks. A change of existing laws to make homosexual acts (performed in private between consenting adults) legal would solve most of the objections proposed for their employment in the government.

There is no place in the Armed Forces for homosexuals because of the nature of their sexual drive, not because they are necessarily security risks. Many so-called "fraudulent" enlistments would be avoided if greater assurance could be given that the information supplied at the time of enlistment in regard to sexual tendencies would be treated confidentially.

CLINIC 12 — NOTES

1. "Report on Homosexuality With Particular Emphasis on This Problem in Governmental Agencies," formulated by the Committee on Cooperation with Governmental (Federal) Agencies of the Group for the Advancement of Psychiatry, 3617 W. 6th Ave., Topeka, Kansas, Report No. 30, p. 6, January, 1955.
2. "Employment of Homosexuals and Other Sex Perverts in Government," Interim Report submitted to the Committee on Expenditures in the Executive Depart-

ments by its Subcommittee on Investigations pursuant to S. Res. 280 (81st Congress), December 15 (legislative day, November 27), 1950. (United States Government Printing Office.)

3. *Ibid.*, p. 1.
4. For a complete report on this defection see *The Great Spy Scandal* by John S. Mather and Donald Seamon (London: Purnell & Sons, Ltd., 1956).
5. This report is given at length so that the official attitude toward sexual deviation may be clearly seen. This is important because "official" attitudes are frequently representative of public reaction or are important in molding public opinion. My principal objection to the report is that it puts all homosexuals in the same package, which is not true. The *italics* in the citations are my own.
6. Interim Report, p. 3.
7. *Ibid.*, pp. 3–4.
8. *Ibid.*, pp. 4–5.
9. *Ibid.*, pp. 8–9.
10. *Ibid.*, p. 19.
11. Norman St. John-Stevas, *Law and Morals* (Volume 148 of the *Twentieth Century Encyclopedia of Catholicism*) (New York: Hawthorn Books, 1964), p. 121. See Clinic 14 for further discussion of changes in the law.
12. See footnote 1.
13. *The GAP Report*, pp. 3, 5.
14. Karl M. Bowman, M.D., "The Problem of the Sex Offender," *The American Journal of Psychiatry*, Vol. 108, No. 4 (October, 1951), p. 253.
15. John F. Oliven, M.D., *Sexual Hygiene and Pathology* (Philadelphia and Montreal: J. B. Lippincott Company, 1955), pp. 441–442.
16. Department of the Air Force, Washington, March 17, 1959.
17. Louis J. West, William T. Doidge, and Robert L. Williams, "An Approach to the Problem of Homosexuality in the Military Service," *The American Journal of Psychiatry*, Vol. 115, No. 5 (November, 1958), p. 393.
18. Karl M. Bowman, M.D., and Bernice Engle, "A Psychiatric Evaluation of Laws on Homosexuality," as submitted to the *Temple Law Quarterly*, Spring, 1956. This article was subsequently published in the *American Journal of Psychiatry*, Vol. 112, No. 8 (February, 1956), pp. 577–583. Quoted at p. 583.
19. See West *et al.*, *op. cit.*, p. 399.
20. *Ibid.*
21. *Ibid.*
22. Rodney Garland, *The Heart in Exile* (London: The Camelot Press, 1954), p. 40.

*Homosexual Sexual Anomalies**

For most people homosexuality is enough of a deviation without adding anomalies to an already anomalous situation. Nevertheless, it is true that the homosexually oriented person is subject to more or less the same sexual disorders as the heterosexual individual. The difference is in the sex object. In the case of the homosexual it will naturally be of the same sex.

CLASSIFICATION OF SEXUAL ANOMALIES

In this grouping, it will be clear that not all sexual anomalies should be classified as sexual offenses. None of them, however, are without legal significance. Those having greater significance will be discussed more fully. The list, while not exhaustive, is sufficiently comprehensive to encompass the experience of most counselors.

1. *Quantitative Disturbances of the Sex Drive*

In this type of disturbance, the sex drive is increased or decreased in relation to the average by homosexuality.

a) Impotence
b) Premature ejaculation
c) Frigidity
d) Vaginismus
e) Nymphomania
f) Priapism
g) Satyriasis

2. *Qualitative Disturbances of the Sex Drive*

In this type of disturbance, the sexual arousal is the result of other than the usual stimulus.

---

* Parts of this chapter are reprinted from the 1963 Winter Edition of *The Catholic Lawyer* with permission.

a) Voyeurism
b) Exhibitionism
c) Transvestitism
d) Transsexualism
e) Fetishism
f) Sadism
g) Masochism
h) Coprophilia
i) Necrophilia
j) Coprophagia
k) Necrosadism (lust murder)
l) Gerontosexuality
m) Pygmalionism
n) Frottage
o) Illusionary cohabitation

3. *Sexual Disturbances Which Are Against Society*

In this group are included the offenses which interfere with the unity of marriage.

a) Fornication
b) Adultery
c) Incest
d) Seduction
e) Rape
f) Artificial insemination
g) Triolism (troilism)
h) Prostitution

4. *Sexual Acts "Contra Naturam"*

In this type of disorder, the disturbance is such that it destroys the "natural order of the act."

a) Fellatio
b) Cunnilingus
c) Sodomy (buggery)
d) Masturbation
e) Bestiality
f) Homosexual acts
g) Pedophilia

5. *Anomalies in Which the Sexual Element Is Not in Consciousness*
a) Kleptomania
b) Pyromania
c) Others

QUANTITATIVE DISTURBANCES OF THE SEX ACT

Impotence (premature ejaculation). Impotence is the inability of the male or female to perform the sex act completely. Impotence may be either (*a*) functional or (*b*) organic. In the male, impotence may appear in several guises. It, for example, may be *erective impotence* (the inability to get an erection), *ejaculatory impotence* (the inability to expel seminal fluid), or *orgastic impotence* (the inability to achieve full orgasm). *Premature ejaculation,* as its name implies, signifies ejaculation even before intromission (or at least before either partner is ready). Impotence is a condition of great significance legally. It is important not only to the counselor who handles marriage problems but to the attorney who practices criminal law. Many sexual offenses occur because the individual is seeking the stimulus necessary to overcome his impotence. The individual who has lost his potency frequently becomes obsessed with the idea that if he could receive a certain type of stimulus he could then perform a sex act quite satisfactorily. He may have previously experienced such stimulation or (more likely) has enjoyed it in fantasy. This stimulus may vary from some simple form of stimulation such as pornographic pictures at one end of the scale to sadistic murder at the other. This is as true of the invert as of the heterosexual. Conflict over the sexual deviation may result in strong feelings of guilt with associated impotence.

Impotence may occur at any age, but it increases in frequency with advancing years. Not all bizarre forms of sexual acts are the result of impotence but they are sufficiently frequent to be thought of as a possible cause in every case. Some anomalous acts merely add zest to the performance; others actually make the act possible.

The impotent individual becomes increasingly dangerous socially to the degree that he is obsessed by the need of vicarious stimulation and the availability of such a stimulus to him.

In the female, impotence, if it occurs, is usually anatomical. In some cases, which are becoming less frequent, vaginismus may be a cause of impotence. This is not unusual in the Lesbian who attempts vaginal intercourse.

Priapism. This condition is named after Priapus, the son of Venus and Mercury, who was the god of procreation. His statues represent him with an erect penis. Priapism is a pathologic erection of the penis unaccompanied by sexual desire (see comment of Patient I in Clinic 8). Priapus has been adopted, but rarely, as a common noun to mean the penis.

Satyriasis. This is a pathologic, compulsive, excessive degree of sexual desire in the male. It is similar to nymphomania in the female and, like that condition, seldom leads to conflict with the law. This is so because, although the desire is excessive, there is no qualitative disturbance in its aim so that usually satisfaction is easily found. The original aim may, of course, be either toward the self sex or the other sex.

Frigidity (sexual anhedonia, anesthesia, anaphrodism, dyspareunia) in the female consists of varying degrees of loss of sexual desire, from complete indifference to complete revulsion. This would be the ordinary reaction of the Lesbian who attempts heterosexual relations.

In the evaluation of frigidity, it is important to bear in mind that sexual orgasm is infrequent in women. It occurs in only 20 to 40 percent of American married women. There are, however, indications that in the new generation of married women, orgasm is more frequent. Such an absence of orgasm does not, of course, indicate lack of affection, desire, pleasurable erotic feelings, or sexual arousal. This knowledge is important because many men and women feel that inability to achieve orgasm is an indication of lack of love, poor sexual technic (usually on the part of the husband), or extramarital affairs. None of these is necessarily true. As a matter of fact, there have been and still are, occasionally, arguments as to whether frigidity is pathological even in the normally sexed woman. Oliven, for example, states:

> There continues to be occasional controversy as to whether frigidity is a pathologic condition at all. A few observers feel that orgasm is not an integral part of female sexuality, but a faculty which the individual women may or may not achieve; and that the "doctrine of universal copulatory orgasm" tends to stigmatize a proportion of normal women as sexually deficient or disordered. However, clinical consensus today favors the view that orgasm capacity is a normal part of a female

sexuality, and that its absence constitutes a significant finding, both as a symptom and as a potential pathogen.[1]

Vaginismus. Extreme degrees of frigidity occur in which there is not only revulsion for the act but physical inability to perform it due to spasm of the abductor muscles of the thighs. This is called vaginismus. This may or may not be associated with feelings of aversion for the act or for the partner. Such a condition, if primary (occurring from the beginning of the marriage), may prevent consummation of the marriage. Frequently this would appear to be evidence of latent homosexuality. In secondary types it may prevent sexual relationships which had once been satisfactorily established. There is some indication that this condition is less frequent than it once was.

Vaginismus in its lesser degree is called *dyspareunia.* Both oi thest conditions may come to the attention of the law. For example, if a man tries to have relations by physical force with a woman who suffers from vaginismus, and inflicts serious injury upon her, criminal action might ensue. In rare cases where muscular spasm occurs after the initiation of intercourse, a condition known as "penis captivus" may result.[2] This, however, must be extremely rare.

Nymphomania. Nymphomania is excessive sexual desire in the female. It may occur in the normally sexed woman as well as in Lesbians. It is usually psychogenic in origin, although I have seen at least two cases in which it was the result of the administration of hormones for a menstrual disturbance. The condition may lead to extramarital relations or masturbation because the average normal husband cannot satisfy the sexual demands of such an individual. Some cases resemble the "Don Juan complex" in the male, since in both cases it is an overcompensation to prove the subject's heterosexuality. Such a condition would seldom lead to conflict with the law unless it resulted in chronic compulsive promiscuity. Nymphomaniacs are generally frigid and seldom experience "vaginal orgasm."[3]

QUALITATIVE DISTURBANCES OF THE SEX DRIVE

Voyeurism (scopophilia). This condition is generally referred to as "Peeping" or "Peeping Tomism." Looking or staring at women is an almost universal characteristic of adult males. Under ordinary circumstances it can hardly be regarded as pathological. Insistence on viewing the partner's body as part of sex play should not be considered voyeurism. The voyeur seeks his view by stealth and usually as an end in itself. In many cases it is a compulsive act. In the homosexual this is not a problem because of the availability of subjects without peeping. Efforts to get surreptitious looks at the genitalia of other males is relatively common.

In young children, peeping is frequent but is usually the result of curiosity. It occurs in the "doctor game" played by many young children. In the course of the game, the children take turns being the "doctor" and performing physical examinations on the "patient."

The child has a natural curiosity about the bodily structure of others. Forcible repression of this tendency may lead in adult life to an intense sense of shame or horror when exposed to such sights. The normal adult sublimation of this tendency is in art, anatomy, or in certain forms of amusement as well as in normal sexual intercourse.

As a rule, voyeurism is a nuisance offense. In only rare instances is an individual so afflicted likely to approach his subject. In a few cases, such as an occasional mental defective or sociopathic personality, the voyeurism may be a prelude to assault. Voyeurism is an offense of males; the interest is exclusively in females, except in the case of inverts whose interest may be in the self-sex. Some peepers are specialized and may be interested only in women at stool, or in children, or in watching couples having intercourse (mixoscopia).

The average voyeur establishes a route where he may expect the shades to be up or where he can see in windows or where holes have been bored for purposes of observation. When he sees what he is looking for, he is sexually aroused and may spontaneously ejaculate or masturbate.

Exhibitionism. This is also a nuisance offense in which the subject, usually a male, exposes his genital organs, usually with the penis erect, to a group of individuals who are as a rule strangers.[4] In the female the breasts are part of the genital system and may also be exposed. According to some authors, the tendency of the female is to exhibit her whole body.[5] A variation of exhibitionism is the tendency of many male homosexuals to wear tight jeans which outline the buttocks and genitalia.

Children are natural exhibitionists and their apparent lack of modesty in running around nude is to be considered normal. This usually stops around the age of four or five, and before this time children of opposite sexes may be allowed to mingle in the nude and to bathe together. Any severe repression of this tendency may result in an excessive sense of shame. The normal sublimation of exhibitionism is taking pleasure in being looked at, as in the case of actors, models, and public speakers.

Exhibitionists tend to be overconscientious and rigidly moralistic in their personality. They may be married but usually have an unsatisfactory sex life. Although exhibitionists are not very aggressive, when they expose themselves they intend to be seen and intend to "shock" their victims. There is a rather constant tendency on the part of exhibitionists to return to the same spot, more or less at the same time, and to the same group. Homosexual individuals also have this same tendency. Age is not a constant factor although most of the cases tend to occur later in life.

In most cases, the subject will experience pronounced restlessness and tension before he goes to "look for an opportunity."[6] In the exhibitionist group there is a compulsive and sexualized need to look and to be looked at. In most cases they are fearful of indulging in a normal sexual experience which the exposure tends to displace or rule out. In some cases, the exposure may serve as an adequate sexual experience; others will masturbate or have a spontaneous ejaculation at the time of the exposure.

The legal term "indecent exposure" is not an exact synonym of exhibitionism, but contains all of its elements.

Some authors divide exhibitionists into three types: (a) visual — the type described above; (b) verbal — those who speak to the sex object in obscene language, e.g., those who call and make lewd remarks on the telephone; (c) ideal — those who have an intense interest in showing lewd pictures or books.

There may be many different etiological factors in exhibitionism. For example, Naville and Duboise-Ferriere suggest that it can be caused by hypersexuality, hyposexuality, feeblemindedness, chronic psychosis, epilepsy, constitutional psychopathy, delirium, nudism, or accidental factors.[7] There are many who agree with the suggestion of Rickles that it occurs mainly in timid men who are dominated by an assertive wife or mother.[8] In almost every case, this element is found to some extent. Exhibitionism is the seeking of love and resembles the love dances of savages and even the behavior of male animals to attract females.[9] Arieff and Rotman believe that it is the most common sexual offense (35 percent of all sexual offenses).[10] As a rule it responds to psychotherapy and environmental manipulation. As in other anomalies, exhibitionism is abnormal only when it takes extreme, fixed, or compulsive forms.

Transvestitism. See p. 93.

Transsexualism. See p. 95.

Fetishism. According to Krafft-Ebing, the fetishist is always a man. In this anomaly the sexual interest is displaced from the whole body to some part of it. For example, the sexual interest may be only in a shoe or a crippled joint. It may extend to more normal aspects of the body such as a lock of hair, or in a symbolic way to touching a woman's breast or other parts of her body. The fetish may be an article of clothing (frequently underclothing) which serves as a stimulus to sexual arousal. This may be followed by masturbatory activity. Most fetishists are afraid of sexual relations in the usual way so they pick a substitute. In this way the fetishist is able to avoid the anxiety which would occur if he were to attempt normal relations.

Although this would appear at first glance to be a relatively benign anomaly, it may lead to serious mutilation and even murder if the fetish is part of the sexual anatomy. Fetishism on a homosexual basis is not uncommon.

Sadism. Cruelty is a normal characteristic of children to some degree. We have all seen children pull the wings from flies or throw a cat off the roof to see how it will land. Any sudden and severe attempt to suppress this tendency may result in a fear of one's self in competition with others or a reluctance to try to control a situation because of fear of hurting others. The normal adult sublimation is in competition, in the struggle for existence, and in such medical specialties as surgery. The adult equivalents are sadism and masochism. Naturally one cannot permit a child to display overt cruelty in his play, but, on the other hand, one should not respond to his childish cruelty with cruel methods of suppression.

In sadism, sexual pleasure even to orgasm is derived from the infliction of pain or humiliation upon a person of the other sex, or upon a person of the same sex if the subject of the disturbance is a homosexual. Such feelings may occur only in fantasy or lead only to masturbation. It becomes a legal concern when put into action against unwilling subjects whether they be adults or children.

Sadistic acts may vary from subtle humiliation to degrading acts, from mild spanking to lust murder. In their milder degrees, such acts may serve as a source of sexual stimulation to married couples as a preliminary to the sex act. The man may make his wife kneel before him or spank her if she refuses. Biting and pinching are not unusual. These sexual stimulation acts are morally correct and should be legally acceptable if they are agreeable to both parties and if the sex act culminates with ejaculation taking place in the vagina.

Sadistic acts become perverse when the anomaly replaces the sex act; when the sadistic act becomes an end in itself. In such cases, the aggressor may actually physically injure his sexual partner who may be of either sex depending on his sexual orientation. It is almost always the male who performs the act; sadism is unusual in women. Alcohol may release such reactions.

A typical situation apparently based on a sadistic type of reaction is the apparently unmotivated attack. A young girl walking home from the movies or from work is followed by a man who may or may not have been drinking. Since he knows that she will become alarmed if he does so, he may follow closely so as to enjoy her anxiety when she realizes she is being followed. He has usually chosen an area in which few people are in the street. As the passersby become less frequent he may attempt to accompany her, but whether he does so or not, or whether she refuses him or not, he will attack her with blows, knife slashes, or kicks of various degrees of severity. Occasionally the girl is seriously injured. The attack, which seems unprovoked, is for the purpose of relieving the assailant's sadistic tension. Some seemingly unprovoked homosexual assaults may have this basis.

As sadism becomes more severe, the violence of the acts becomes greater. More severe beatings of the sexual partner, frequently associated with elaborate rituals, may be insisted upon. In such cases, some degree of impotence may be a factor. Scratching, biting, and sticking needles into the body are not infrequent. These may occur with or without coitus.

Murder associated with sadistic acts is an extension of these practices. The sadistic murderer may accidentally kill his sexual partner as a result of allowing his sex play to get out of hand but death is more likely to occur as a necessary condition to his sexual arousal. This type of murderer is frequently a quiet, apparently well-behaved man of indefinite age. He is usually quite particular in regard to his personal cleanliness. The background of such individuals is rich in neurotic traits:

> The typical lust murder is characterized by periodic outbreaks. Cutting and stabbing, particularly of the breasts and genitalia, occur as do sucking, licking, or mouthing the wounds. Biting the skin or drinking the blood may also occur. Erection and ejaculation may be followed by violation of the dying or injured victim. . . . The behavior is accompanied by intense sexual pleasure and excitement, and the pervert usually behaves normally until the next outbreak.[11]

There may be dismemberment and mutilation of the body. In some cases, the sexual parts of the body are amputated and saved for later erotic acts. This may be the primary purpose of the murder. In some cases, the body parts may be eaten (anthropophagia).[12]

For a long period before the murder, the sadistic killer has an increasing sense of sexual tension. He anticipates, plans his deed in fantasy; he may recognize the "wrongness" of his intended act but the urge may persist. He may be leading an active sex life but the insistent urge to sadistic murder persists.[13]

Masochism. This condition is the opposite of sadism. The subject in this case desires to be humiliated, degraded, or hurt by a member of the other sex as a means of sexual stimulation. This may occur with the same sex in homosexually oriented individuals. This anomaly derives its name from Leopold von Sacher Masoch (1836–1895), an Austrian novelist, whose characters indulged in variegated sex activity during which they derived sexual pleasure from being cruelly treated.

Krafft-Ebing defined masochism as:

> A peculiar perversion of the psychical *vita sexualis* in which the individual affected, in sexual feeling and thought, is controlled by the idea of being completely and unconditionally subject to the will of a person of the opposite sex, of being treated by this person as by a master, humiliated and abused. This idea is colored by sexual feeling; the masochist lives in fancies in which he creates situations of this kind, and he often attempts to realize them.[14]

Masochism occurs in two types: (*a*) the *ideal* in which the desires are strictly psychic and begin and end in fantasy; (*b*) the *active* type in which there is a desire to carry the process into actual practice. The extreme of this state is the masochistic suicide. This is the result of self-inflicted practices which are carried too far and get beyond the subject's voluntary control.

The following case is fairly typical of mild masochism:

In the last few years this patient had difficulty in becoming aroused enough to have an orgasm easily. She experimented to seek satisfactory means of stimulation. Her husband described this as follows: "Often during these preliminaries she would bite me. I would then slap her buttocks hard and this would immediately excite her.

"One evening when we were coming home from a party I remember breaking off a switch from a bush in the yard and telling her that I was going to switch her bare bottom with it. Almost as soon as we got into the house she could hardly wait to go to bed. At other times I would take a belt and slap my hand with it or slap the bed alongside of her. She seemed to become worked up very rapidly. I have whacked her with a belt several times. Never too hard, but occasionally she has cried out that it wasn't hard enough. Several times she has said while we were in the bedroom prior to marital relations, 'You want to beat me, don't you.' If I said 'Yes,' she would cringe away and pretend to be afraid. If I grabbed her and paddled her backside with my hand she would be excited in a few moments."

Coprophilia. In this condition the sexual stimulus is displaced from the sex object to his excrement. The feces then become a cause of sexual stimulation. Similar displacement may occur to any bodily excretion. Watching the excretory act may also serve as a sexual stimulus.

Coprophagia. In this anomaly, due to a displacement, the eating of the sexual object's feces serves as a sexual stimulus. In a similar way, there may be a desire to eat or drink other secretions or excretions as a source of sexual satisfaction.

Necrophilia. Necrophilia is a desire to have sexual relations with a dead body. It is uncommon.

Gerontosexuality. In this condition a young person desires sexual relations with an old man or woman. In some cases it may be difficult to decide whether the interest of a young boy or girl is the old man or woman or his money. If, however, he prefers relations *per se* with the older person, it is probably an anomaly.

Pygmalionism. This is a relatively uncommon anomaly in which the individual develops a sexual interest in statues. This may manifest itself clinically (*a*) by masturbating and ejaculating on the statue or (*b*) by having a man or woman pretend to be a statue and then arousing it to life by appropriate sexual stimuli. It may be that some cases of necrophilia belong in this category.

Frottage. A frotteur is an individual who gains sexual satisfaction by rubbing against the desirable sex in crowds, streetcars, or buses. It is a nuisance offense.

Illusionary cohabitation. This condition is so common that in most cases it should probably not be considered an abnormality. It consists of looking at a clothed woman and imagining her naked. In homosexuals the fantasy is more likely to be of the size of the penis. If, however, such use of the imagination leads to mental or even actual masturbation, it assumes the significance of an anomaly. This condition is unlikely to come to the attention of the law.

SEXUAL DISTURBANCES WHICH ARE AGAINST MARRIAGE

Fornication. This is an act of intercourse between two persons, neither of whom is married. The significance of this condition from the standpoint of our present discussion is that, in most jurisdictions, it is a violation of the penal code. This is another act which, when performed between consenting adults, should be considered legal.

Adultery. This is an act of sexual intercourse between two persons, at least one of whom is married. Adultery is a violation of the penal code in most jurisdictions. It is a statute infrequently invoked and then usually out of spite or pique. As with fornication, consenting acts between adults should be legalized. Such a change would have no effect on its frequency and it would, to a large extent, remove the possibility of blackmail. An interesting question would be: Is it properly called adultery if a homosexual male has relations with a married man?

Incest. Incest is sexual intercourse with an individual related within forbidden degrees (depending on the local statute) of blood relationship. It usually takes place between mother and son, father and daughter, brother and sister, father and son, brother and brother, and among cousins. Incest is not infrequent. The concept of the Oedipal situation is based on incest and has caused much discussion. Freud, for example, wrote:

> None of the discoveries of psychoanalytical research has evoked such embittered contradiction, such furious opposition, and also such entertaining acrobatics of criticism, as this indication of the incestuous impulses of childhood which survive in the unconscious.[15]

From the legal standpoint it is important to remember that it is not unusual for children to wander at night. Boys may go to the mother's bed and girls may go to the father's bed. Somnambulism[16] is not unusual. I have seen occasional cases in which there was a long incestuous relationship which was rationalized by the statement that it was not realized that it was the child who was in bed with the parent. An amnesia for such acts is possible but the burden of proof would be on the adult involved.

Although complete incest is unusual, sexual petting and fondling by both parents of their children is not unusual. This is a frequent source of sexual conflict in the child in later life. As uncomplicated a crime as incest would seem to be, confusions, disparities, and unnecessary complexities exist within the statutes of the various states.

Seduction. In *King John,* Shakespeare, in these lines, describes the essence of seduction:

> King Richard Coeur-de-Lion was thy father:
> By long and vehement suit I was seduc'd
> To make room for him in my husband's bed.
> Heaven lay not my transgression to my charge!
> Thou art the issue of my dear offense,
> Which was so strongly urged, past my defence.[17]

The words "long and vehement suit" constitute the difference between rape and seduction. This condition has no special psychiatric interest. See Clinic 5 for a discussion of seduction as a cause of homosexuality.

Rape. Legal and medical literature differ widely in regard to the terminology used for rape. The term itself is common to both disciplines and is understood by both in the same way. Other terms sound strange to medical ears and are quite likely to be misunderstood. Perkins discusses these terms:

> The ancient term for the act (sexual intercourse) itself was "carnal knowledge" and this is found in some of the recent cases and existing statutes. The phrase "sexual intercourse," more common today apart from legal literature, is also found in recent cases and existing statutes. Either term, when the reference is to rape, is sometimes coupled with the word "ravish." And unlawful intercourse with a girl under the age of consent is often characterized as "carnal knowledge and abuse."[18]

It would be best if we could all speak the modern language. Rape is unlawful sexual intercourse with a female person without her consent.[19] The equivalent homosexual attack on a male person has been given a variety of names.

Artificial insemination. The medical and eugenic problems in artificial insemination are mild compared to the legal difficulties. According to both French and English law, a wife who becomes artificially inseminated by a donor (either by consent of her husband or without his consent) is guilty of adultery.[20] In the United States, the question of donor insemination has not yet been directly the subject of decision by the courts.[21] It is possible that in the United States it would also legally constitute adultery. Semour, Koerner, and Guttmacher suggest procedures to obviate the difficulties of adultery and illegitimacy. Guttmacher suggests that delivery of a woman be performed by some doctor other than the one who performed the insemination. This is suggested so that the doctor who delivers the child could honestly say that, so far as he knows, the husband of the woman is the father of her child. Guttmacher recognizes that lying is involved here but he insists that it is a permissible lie. I wonder, then, arguing from the permissibility of falsifying birth records in these circumstances, if Guttmacher would say that it is also permissible for the poor to print their own counterfeit money whenever they feel the pinch of circumstances.[22] This topic is not directly pertinent to our present discussion and is mentioned only for the sake of completeness. It is conceivable, however, that the wife of an impotent homosexual might have recourse to this method for the achievement of pregnancy.

Triolism. This is a condition in which a man shares his wife or girl friend with another man. The husband may compel his wife to have sexual relations with another man while he watches. This condition has rather obvious psychiatric implications. Its legal implications are clear. I have never heard of such a disturbance in a homosexual.

SEXUAL ACTS WHICH ARE *CONTRA NATURAM*

The reason these acts are considered as *contra naturam* is explained in this way by St. Thomas:

> Wherever there occurs a special kind of deformity whereby the venereal act is rendered unbecoming, there is a determinate species of lust. This may occur in two ways: First, through being contrary to right reason, and this is common to all lustful vices; secondly, because, in addition, it is contrary to the natural order of the venereal act as becoming to the human race; and this is called *the unnatural vice*. This may happen in several ways. First, by procuring pollution, without any copulation,

for the sake of venereal pleasure. This pertains to the sin of *uncleanness* which some call *effeminacy* Secondly, by copulation with a thing of undue species, and this is called *bestiality*. Thirdly, by copulation with an undue sex, male with male, or female with female, as the Apostle states:[23] and this is called the *vice of sodomy*. Fourthly, by not observing the natural manner of copulation, either as to undue means, or as to other monstrous and bestial manners of copulation.[24]

Note that St. Thomas uses the term "sodomy" to refer to homosexual acts between either sex. Most of the statutes I was able to review are vague and seem to consider sodomy and acts *contra naturam* as synonyms. For example, all subjects seem included in this typical statute:

Every person who shall carnally know, or shall have sexual intercourse in any manner with any animal or bird, or shall carnally know any male or female by the anus (rectum) or with the mouth or tongue or shall attempt intercourse with a dead body is guilty of Sodomy.[25]

It would be better to reserve the term "sodomy" for entry of the penis into the rectum of either the male or female and to use the more accurate terms for other acts "against nature."

Fellatio. In fellatio, the act is performed by inserting the penis into the mouth of the partner. This term is more frequently used to refer to the complete act in which the ejaculation takes place in the mouth. Oral stimulation of this type by the woman is a relatively common act between married couples, but if the ejaculation does not take place in the oral cavity, it is not fellatio properly speaking. Fellatio is a common practice among homosexuals as well as heterosexual individuals.

Cunnilingus. This is a practice in which the vulva is orally stimulated by the male or female partner depending on the sexual orientation of the couple. The partner may be stimulated to orgasm. The pleasure to the active partner may be such that he will achieve his orgasm as a result of his act. More frequently, however, cunnilingus is merely a source of stimulation to both parties and will be followed by some other type of relationship.

Sodomy. This term is probably derived from Sodom, an ancient Palestinian city which was destroyed, according to Genesis 18 and 19, because of the prevalence there of unnatural sex relations (see p. 2). The term is today most commonly used to designate *coitus per anum,* performed between homosexual partners. It may, however, take place between heterosexual partners. If it is performed with a person of the same sex, it is known by the moralists as perfect sodomy. In some modern texts the term is used for coitus of humans with animals.[26] A better and more commonly used term for this activity is "bestiality."

Sodomy is defined in the U. S. Code (50 #719) as:

Unnatural carnal copulation with another person of the same or opposite sex or with an animal.

Penetration, however slight, is sufficient to complete this offense.

English Common Law restricted sodomy to sexual intercourse *per anum* between two individuals one of whom had to be a male, or between a human being and a beast of the opposite sex. The Common Law definition has now been extended by the courts to include acts of bestiality, pederasty, fellatio, buggery, and cunnilingus as acts of sodomy.[27]

When we look at the expression "unnatural carnal copulation" in this definition we realize that the crime of sodomy can be charged against a husband and wife who might engage in some sexual practice other than vaginal intromission.

Cases involving the charge of sodomy are not treated with exactly the same procedure as other criminal cases. Since any form of sodomy is believed to be degrading, the offense need not be described "with the same particularity" required in other criminal charges. Ordinarily the charge "need not allege the exact date of commission of the crime." It need not specify in detail what the act was. Nor is it always necessary to state whether the other individual was a human being or an animal. A statement of the offense in the language of the statute is all that is required. Since the charge is usually made in the language of the statute, it becomes the duty of the courts to decide which particular kinds of sexual acts are to be included within the scope of the statute. Commission of the act must be proven beyond a reasonable doubt. It must be proven by the prosecutor that penetration was effected. This proof may be established on circumstantial evidence. However, it is not necessary to prove an emission, as it used to be in English Common Law.

Penalties for acts of sodomy vary; but in every case they are severe. Missouri assigns a minimum of two years. Montana and Idaho assign a minimum of five years. These three states do not specify a maximum term. Georgia and Nevada specify a maximum of life imprisonment. In North Carolina there is a maximum of sixty years. In other states the maximum ranges from twenty to thirty years. This disparity of sentence was demonstrated recently in North Carolina, as reported in *Time Magazine,* for December 25, 1964:

> Indicted by a North Carolina grand jury for committing an homosexual act, Defendant Robert McCorkle pleaded no contest, got a five-year sentence and served only 17 months before being paroled. Max Doyle pleaded not guilty, was tried and sentenced to not less than 20 nor more than 30 years in prison.

> The oddly disparate sentences were handed down by the same judge, acting under an equally odd state law based on an English statute of 1533 that made homosexuality a capital offense. As adopted in 1837, the euphemistic North Carolina law reads: "Any person who shall commit the abominable and detestable crime against nature, not to be mentioned among Christians, with either mankind or beast, shall be adjudged guilty of a felony, and shall suffer death without the benefit of clergy." As it stands today, the law omits death and Christians, but prescribes a whopping sentence of up to 60 years.

In France homosexual acts among adults are penalized only when some kind of coercion has been used or when the acts are publicly indecent. But there is no penalty for adult homosexual acts which are committed voluntarily and privately.

In England there is a maximum prison term of two years for any kind of homosexual act among males. There is no similar legal statute for female homosexuals.

Much of the punishment against homosexuality will probably be mitigated in the future. In England there have been attempts to change some of it especially since the conviction of a famous actor and a member of the House of Lords. And in the United States there is unanimous agreement that punishment in some cases should be lessened.

Masturbation. See p. 24.

Bestiality. This terms refers to sexual intercourse between humans and animals. Although the condition is not frequent, it is not rare. Most commonly it is practiced by boys and young men in remote areas, not so much because of preference for animals but because of a lack of human association. In urban communities, it is seldom practiced by men, but relations or attempted relations between middle-aged women and their pets are not rare.

Homosexuality. This title was included in the classification only for the sake of completeness.

Pedophilia. Se p. 97.

Prostitution. This condition is included here only for the sake of completeness. The legal and psychiatric implications of prostitution are too extensive for a brief treatment. Certain aspects of homosexual prostitution are considered in other sections of this book.

ANOMALIES IN WHICH THE SEXUAL ELEMENT IS NOT IN CONSCIOUSNESS

There are many conditions, of which pyromania and kleptomania have been mentioned, in which the sexual factor is not clearly in consciousness. It may, in fact, be completely unconscious. Space does not permit a lengthy discussion of this subject but an example may help. A young man developed a compulsive desire to set fires to the extent of over several million dollars before he was caught. He had discovered that the jumping flames, the excitement of the fire fighting, and the sense of power he experienced were sexually exciting. He would set the fire, go off to a safe distance, and watch the excitement. As the excitement increased, he would ejaculate spontaneously. This may occur in individuals of either sexual orientation.

CLINIC 13 — NOTES

1. John F. Oliven, M.D., *Sexual Hygiene and Pathology* (Philadelphia: J. B. Lippincott Co., 1955), p. 352.
2. *Ibid.*, p. 365.
3. William S. Kroger and Charles S. Freed, *Psychosomatic Gynecology* (Philadelphia: W. B. Saunders Co., 1951), p. 407.
4. Oliven, *op. cit.*, p. 403.
5. O. Spurgeon English and Stuart M. Finch, *Introduction to Psychiatry* (New York: W. W. Norton and Co., 1954), p. 273.
6. Oliven, *op. cit.*, p. 404.
7. F. Naville and H. Duboise-Feriere, *"Etude sur l'exhibitonisme,"* *Schweiz. Neurol. u. Psychiat.,* 19 (1938), pp. 79–84, 575.
8. N. Rickles, "Exhibitionism," *Journal of Nervous and Mental Diseases,* 95 (1942), pp. 11–17.
9. *The Encyclopedia of Sexual Behavior,* Albert Ellis and Albert Abarbanel (eds.) (New York: Hawthorn Books, Inc., 1961), 2 vols., p. 808.
10. A. J. Arieff and D. B. Rotman, "Psychiatric Inventory of 100 Cases of Indecent Exposure," *Archives of Neurology and Psychiatry,* 47 (1942), pp. 495–498.
11. *Encyclopedia of Sexual Behavior,* p. 806.
12. George W. Jacoby, *The Unsound Mind and the Law* (New York: Funk and Wagnalls Co., 1918), pp. 344–345.

13. Oliven, *op. cit.*, p. 419.
14. R. v. Krafft-Ebing, *Psychopathia Sexualis* (New York: Sam Logen, 1908), p. 115.
15. Sigmund Freud, *Basic Writings,* translated and edited by Dr. A. A. Brill (New York: Random House, 1938), p. 308, footnote 1.
16. Somnambulism, also called sleep walking, is quite common in neurotic, especially hysterical, types of children.
17. William Shakespeare, *King John,* Act I, Scene I. Words spoken by Lady Faulconbridge, mother of the bastard.
18. Rollins M. Perkins, *Criminal Law* (Brooklyn: The Foundation Press, Inc., 1937), p. 113.
19. *Ibid.,* p. 110.
20. R. Savatier, "Artificial Insemination and the Law of France," *New Problems in Medical Ethics,* Vol. II, pp. 15–19; Charles Larere, "Artificial Insemination in England," *New Problems in Medical Ethics,* Vol. II, pp. 26–30; A. Gemelli, "Artificial Insemination" (Milan, Italy: Catholic University of the Sacred Heart, n.d.); H. U. Willink, "Legal Aspects of Artificial Insemination," *The Practitioner* (London, 1947), Vol. 158, p. 349. The editorial staff of the *British Medical Journal* held that it is generally agreed that a child conceived by artificial insemination from a donor would be illegitimate. Editorial: "Artificial Insemination," *Justice of Peace and Local Government Review,* Vol. 109 (1945), pp. 194, 448 f.
21. In the Strnad case in New York City, 1947, the former wife of Strnad attempted to prevent him from visiting her child who, she declared, was conceived by donor insemination. The judge in this case refused to make any decision on the question of donor insemination since it was not the immediate issue in the case. Cf. also: J. P. Greenhill, "Artificial Insemination: Its Medico-Legal Implications," chapter in *Symposium on Medico-Legal Problems,* edited by Samuel A. Levinson (Philadelphia: J. B. Lippincott Co., 1948), pp. 43–87. Judge Gibson E. Corman (Doornbos v. Doornbos, N. 54 S. 14981; Superior Court, Cook County, December 13, 1954) said: "Homologous artificial insemination (when the specimen of semen used is obtained from the husband of the woman) is not contrary to public policy and good morals, and does not present any difficulty from the legal point of view. Heterologous artificial insemination (when the specimen of semen used is obtained from a third party or donor) with or without the consent of the husband is contrary to public policy and good morals, and constitutes adultery on the part of the mother. A child so conceived is not a child born in wedlock and therefore is illegitimate. As such it is the child of the mother, and the father has no right or interest in said child." The Ontario (Canada) Supreme Court in 1921 (58 D.R.L. 251) also declared that heterologus artificial insemination constituted adultery.
22. A. F. Guttmacher, "The Role of Artificial Insemination in the Treatment of Human Sterility," *Bulletin of the New York Academy of Medicine,* Vol. 19 (1943), p. 590.
23. Romans 1:26–27: "For this cause God has given them up to shameful lusts; for their women have exchanged the natural use for that which is against nature, and in like manner the men also, having abandoned the natural use of the woman, have burned in their lusts one towards the other, men with men doing shameful things and receiving in themselves the fitting recompense of their perversity."
24. *The Summa of St. Thomas Aquinas* (New York: Benziger Brothers, Inc., 1947), 3 vols.; II–II, Q. 154, Art. 12, p. 1825.
25. *Encyclopedia of Sexual Behavior,* p. 626.
26. Leland Hinsie and Jacob Shatzky, *Psychiatric Dictionary* (New York: Oxford University Press, 1953), p. 493.
27. Sodomy may be committed between two persons both of whom consent, even

between husband and wife; 8 Carrington and Payne's Reports, 604; and both may be indicted; 1 Denison's Crown Cases, 464; 2 Carrington and Kirwin's Reports, 869. Penetration of the mouth is not sodomy; Russell and Ryan's Crown Cases, 331. As to emission see 12 Coke's Reports, 36; 1 Virginia Cases, 307. See 1 Russell and Ryan's Crown Cases, 698; 1 Moody's Crown Cases, 34; 8 Carrington and Payne's Reports, 417; 3 Harris and Johnson's Reports (Maryland), 154.

Homosexuality and the Law*

Statistics concerning the incidence of homosexual offenses in the United States are difficult to find. The Federal Bureau of Investigation, for example, reports that in 1961 there were 7143 arrests for forcible rape and 46,204 arrests for other sexual offenses. The latter figure includes statutory rape, offenses against chastity, common decency, and the like; it does not include forcible rape, prostitution, or commercialized vice. There are no separate figures for inverts. An interesting feature of this figure is that when the 46,204 arrests were broken down by race, 29,680 of the offenders were found to be white and only 11,006 Negro. This is important because of the popular belief that most sexual offenders are Negro.[1]

The laws of the individual states in regard to sexual offenses vary widely. Homosexuality as such is not illegal, but homosexual acts are forbidden under various statutes in 49 states and the District of Columbia. Illinois in 1961 became the first state to exempt such acts from legal sanctions. In Alaska, for example, the statute forbids "sodomy, the crime against nature by mouth or otherwise."[2] The penalty is one to ten years. Connecticut[3] describes the offense as "carnal copulation with any beast or any man against the order of nature." The maximum penalty is thirty years. Massachusetts law speaks of the crime against nature "with man or beast"[4] and also of "unnatural and lascivious acts with any person."[5] In Massachusetts the maximum penalty for these acts is five years in prison. For North Carolina, see p. 194. Oregon Revised Statutes, 1953, Section 167 (040) uses this unusual language: "Sustaining osculatory relations with the private parts of any person or permitting such relations to be sustained with his private parts."

This variety makes it difficult to summarize what is known concerning such offenses. There is also little agreement among medical

---

* Parts of this chapter are reprinted from the 1963 Winter Edition of *The Catholic Lawyer* with permission. The term "sexual offender" is used throughout this clinic as a broad term which should be understood to include homosexual offenders.

men who write on this subject. This is to some extent understandable because the problem is not the offense but the offender. The concern is with the person who committed the offense. Since no two individuals are alike, it is important to realize that when one speaks of a sexual offense, he is not describing a definite entity but is speaking of a person who has committed a sexual crime. An exhibitionist, for example, is a person and his sexual disturbance will be conditioned by his basic personality. As one reads through the voluminous literature on the subject of sex and the law, there are many areas which immediately attract attention:

1. Much of the terminology of the law is outdated and confusing. This may lead to misunderstanding.

2. The laws as they are written do not seem to recognize that sexual crimes may be committed by individuals who are not sexual perverts.

3. There seems to be little recognition that pyromania, kleptomania, and similar conditions may be based on sexual pathology.

4. The courts tend to deal primarily with the sexual offense, although this may be, and frequently is, only a surface manifestation of a more deep-seated disorder.

These four points represent only a few of the problems with which a counselor is confronted when he looks at sexual anomalies vis-à-vis the law.

Another disturbing element that becomes apparent as one reviews the literature is that many of the sex laws seem to have been promulgated in anger in response to a public demand which had been aroused by some particularly flagrant sexual crime. Many laws appear to have been written hurriedly. As a consequence, the full implication of the statute was often not fully realized. The penalties imposed by such laws vary widely, some of the penalties being overly severe and others sending too many offenders to mental hospitals. Judges and legislators often decide who should be sent to mental hospitals without consulting psychiatrists who might be considered more likely to understand the value and limitations of such a procedure. As a matter of fact, the mere commitment of an individual to a mental hospital may serve little purpose. Many psychiatrists feel that there are no available technics for the treatment of the sexual offender (see p. 206). Even if such technics were available there would not be enough psychotherapists, in most instances, to apply them. Many sexual offenders are sent to the hospital "to remain until cured." This in spite of the fact that there are no criteria of cure. It is conceivable that under such laws the relatively harmless voyeur or exhibitionist could remain in the hospital for life for an offense whose penalty otherwise might be a few days in jail. The editors of *The Mentally Disabled and The Law* look at the problem in this way:

> The reforms that have swept our penal institutions from the eighteenth to the twentieth century have left mental institutions substantially untouched. Physical restraints have departed from the prison but are still standard equipment in many mental institutions. There is no doubt about the legality of sterilizing criminals, but sterilization, lobotomy and electric shock treatment are permissible for sexual psychopaths. Substantial constitutional questions can be raised about the right of a criminal court to expose a defendant to the possibility of sterilization, lobotomy, and electric shock treatment.[6]

One can hardly agree that our mental hospitals have not improved in the past two centuries. Even to one who is not a lawyer, however, the constitutional question which is raised sounds logical.

More study needs to be devoted to the sexual offender in academic circles so that more reasonable laws may be written. Public indignation and public guilt should not play any part in the writing of laws dealing with sexual offenses. As Bowman stated:

> Exhibitionists and peeping Toms are looked upon as terrible sex criminals. Yet many of those upset at such types of behavior will go to night clubs to see nude women dancing in suggestive fashions. These same persons become indignant, however, if some individual is caught peeping through a window while a girl is undressing.[7]

In addition to emotional attitudes on the part of the public and the courts, ignorance plays a part in the enactment of some of the sex statutes. For example, the frequency of coitus has been the subject of review in some recent divorce cases. The judge was called upon to consider the reasonableness of the coital frequency which the husband had demanded. In such cases, nearly daily coitus has been ruled to be unreasonable and cruel and sufficient grounds for securing a divorce. This is an example of the law's failure to allow for the fact that such apparently high rates of coitus are maintained by a not inconsiderable portion of the population.[8]

Surprisingly few persons, including attorneys, are aware that the "crimes against nature" can be extended to include married partners. The penalties for such acts may in some jurisdictions be exceeded only by the penalties for murder, kidnapping, and rape. There are court decisions on the applicability of these sodomy statutes, one of which goes so far as to uphold the conviction of a man for soliciting his wife to commit sodomy.[9]

ENTRAPMENT

Another aspect of the law which should be reexamined is that which permits entrapment:

> . . . A debatable police practice which reportedly exists in a number of localities is the use of plain-clothes officers serving as "decoys," waiting to be accosted by a homosexual, e.g., in public washrooms ("entrapment").[10]

This practice in itself would not be so bad, but in many instances the officer accosts the homosexual. After the proposition, when the invert shows interest, he is arrested and charged. Such practices, to the best of my knowledge, are not permissible in regard to other offenses. This would appear to be the opinion, also, of Clark and Marshall. These authors state:

> Public sentiment, as well as the leaning of the courts, is strongly against the practice of entrapping persons in the commission of crimes by the common detective methods. The practice has frequently been condemned by the courts, and there are reported cases in which it has been held, independently of any question of consent on the part of the person injured, that a criminal act may not be punishable if the accused was induced to commit it by active cooperation and instigation on the part of public detectives.[11]

> A sound public policy requires that the courts shall condemn this practice by directing an acquittal whenever it appears that the public authorities, or private detectives, with their cognizance, have taken active steps to *lead* the accused into the commission of the act. It is perfectly legitimate and proper, however, to adopt devices and traps for the purpose of detecting crime and securing evidence, provided the device is not a temptation and solicitation to commit it. . . .[12]

> As was said by Judge Marston in a Michigan case: "Human nature is frail enough at best, and requires no encouragement in wrong-doing. If we cannot assist another, and prevent him from committing crime, we should at least abstain from any active efforts in the way of leading him into temptation" (Caunders *v*. People, 38 Mich. 218, 222).[13]

I find myself in complete agreement with Judge Marston (see Case X, p. 171).

Following the arrest of a prominent citizen in Washington, D. C., *The Washington Post* reported on Feb. 3, 1965, that the National

Capital Area Civil Liberties Union had written the District Com-
missioners to protest against "peephole" surveillance and the use of
police decoys in civilian clothes to apprehend sex offenders. The use
of "peepholes," the statement emphasized, is "an unreasonable invasion
of the privacy of all members of the public who use" the facilities.

The Civil Liberties Union stated that the right of the public to
be free of solicitation and annoyance would be better secured by
patrols of uniformed policemen than by secret peeking and "enticement of a special undercover squad."

The *Post* also noted that the police defend their practices and
feel they have been unjustly branded by such catchwords as "enticement" and "entrapment." This, the *Post* reported, is how one veteran
officer sums up the case for the police:

> People can't understand a problem they don't see. We see them — these
> men are predatory. They hang around theater, store, and public rest-
> rooms. It is a question of public decency. We're not interested in the
> non-predatory ones or acts in private. . . .

It would seem that "to the law, the homosexual offender may be
a confirmed, casual, or even one-time homosexual. All are equal in
having been caught in the act. The background of the offender makes
no difference."

THE WOLFENDEN REPORT — A CATHOLIC VIEWPOINT

This is the name given to a proposal in Great Britain which
recommended, in effect, that the law should make no effort to
interfere in the purely private relations of adult homosexuals, male
or female, where the element of seduction or duress is absent.[14]
While this report has failed of adoption, the issue raised is of interest
to clergymen because their position on such questions is often re-
quested. They are asked whether they as clergymen can accept
the recommendations of the report. The briefest and most authoritative statement on this subject was published by the Archbishop of
London in the December 2, 1957, issue of the Westminster Cathedral
Chronicle. The statement is as follows:

> In view of the inquiries which have reached Archbishop's House fol-
> lowing publication of the report of the House Office Departmental
> Committee on Prostitution and Homosexuality, His Grace the Arch-
> bishop of Westminster has thought it useful to set forth the following
> principles which should be borne in mind when consideration is given
> to the proposals regarding homosexual acts between consenting adults:

The civil law takes cognizance primarily of public acts. Private acts as such are outside its scope.

However, there are certain private acts which have public consequences in so far as they affect the common good. These acts may rightly be subject to civil law.

It may be, however, that the civil law cannot effectively control such acts without doing more harm to the common good than the acts themselves would be. In that case it may be necessary in the interests of the common good to tolerate without approving such acts.

It has, for example, invariably been found that adultery or fornication (which, however private, have clear public consequences) cannot effectively be controlled by civil law without provoking greater evils.

Applying these principles to the question of homosexual acts between consenting males:

1. As regards the moral law, Catholic moral teaching is:
   a. Homosexual acts are grievously sinful.
   b. That in view of the public consequences of these acts, *e.g.*, the harm which would result to the common good if homosexual conduct became widespread or an accepted mode of conduct in the public mind, the civil law does not exceed its legitimate scope if it attempts to control them by making them crimes.
2. However, two questions of fact arise:
   a. If the law takes cognizance of private acts of homosexuality and makes them crimes, do worse evils follow for the common good?
   b. Since homosexual acts between consenting males are now crimes in law, would a change in the law harm the common good by seeming to condone homosexual conduct?

Ecclesiastical authority could rightly give a decision on this question of fact as well as on the question of moral law, if the answers to questions of fact were overwhelmingly clear. As, however, various answers are possible in the opinion of prudent men, Catholics are free to make up their own minds on these two questions of fact.

DEFINITION OF TERMS

A *sexual offense* for purposes of this discussion will be considered to be any act not included in the definition of legal marriage (given below). This may be inexact in terms of the laws of some jurisdictions but it is the consensus of those authors available to me. It will be stressed as the discussion proceeds that many acts which are now offenses could be made legal without harm to the public good, e.g., consenting sexual acts between mentally competent adults. This would decrease the possibility of blackmail and eliminate the need of solicitation and force. The vast percentage of individuals who commit sex offenses which are punishable under our present law are not engaged in behavior basically different from that usual in the population as a whole: such persons are not necessarily to be regarded as psychiatrically ill nor as a danger in the community.[15] Sexual acts outside of marriage which involve force or disparity of age should, of course, be regarded as illegal.

Psychiatrically, those sexual offenses which are significant are those which, following a repetitive obsessional fantasy, lead to compulsive acts of forced sexual assault either on adults or children. These may be of the nature of an unresisted urge (irresistible impulse) (see p. 243). Such a compulsive sexual act is more often a surface symptom of a more profound psychic disturbance. As a matter of fact, the symptom may be less significant than other psychopathological features of the total personality which can only be detected by a thorough examination. Too frequently, the more dramatic symptom gets attention because it shocks the public conscience.[16]

For other definitions see Clinic 2.

CLASSIFICATION OF SEXUAL OFFENDERS

Many attempts have been made to classify sexual offenders into significant groups. Law-enforcement officials seeking for a behavior classification frequently divide sexual offenders into (a) those who are a menace and (b) those who are only a nuisance.[17] The sociologist and the psychiatrist are likely to divide the offenders into (a) traumatizing and (b) nontraumatizing.[18]

Both of these classifications have value, but there is much difference of opinion concerning which offenses, except in a few categories, belong in each. It takes little imagination to realize that what would be traumatizing for one individual would not be for another. A neurotic young adolescent girl might be strongly affected by an exhibitionist, whereas a mature married woman might only laugh.

Another classification which has merit is that which divides offenses into those involving physical contact and those not involving physical contact. From the legal standpoint, this is a useful classification.

Sexual offenders do not represent discrete types of individuals. Not all things are black or white. This is a fundamental principle of classification. It is the human mind which invents categories and tries to force the facts into manufactured groups. The world of people is a continuum in all its aspects. "We must bear this in mind because the sooner we realize this fact of human sexual behavior the sooner we shall reach a sound understanding of the real ties of sex."[19]

Kinsey classified sex acts in regard to the outlet sought; i.e., he described six chief sources of orgasm in the male:

1. Masturbation;
2. Nocturnal emissions;
3. Heterosexual petting;
4. Heterosexual intercourse;
5. Homosexual relations;
6. Intercourse with animals.[20]

Although this grouping includes the vast majority of sexual outlets, it has little use for our present purpose.

Psychiatrists are more inclined to seek the underlying pathology rather than the sexual act which shows on the surface. Psychiatrically, most sexual offenders may be classified in the following categories:

1. Mental defectives;
2. Alcoholics;
3. Personality disorders — this would include most homosexuals;
4. Sociopathic personalities (psychopaths);
5. Psychoneurotics;
6. Psychotics.

From this listing it is apparent that the sexual offender may have one of a great variety of psychiatric syndromes. In reporting the sexual offender to the court, the psychiatrist should be expected to report the basic psychiatric difficulty. If, for example, a schizophrenic is accused of incest, the psychiatric report should list schizophrenia as the primary diagnosis and incest as a secondary one. This is desirable because the individual's responsibility for his offense depends upon his basic mental state, not upon his sexual offense.

For didactic purposes, it is helpful to realize that most sexual offenders have a more serious underlying disorder. In the courtroom this is of primary importance because the proper handling of the patient depends on it. For an insight into sexual offenses, an understanding of the sexual pathology is important (see Clinic 4).

LEGALLY PERMISSIBLE SEX ACTS

A consideration of sex acts which are legally permissible will help to keep this discussion oriented. In most states, only penile-vaginal sexual relations are permissible under the law. These must take place between a man and a woman who are legally married to each other. To be legally married, the couple must be above the legal age for marriage, at the time of their marriage they must have been free to marry each other, and the act must be voluntary on the part of each. In many jurisdictions, both partners must be of the same race since miscegenation is forbidden.[21]

Any other sex act is illegal and as such is subject to punishment. Such a legalistic interpretation fails to take into account certain acts which are employed by many couples as sexually stimulating before intercourse. These include such sexual play as oral stimulation of the genitals, anal intromission, spanking, biting, and so forth. These practices are so common, and from the moral standpoint so acceptable, that one cannot find fault with them, as long as they are acceptable to both partners and as long as the act ends properly with the ejaculation taking place in the vagina. Legally, however, most such acts are forbidden and punishable. The reality of the situation is that, although such acts are unlikely to come to judicial attention, the possibility that they will do so through pique or anger is always present. This happened in the case of a masochistic woman who could only achieve orgasm if she was spanked or slapped by her husband. He was unable to understand her sexual needs but she could easily provoke him to anger and thus get him to slap her. On one occasion, she provoked him too much and he knocked out two of her front teeth. She swore out a warrant for assault because it was too much for her narcissistic ego to have her self-image distorted by loss of her teeth. A judge issued a peace warrant. Now her sex pleasure is nil because her husband is afraid to give her the sexual stimulus she needs.

RECIDIVISM IN SEX OFFENDERS

The sexual psychopath laws are based on a number of assumptions, many of which are not proven. One of the principal assumptions is that there is a high degree of recidivism in sexual offenders. It seems to be assumed not only that the sex offender is more dangerous than other offenders, but that he has a higher rate of recidivism than other criminals. Statistics are incomplete in regard to recidivism but those available do not support this view.

Pacht *et al.,* reporting on their experience with the Wisconsin Sex Crimes Law, state:

> Of 1,065 male offenders examined under this law over a nine-year period, only 783 were found to be in need of specialized treatment. Parole experience with this group has been excellent. Of the 475 individuals granted parole through May 31, 1960, only 81 have violated that parole — a rate (17 percent) considerably lower than that found with parole granted to the general prison population. It is particularly noteworthy that only 43, or 9 percent of the total paroled, violated their parole by commission of a further sex offense. For individuals who have been discharged following a period of institutional treatment and parole supervision, the results are even more outstanding. Through May 31, 1960, 414 individuals were discharged from departmental control: only 29, or 7 percent of this group, committed a new offense following discharge.[22]

The Illinois Commission Report concludes: "Not more than about 5% of convicted sex offenders are dangerous."[23]

Paul W. Tappan reported:

> There are very few aggressive and dangerous sex offenders in the criminal population. Most of the deviates are mild and submissive, more an annoyance than a menace to the community.[24]

He concluded:

> Our sex offenders are among the least recidivous of all types of criminals. They do not characteristically repeat as do our burglars, arsonists, and thugs.[25]

In addition, other studies have concluded that the danger represented by sex offenders is overemphasized.[26] Not all authors agree. For example, Neilson states:

> . . . homosexuality very often is a condition dangerous to society. Well-meaning lay people often believe that homosexuality is an affair between adult responsible persons, who have a right to arrange their sexual life as they like. The fact is that most homosexuals decidedly prefer youngsters, whose mental health and social adaptation may be very much endangered by these assaults. Society has a right and duty to protect immature persons.[27]

Closely related to recidivism is the theory that sex deviates progress from minor sex crimes to major sex crimes of force and violence. The studies undertaken have proved that such is not the case.[28] For example, Guttmacher and Weihofen[29] stated: "It is believed that sex offenders regularly progress from minor sex offenses such as exhibitionism to major offenses like forced rape. Such a gradation is almost unknown."

All students of the subject do not agree on the findings recorded above. Davidson, for example, states that "both the dynamics of sex psychopathy and the actual statistics seem to contradict that optimism (that the sex offender is not a repeater)." Davidson, however, does not present any convincing figures.[30]

My own experience has been that, in offenses involving physical contact with another person, the rate of repetition is low. In those offenses not involving bodily contact, the repeat rate is quite high. Progression from a mild anomaly to a more serious one has not happened in my experience.

LEGAL RESPONSIBILITY OF THE SEXUAL OFFENDER
(For Questions of Moral Responsibility see Clinic 16)

Some psychiatrists are reluctant to admit that anyone is "normal," i.e., "responsible," on the theory that no one is free of some personality distortion. They apparently feel that, since the act which has been committed is foreign to their own personality, it is abnormal. This is certainly not true. It is especially not true of sexual disorders. Rather, in many cases the sex offender should be considered responsible because his offense represents absence of control over normal temptations and normal sexual desire.

I find it hard to accept the concept of sexual psychopathy. This concept seems to presume responsibility in all areas of conduct except the sexual.[31] Many of the statutes include the words "not insane." For example, the "sexual psychopath" is defined in the following terms in the District of Columbia Code:

> "Sexual psychopath" means a person, *not insane*, who by a course of repeated misconduct in sexual matters had evidenced such lack of power to control his sexual impulses as to be dangerous to other persons because he is likely to attack or otherwise inflict injury, loss, pain, or other evil on the object of his desires. [Italics are mine.][32]

In the District of Columbia, "insanity" is defined as:

> A condition in which an individual is incapable of managing his own affairs, and is not a fit person to go at large or to go unrestrained, and if permitted to remain at liberty in the District of Columbia, the rights of persons and property will be jeopardized or the preservation of public peace imperiled and the commission of crime rendered probable.[33]

If we substitute this meaning for the word "insane" in the above definition, the latter portion seems redundant. The Code implies that the sexual aspect of personality can be isolated from the rest. This is impossible. Man is a psychosomatic unit. He functions as a whole. The basic problem here is that the sexual manifestation is isolated from the rest of the personality. The individual should not be judged on the basis of symptoms.

If we can accept the statement made above that, psychiatrically, "those offenses which are significant are those which, following a repetitive obsessional fantasy, lead to compulsive acts of forced sexual assault on adults or children," then the problem of responsibility is greatly clarified. A few terms need definition:

Repetitive means frequently repeated.

Obsessional is derived from *obsession* which "is an overpowering, persistent, and irrational idea accompanied by feelings of tension and fear."[34] Such an obsession may, of course, vary in degrees of severity.

Fantasy or daydreaming is "the act or state of dwelling amid people or scenes created by the imagination."[35]

Compulsive is derived from *compulsion* which "is an overpowering, unreasonable urge to perform certain actions and is associated with the development of tension or anxiety if the act is not performed."[36]

Forced means against the wish or will of the individual attacked.

In evaluating responsibility, therefore, the above factors must be considered.

The question of "irresistible impulse" would certainly arise if these conditions are present (see p. 243). Each case must be considered on its own merits and there will quite likely be differences of opinion among psychiatrists. This will result because the degree of compulsion will be a matter of the judgment of each psychiatrist.

There are three legal rules under which the responsibility of the sexual offender may be considered:

1. The M'Naghten Rule;[37]
2. The Proposed American Law Institute Rule;[38]
3. The Durham Rule.[39]

In following any of these rules, it is important that it be applied to the basic personality disturbance of the individual. It should not be applied to a symptom. Just as a diagnosis of "hallucinations" would not be considered adequate, neither is exhibitionism or voyeurism. The responsibility of the individual depends on his primary diagnosis. There will usually be no problem in applying either the M'Naghten Rule or the A.L.I. Rule to sexual offenders except for the inevitable differences of opinion between psychiatrists. The Durham Rule presents a different problem.

The Durham Rule. The use of the Durham Rule in sex offenses leads to even more confusion than in other types of criminal cases. Under this rule, the individual is not guilty if his crime is the product of mental illness or defect. As this rule has been interpreted by the courts in the District of Columbia, the only jurisdiction in which it has been accepted, almost any type of psychiatric disorder would result in a finding of not guilty. If, as seems to be the tendency, the sexual symptom is accepted as a diagnosis, then no one having a sexual problem would be considered responsible. If, for example, pedophilia (se p. 97) is accepted as a basic diagnosis rather than a symptom, then under the Durham Rule such an individual would always be "not guilty by reason of mental illness" in all his offenses against children. This is so because it is obvious that if pedophilia is the diagnosis, then it is equally obvious that the crime against the child is the "product of his illness." Thus, also, the homosexual would be "not guilty" because any homosexual offense would be the product of his illness. On the contrary, the homosexual is as responsible as the heterosexual individual for equivalent offenses.

Conclusions. (1) The sexual offender will in many cases be legally responsible. (2) His responsibility will depend on his basic disorder, not his sexual offense. (3) His responsibility will also depend on the degree of compulsiveness involved in his condition. (4) The M'Naghten and the American Law Institute Rules may be applied without difficulty. Under the Durham Rule, the problem will be much more complicated because of its failure to adequately define "cause." This is one of the fatal effects of the Durham Rule which has undoubtedly contributed to keeping it from being adopted by all jurisdictions except the District of Columbia. (5) Many problems would be avoided if the laws could be changed to permit consenting sexual acts between competent adults.

Enforcement of many of the present sex laws is impossible. The report of the Group for the Advancement of Psychiatry, for example, comments:

Moreover, if they were strictly enforced we should be indeed witness to a colossal travesty reaching all levels of American society. Absolute law enforcement would perforce touch about 95% of the total male population. In contrast to the universality of illegal sexual behavior actually only a meager number of persons falls into the law enforcement net to suffer inordinate punishment for the conduct of many. In one category alone recent statistical studies bring to light that 6 million homosexual acts take place each year for every 20 convictions. In the area of extra-marital copulation the frequency to conviction ratio is nearly 30 to 40 million to 300.[40]

GENERAL CONCLUSIONS

An attempt has been made to present in brief outline form the classification and basic psychopathology of sexual anomalies. It is suggested that legal and psychiatric terminology be brought up to date. This would include adopting the term *sexual anomaly* as a substitute for sexual perversion because it is more meaningful. It is also suggested that consenting sexual acts between competent adults be legalized.[41] This would bring the law into conformity with the modern knowledge of sex. Most sexual offenders are a nuisance rather than a danger to the community. The recidivism rate is low in offenses involving physical contact but high in noncontact offenses. An enlightened and progressive approach to these problems and the development of an enthusiastic communication between the law and psychiatry can only lead to the betterment of society — the end which gives to each science its meaning.

CLINIC 14 — NOTES

1. *Crime in the United States*, 1961, edited by the Federal Bureau of Investigation, United States Department of Justice. These arrests were in 2776 cities of over 2500 citizens with a total population of 85,158,360.
2. Alaska Compiled Laws, 1948, Sec. 65–9–10.
3. Connecticut, General Statutes, 1958, Sec. 53–216.
4. Massachusetts Annotated Laws, 1932, Sec. 272–34.
5. *Ibid.*, 272–35.
6. Frank T. Lindman and Donald M. McIntyre, Jr. (eds.), *The Mentally Disabled and the Law* (Chicago: The University of Chicago Press, 1961), p. 310.
7. Quoted in Henry A. Davidson, *Forensic Psychiatry* (New York: The Ronald Press, 1952), p. 109.
8. Alfred C. Kinsey, *et al.*, *Sexual Behavior in the Human Female* (Philadelphia: W. B. Saunders Co., 1953), p. 369.
9. *Ibid.*, p. 370.
10. John F. Oliven, M.D., *Sexual Hygiene and Pathology* (Philadelphia and Montreal: J. B. Lippincott and Company, 1955), p. 441.

11. Saunders v. People, 38 Mich. 218; People v. McCord, 76 Mich. 200, 42 N.W. 1106; State v. Hayes, 105 Mo. 76, 16 S.W. 514, 24 Am. St. Rep. 360; State v. Dudoussat, 47 La. Ann. 977, 17 So. 685; Love v. People, 160 Ill. 501, 43 N.E. 710.
12. William L. Clark and William L. Marshall, A Treatise on the Law of Crimes (Chicago: Callaghan and Company, 1912), pp. 226–227.
13. Ibid., p. 227, fn. 213.
14. Charles Berg and Clifford Allen, The Problems of Homosexuality (New York: The Citadel Press, 1958). This book has a complete text of The Wolfenden Report on "Homosexuality and Prostitution."
15. Group for the Advancement of Psychiatry, Psychiatrically Deviated Sex Offenders, Report No. 9, New York, February, 1950.
16. Ibid., p. 1.
17. Davidson, op. cit., p. 111.
18. Ibid., p. 112.
19. Alfred C. Kinsey et al., Sexual Behavior in the Human Male (Philadelphia: W. B. Saunders Co., 1948), p. 638.
20. Ibid., p. 193 f.
21. This is likely to change under new desegregation laws. Some thirty states now have antimiscegenation laws (Harper, Problems of The Family [1952], p. 268). Almost half of the states are in the North and West. Most laws prohibit intermarriage between members of the Caucasian race and Negroes. In the states having these laws, Negroes comprise from 50 percent or more of the population to less than 1 percent ("Intermarriage with Negroes — A Survey of State Statutes," 36 Yale L. J. 858, 1928). The prohibition in other states is extended to Mongolians, Malayans, Hindus, Indians (Harper, op. cit., pp. 266–268. See note, 58 Yale L. J. 472, 480, 1949). Some statutes specify "Negro or Mulatto" (for example: Idaho Code [1947], Sec. 32–206) or "persons possessed of one-eighth or more" Negro blood (for example: Mississippi, Constitution, Art. 14, Sec. 263; Code, 1942; Secs. 4–459, 11–2002, 11–2234, 11–2339; Missouri Revised Statutes [1942], Secs. 3361, 4651). All such states make the prohibited marriage void and most of them characterize the offense as a felony subject to severe penalties (Charles W. Lloyd [ed.], Human Reproduction and Sexual Behavior [Philadelphia: Lea and Febiger, 1964], p. 542).
22. In Current Psychiatric Therapies, Jules H. Masserman (ed.) (New York: Grune and Stratton, Inc., 1962), Vol. II, p. 179.
23. Report of the Illinois Commission on Sex Offenders to the Sixty-Eighth General Assembly of the State of Illinois, 11 (1953).
24. Paul W. Tappan, "Sentences for Sex Criminals," Journal of Criminal Law, Criminology and Police Science, Vol. 42 (1951), pp. 332–336.
25. Ibid., p. 336.
26. The Mentally Disabled and the Law, p. 304, n. 48.
27. Nils Nielson, "What is Homosexuality?" International Journal of Sexology, Vol. VI, No. 3 (February, 1953), p. 188.
28. The Mentally Disabled and the Law, p. 304, fn. 51.
29. M. S. Guttmacher and H. Weihofen, Psychiatry and the Law (New York: W. W. Norton Co., Inc., 1952), p. 111.
30. Davidson, op. cit., p. 114.
31. The Mentally Disabled and the Law, p. 318.
32. D.C. Code 22–3503 (1951).
33. Ibid., 21–311.
34. John R. Cavanagh and James B. McGoldrick, Fundamental Psychiatry (Milwaukee: The Bruce Publishing Company, 1958), p. 264.
35. Ibid., p. 122.
36. Ibid., p. 265.

37. M'Naghten's case, 10 Cl. and Fin. 200, 203, 208, 8 Eng. Rep. 718, 720, 723 (H. L. 1843) (A. II and III) ". . . (A)s: These two questions appear to us to be more conveniently answered together, we submit our opinion to be that the jury ought to be told in all cases that every man is to be presumed to be sane, and to possess a sufficient degree of reason to be responsible for his crimes, until the contrary be proved to their satisfaction; and that to establish a defence on the ground of insanity, it must be clearly proved that, at the time of committing the act, the accused was laboring under such a defect of reason, from disease of the mind, as not to know the nature and quality of the act he was doing, or, if he did know it, that he did not know he was doing what was wrong."

38. The American Law Institute's proposed Criminal Code: "(1) A person is not responsible for criminal conduct if at the time of such conduct as the result of a mental disease or defect he lacks substantial capacity either to appreciate the criminality of his conduct or to conform his conduct to the requirements of law. (2) The terms 'mental disease or defect' do not include an abnormality manifested only by repeated criminal or otherwise anti-social conduct." A.L.I. Model Penal Code Appendix A4.01 (tent. Draft No. 4, 1955). Substantially the same formula has been adopted by the Governor's Conference on the Defense of Insanity of the State of New York and by H. R. 13492 introduced in Congress by Representative Davis of Georgia.

39. Durham v. United States, 214 F. 2d, 862 (D.C. cir. 1954).

40. Group for the Advancement of Psychiatry, op. cit., p. 2.

41. Paul Friedman, "Sexual Deviations," Chapter 29 in American Handbook of Psychiatry, Silvano Arieti (ed.) (New York: Basic Books, Inc., 1959), Vol. I, p. 605: "The fact that sexual perversions are punishable by law is meeting with increasing opposition based upon the view that sexual morality is a private matter and should be subject to public regulation only if (1) the acts are carried out in public places, (2) one of the partners is a minor, or (3) violence or coercion is involved."

CLINIC 15

Homosexual Organizations and Publications

Homosexuals do not seem to be well organized although there are a large number of homophile organizations. This would, however, be consistent with one of the invert's better known traits — his inability to form lasting associations. Most of the organizations appear to be for one of three purposes: (1) to improve the social position of the invert; (2) to promote a better public image of the homosexual; and (3) to improve his legal status.

In the United States there are three large organizations besides a number of lesser ones. The Big Three, as they are called, are the Mattachine Society, the Daughters of Bilitis, and One, Incorporated.

The *Mattachine Society, Inc.,* was founded in San Francisco, California, in 1950. The society was named after the court jester of the Middle Ages who dared to speak the truth in the presence of his lord and master. There are also Mattachine Societies in New York and Washington, D. C. At the present time these organizations seem to be independent of the San Francisco group.

The aims and principles of the organization are set forth as follows in *Mattachine Society Today,* an explanatory brochure issued by their national headquarters (Room 312, 693 Mission Street, San Francisco, California):

To sponsor projects of education:
1. Education of the general public so as to give them a better understanding concerning sex variation, so that all persons may be accepted as individuals for their own worth and not blindly condemned for their emotional make-up; to correct general misconceptions, bigotries, and prejudices resulting from lack of accurate information regarding sex variants.
2. Education of variants themselves so that they may better understand not only the causes and conditions of variation, but formulate an adjustment and pattern behavior that is acceptable to society in general and compatible with recognized institutions of a moral and civilized society with respect for the sanctity of home, church, and state.

To aid the variant through integration:

1. Since variants desire to be accepted by society, it behooves them to assume community responsibility. They should, as individuals, actively affiliate with community endeavors, such as civic and welfare organizations, religious activities, and citizenship responsibilities, instead of attempting to withdraw into an invert society of their own. For only as they make positive contributions to the general welfare can they expect acceptance and full assimilation into the communities in which they live.
2. The long-term aid is not only to support well-adjusted variants with full integration into society, but to give social aid to maladjusted homosexuals for their own welfare as well as that of the community.

To conduct a program of civil action:

1. To secure the active cooperation and support of existing institutions such as psychology departments of universities, state and city welfare groups, mental hygiene departments, and law-enforcement agencies in pursuing the programs of education and integration.
2. To contact legislators regarding both existing discriminatory statutes and proposed revisions and additions to the criminal code in keeping with the findings of leading psychiatrists and scientific research organizations, so that laws may be promulgated with respect to a realistic attitude toward the behavior of human beings.
3. To eliminate widespread discrimination in the fields of employment, in the professions and in society, as well as to obtain personal social acceptance among the respectable members of any community.
4. To dispel the idea that the sex variant is unique, "queer" or unusual, but is instead a human being with the same capacities of feeling, thinking, and accomplishment as any other human being.

General Aims:

1. To accomplish this program in a law-abiding manner. The Society is not seeking to overthrow or destroy any of society's existing institutions, laws, or mores, but to aid the assimilation of variants as constructive, valuable and responsible citizens. Standard and accepted democratic processes are to be relied upon as the technique for accomplishing this program.
2. The Society opposes indecent public behavior, and particularly excoriates those who would contribute to the delinquency of minors and those who attempt to use force or violence upon any other person whatsoever.
3. The Mattachine Society is a non-sectarian organization and is not affiliated with any political organization. It is, however, unalterably opposed to Communists and Communist activity and will not tolerate the use of its name or organization by or for any Communist group or front.

The Society publishes a monthly, *The Mattachine Review,* in English. The advertisement states that it "seriously examines and discusses human sex problems, especially homosexuality, with emphasis on legal, medical, social, religious, and cultural aspects."

The *Daughters of Bilitis* (headquarters: 1232 Market Street, Suite 108, San Francisco, California 94102) also has chapters in New York and Chicago. According to the San Francisco headquarters director of public relations:

> DOB is still working primarily with the education of the Lesbian herself rather than the education of the public. We feel that social acceptance will come more easily if the homosexual accepts himself or herself as a human being and is able to work in and with the total societal structure. We have, however, been doing more and more actual public relations work — speaking before groups and appearing on radio and television programs. Our primary means of communication remains THE LADDER which is growing in circulation all the time and is now available in many newsstands, bookstores and libraries throughout the nation.[1]

The name of this organization arouses curiosity. Waring and Bryce give this explanation:

> The name "Bilitis" has attracted attention and curiosity from time to time. According to the organization, the name was taken from Pierre Louys' group of prose poems entitled "Songs of Bilitis" ("And Now We Are Three," *The Ladder,* Vol. 3, No. 1 [San Francisco, October, 1958], p. 4). Louys represented in this writing that the poems were written by the young Pamphylian poetess, Bilitis, who lived on the Aegian island of Lesbos concurrently with the famous poetess, Sappho, during the 6th century, B.C. The "Daughters of Bilitis" claim that Sappho and Bilitis were Lesbian "sweethearts." However, there is substantial information to the effect that Bilitis was merely a fragment of Louys' imagination (The Collected Works of Pierre Louys [New York: Liveright Publishing Corporation, 1932]).[2]

The Daughters of Bilitis, Inc., publish *The Ladder,* a monthly publication now in its tenth year, which is regarded as "a sounding board for various points of view on the homophile and related subjects and does not necessarily reflect the opinion of the organization."[3]

The purpose of the organization is stated more specifically than noted above on the inside front cover of its journal:

Purpose of the Daughters of Bilitis:

A Women's Organization for the Purpose of Promoting the Integration of the Homosexual into Society by:
(1) Education of the variant, with particular emphasis on the psychological, physiological and sociological aspects, to enable her adjustment to society in all its social, civic and economic implications — this is to be accomplished by establishing and maintaining as complete a library as possible of both fiction and non-fiction literature on the sex deviant theme; by sponsoring public discussions on

pertinent subjects to be conducted by leading members of the legal, psychiatric, religious and other professions; by advocating a mode of behavior and dress acceptable to society.

(2) Education of the public at large through the acceptance first of the individual, leading to an eventual breakdown of erroneous taboos and prejudices; through public discussion meetings aforementioned; through dissemination of educational literature on the homosexual theme.

(3) Participation in research projects by duly authorized and responsible psychologists, sociologists and other such experts directed towards further knowledge of the homosexual.

(4) Investigation of the penal code as it pertains to the homosexual, proposal of changes to provide an equitable handling of cases involving this minority group, the promotion of these changes through due process of law in the state legislatures.

Of special interest to the counselor is an organization called *The Council on Religion and the Homosexual, Inc.* (330 Ellis Street, San Francisco, California):[4]

This Council was formed the latter part of last year (1963) to "promote a continuing dialogue between the Church and the homosexual." . . . This group is made up of approximately 50 ministers from many different Protestant faiths, members of the homophile community, and other interested persons in the San Francisco Bay area. Its formation is indicative of the slowly-awakening realization by the churches that they must deal with the subject of homosexuality — and the homosexual — if they are truly to fulfill their mission of spreading the word of God.

A part of the concern which prompted the formation of the Council is the problem of counseling young people. The organization cannot deal with persons under 21 years of age, and we feel that it is of paramount importance that these youngsters have somewhere to turn. The Council is endeavoring to orient ministers on the subject of homosexuality so they will be better qualified to counsel on this problem.

The goals and purposes of "The Council on Religion and the Homosexual," as stated, are:

OBJECTIVE: "TO PROMOTE CONTINUING DIALOGUE BE-TWEEN THE CHURCH AND THE HOMOSEXUAL."

In order to promote a continuing dialogue between the church and the homosexual and in an endeavor to better understand human sexuality and to promote understanding of the broad variations and manifestations within the spectrum of human sexuality, the Council on Religion and the Homosexual sets forth these goals and purposes:

1. To orient the clergy on aspects of homosexuality (i.e., physical, economic, legal, intellectual, emotional, etc.) in accordance with homosexual testimony and available scientific data.

2. To encourage pastoral clergy to provide homosexuals of both sexes an opportunity to present the homosexual views on sex, religion, morals, and ethics before lay organizations within their churches.

3. To open up channels of communication so that clergy and lay churchmen may engage in dialogue with the homosexual so that new understandings of the church and religious faith may be developed.

4. To conscript the aid of religious publications and other appropriate communication media urging a broadened editorial policy that will include accurate and objective articles on homosexuality. [The word "conscript" in this paragraph is an aggressive choice if it really means what it says. — AUTHOR]

5. To provide an effective voice throughout the nation in the matter of laws, policies and penal reforms governing adult sexual behavior.

6. To encourage the formation of similar councils on religion and the homosexual in other areas.

7. To help the clergyman to better understand his role as counselor in dealing with problems of human sexuality in our society with special reference to young people.[5]

One, Incorporated (headquarters: 2256 Venice Boulevard, Los Angeles, California 90006) is the third large homophile organization in the United States. It publishes "One — The Homosexual Magazine of America" which is described as containing "fiction, poetry, essays, scientific research, legal reports, written for readers of all ages and for acceptance in every home." In a letter to the author, the director of ONE Institute (see list below) states:

> We tend to be highly respectful of biologically oriented approaches, far less so of psychoanalytical methods, highly critical of religiously based counselling.[6]

In the United States there are numerous smaller organizations, not all of which would be readily recognized by their names. The following list is probably incomplete, since it contains only the organizations with which I have had correspondence:

HOMOPHILE ORGANIZATIONS IN THE U. S. AND CANADA

Association for Social Knowledge	P.O. Box 4277	Vancouver 9, British Columbia
Atheneum Society of America, Inc.	P.O. Box 2278	Miami, Florida 33101

Dionysus, Inc.	P.O. Box 804	Huntington Beach, California
Homosexual Voters Advisory Council	P.O. Box 5131 — Terminal Annex	Denver 17, Colorado
Janus Society of America	34 South 17th Street, #229	Philadelphia, Pennsylvania 19103
National League for Social Understanding	8214 Sunset Blvd.	Los Angeles, California
One Institute of Homophile Studies (The Education Division of One, Inc.)	2256 Venice Boulevard	Los Angeles, California 90006
Society for Individual Rights (SIR)	529 Clayton St.	San Francisco, California
United States Mission	406 South Main Street	Los Angeles, California 90013

Each of these organizations was asked for some description of itself and its purposes.

1. *Atheneum Society of America, Inc.*

This organization states its purpose quite well in its description of the aims of its *Newsletter:*[7]

The Atheneum Newsletter will have two major aims:

1. To urge all homosexuals to demand their constitutional rights by going to the highest court, if necessary, whenever their rights are infringed upon by anyone; 2. We will urge all homosexuals to join, or support, at least one of the homophile organizations, whose entire existence is for the purpose of helping homosexuals to obtain fair and equal treatment under the law, and where necessary, to get unfair laws repealed.

We will present news notes of the current activities of the various organizations, their programs, events, policies, etc. We will include the latest news about old and new laws planned, court actions, law enforcement notes, occasional book reviews, a list of organizations, and other happenings of interest.

The *Newsletter* is published monthly.

2. *Janus Society of America*

The official publication of this society is *Drum*. This is "circulated throughout the United States and Canada, and sold on newsstands in eleven foreign cities as well. It is already, in the half-year of its existence, the widest-selling homophile publication of its type."[8]

3. *The National League for Social Understanding*

The only information received from this group consisted of mimeographed material in which the purpose of the organization was not specifically stated. It would appear to be a militant group now beginning its fifth year. It has branches in San Francisco, Phoenix, and Long Beach and plans branches in Chicago and Denver soon.

An action report which is undated concludes with these two paragraphs which undoubtedly give some insight into its purposes:

> You pay your fair share of taxes, why allow yourself to be persecuted? The League needs your support. We invite you to become a member in one of our three different categories. If you would rather be a contributor only, this would also be greatly appreciated. We need your enthusiasm, interest, talent, and financial support.

> With your help we will be able to expand our publications, up-grade our employment service by having a paid staff available to search out and collect employment data. We will be able to reach out to many new agencies, news media, professional leaders, and news programs with the *truth*. We will be able to expand all of our services and be of more help to the homosexual community. Come join our membership, we welcome you.

> In organization is there strength. . . .

4. *Society for Individual Rights*

The abbreviation of this organization appropriately is SIR. Its publication, *Vector,* is still in its first volume (February, 1965, is Volume I, No. 3). The by-line of the bulletin is "Responsible Action by Responsible People in Responsible Ways." As stated in a brochure, the policy of SIR "is to create a social fabric in which all may share equally in the guarantees of democracy under the constitution of the United States."

In answer to the question "What does SIR do?" the brochure lists the following committees:

Community Services Committee
Provides referrals for employment, apartments, legal counsel, and other problems. It has promoted the V33 campaign to combat VD, and sent out a brochure of danger spots in the community. The answering service is maintained under the auspices of this committee.

Legal Committee
Disseminates information regarding legal rights in case of arrest and other situations. Establishes liaison with other civil rights organizations, and discusses policies of liaison with other non-homophile organizations, and law enforcement agencies.

Political Committee

Registers voters and informs the Community of the attitudes of the political aspirants. Wrote and published a brochure covering attitudes of persons running for political office.

Publications Committee

Prepares for printing all material submitted them representing the organization. Such material included SIR's VD prevention material, political brochures, membership brochures, and general advertising.

Membership Committee

Advises the Membership and Community of the organization's activities, and provides information on the proposed programs of the organization. The committee also handles the maintenance of membership lists, voting results, and campaign drives.

Social Activities Committee

Sponsors and arranges parties, sets the location for meetings, sets up maintenance procedures for the halls during and after functions, and oversees the interest groups as listed below.

Bowling	Roller Derby	Opera
Art Groups	Tennis	Movies
Cards	Theatre	Weightlifting
Dining	Swimming	Excursions
Sunbathing	Barring	Others
Conversation	Hiking	

5. The United States Mission

In a letter from the secretary general of this group, dated February 24, 1965, the mission was described in this way:[9]

The United States Mission was formed on March 19, 1962 as a non-profit, religious, homophile, organization under the auspices of the Church of the Androgyne. Its purposes are:

1. the dissemination of the religious beliefs of the Church of the Androgyne.
2. aiding the homosexual and the existing religious groups, in the realization of homosexuality as simply one facet of God's Creation, neither good nor bad, in and of itself.
3. the maintenance of religious freedom for all people, in accord with the Spirit of the First Amendment to the United States Constitution, insofar as this religious freedom does not involve physical injury to any other person.

Also enclosed, please find a statement of the religious beliefs of the Church of the Androgyne which is headed by Robert Humphries, termed His Androgynous Highness, Robert, Dei Gratia, Prince Bishop of the Church of the Androgyne.

Religious Belief
of the
Church of the Androgyne

The Church of the Androgyne is founded upon the belief that God has many aspects and that one of these aspects is that of the Androgyne. We believe that this Androgynous Aspect is the synthesis of the masculine and feminine dualities and that the individual can enter a spiritual consciousness called the Androgynous Awareness, in which one realizes oneself as a combination of the apparently opposing elements of masculinity and femininity and becomes able to transcend both of them; thereby recognizing The Androgynous Unity, inherent with all creation. We believe that as one loves another, be that other physically male or female, one draws closer to the Androgynous Awareness and the perception of God's aspect as the Androgyne. We believe that both the heterosexual and the homosexual drives are different ways of approaching the Androgynous Awareness. We believe that the various concepts of God, as manifested in different religions and philosophies, are the many paths The Deity uses to draw Its Creation unto Itself and that each of them is necessary for the accomplishment of this purpose.

INTERNATIONAL SOCIETIES

1. *The Circle* (Der Kreis), Postfach 547, Fraumunster, Zurich 22, Switzerland.[10]

   Organized: 1932 in Zurich, Switzerland.

   Publication: Der Kreis, monthly, in three languages — German, French, and English. The purpose of the publication is to elevate the social status of the homosexual. In the words of the publisher:

   Der Kreis (The Circle) is a cosmopolitan magazine, presenting every month a collection of stories, articles, poems, and book reviews in German, French, and English. Save in rare cases, the material in one language is not duplicated in another. Our magazine is the oldest publication of its kind, having appeared without interruption for thirty years. Each issue contains from thirty-six to fifty-five pages. *Der Kreis* is famous for its beautiful photographs of the male figure, four to six full-page photos appearing in each issue.

   Der Kreis is dedicated to increasing fraternal relations among homosexuals throughout the world, and to creating a means of communication among them, thus relieving their sense of isolation. One of the regular monthly features of our magazine is a supplement designed to help homosexuals all over the world to make contact with one another through correspondence.

   The basic aim of *Der Kreis* is to give pleasure and information to homosexual readers, and to provide a medium through which homosexual writers and artists can express themselves as freely as possible. We realize, of course, that homosexuals are a minority group, and that our way of life and our goals can hardly hope ever to gain widespread mass support. Accordingly, we feel that the wiser course for the leaders of the homosexual cause to follow is that of direct appeal to legislators, jurists, scientists, and churchmen, for the abolition of unjust, discriminatory, and obsolete laws.

2. *Culture and Recreation Center* (Cultuur-En Ontspanningscentrum, C.O.C.), Postbox 542, Amsterdam, Holland.

   Organized: 1946 in Holland.

   Publication: De Schakel, monthly in Dutch. *Dialoog,* bi-monthly, in Dutch — a periodical for society and homophily (Postbox 1564, Amsterdam, Holland).

   Purpose: Social and cultural.

3. *International Committee for Sexual Equality* (I.C.S.E.), Postbox 1564, Amsterdam, Holland.[11]

   Organized: 1951 in Holland (headquarters). There are branches in 7 countries.

   Publication: I.C.S.E. *Newsletter,* monthly.

   Purpose: To improve the social and legal position of homosexuals and to increase knowledge of the condition.

4. *Arcadie,* 19 rue Beranger, Paris-3°, France.

   Publication: Arcadie, monthly, in French — *revue litteraire et scientifique.*

WHAT DO HOMOSEXUALS WANT?

The aims stated in the official publications of the homosexual organizations are not always those of the "unorganized" homophile. These are not always so restrained and acceptable. According to Masters, who asks the question — "What do homosexuals (say they) want?":

> Most basically — and most obviously — what homosexuals want is to be regarded as ordinary citizens who differ from the rest of the population only in terms of their sex object-choices (which they would wish to have regarded as, for them, natural); and they would wish to be accepted on the basis of their worth as individuals (apart from their sexual inclinations and behavior). Almost equally basically, and perhaps prerequisite to social acceptance, they want to be freed from the laws that brand them criminals even though, as is usually the case, their prohibited sex acts occur between consenting and responsible adults.[12]

More specifically, Masters then summarizes some of the demands made by homosexual spokesmen. How many homosexuals would want any or all of these demands satisfied one could never know. They are listed here after the order of Mr. Masters, but they are a paraphrase of his summary:

1. The homosexual, both male and female, wants the right to serve in the armed forces (see Clinic 12).

2. The homosexual does not feel that he should be excluded from government service for "security reasons" (see Clinic 12).

3. Marriages between homosexuals should be legalized and the various consequences of this should follow, such as joint ownership of property and income tax deductions (see Clinic 10).

4. Married homosexuals should be allowed to adopt children.

5. Realistic presentation of homosexual life should be allowed in movies, in TV, and in literature. Such presentations should be subject only to the good taste applied at present to heterosexual themes.

6. Homosexual marriages should be accepted by the various religious groups (see Clinic 10).

7. Homosexuals should be allowed to wear such clothing, makeup, and perfumes as their personality dictates (see Clinic 6).

8. The homosexual press should enjoy the same freedom as that of the heterosexual press in the matter of pinups, etc.

9. Homosexuals should be allowed to display their affection for each other as openly as do heterosexuals within the limits of good taste.

It seems unlikely that many of these objectives will be achieved. The aims fostered by the Mattachine Society and the Daughters of Bilitis are more realistic and more likely to be acceptable. The individual homosexual would do well to follow the aims expressed by responsible leadership.

CLINIC 15 — NOTES

1. Personal communication, February 13, 1965.
2. Paul Waring and Dean Travis Bryce, "Homosexual Freedom," privately published, 1961, p. 16.
3. *The Ladder,* Vol. IX, No. 3 (December, 1964), p. 3.
4. This organization was called to my attention in a letter from the Public Relations Office of the Daughters of Bilitis, February 13, 1965, which I quote.
5. From a mimeographed note obtained through the Daughters of Bilitis.
6. Personal communication, March 1, 1965.
7. Form letter to subscribers to the *Newsletter* dated December 7, 1964.
8. Personal communication, February 24, 1965.
9. Personal communication, February 24, 1965.
10. Personal communication from *Der Kreis,* received February, 1965.
11. Note that the mailing address for the I.C.S.E. is the same as that for the C.O.C.'s publication, *Dialoog.*
12. R. E. L. Masters, *The Homosexual Revolution* (New York: The Julian Press, Inc., 1962), p. 130.

Moral Responsibility of the Homosexual

STATISTICAL ETHICS

There is a trend today to deny an objective code of morality and to accept as moral the criteria of the group. Standards are set and moral values established, as it were, by popular vote. Nowhere is the principle that an action is moral because "everyone does it" more accepted than in the field of sex. Because many do it, they say, it is normal; what is normal is moral. Morality then becomes a statistical norm.

M. R. Sapirstein in speaking of the Kinsey Report wrote as follows:

Almost every possible cultural variation has been described in our own culture by Kinsey, and the experimental biologists use this as evidence that man is basically an "animal." They use this evidence to encourage a greater permissiveness toward socially unacceptable practices in our own society by bringing forth evidence that "perversions" are acceptable in other cultures and other species of animals. This type of reasoning which is rapidly becoming fashionable further destroys conformity of sexual patterns as a means of finding security. The anthropologists and the biologists do not suggest that we adopt the religion, the family organization or economic practices of the many societies which they describe. Yet they seem to indicate that any variation of sexual practice, taken out of context, is "normal" for our society.[1]

There exists, therefore, especially in the field of sexual ethics, a great deal of confusion as to what is normal, what is natural, what is perverse, "especially in an age which bases its arguments or its prejudices so largely on statistical evidence."[2]

No counselor can accept this "statistical norm" of sex morality. He must recognize an objective norm of morality which is based on the natural law as well as the law of nature. He must recognize that the purpose of coition is twofold. It is "conceptional," and it is "relational." He must also know that these purposes may never be entirely and permanently separated. This separation would, of necessity, happen in a homosexual relationship. Therefore, he would readily conclude that homosexual acts are intrinsically wrong in that by their very nature they frustrate the natural purpose of the sex act. Homosexual acts are, therefore, *contra naturam*. This has been the opinion of moralists and thinking men as long as there has been a recorded history.

THE MORAL QUESTION

The problem here for the counselor is: Does a homosexual continue to be responsible for his offenses against morality or does the fact that there is a deviation involved remove, or at least diminish, culpability for his actions? Obviously no hard and fast rule can be put down to cover all cases and all persons. We do know that very often a deviate will claim inculpability on the grounds that he is not free when it is a question of his particular form of perversion, or that his will is weakened because of it. This may be true in some cases, but not infrequently it is merely a cloak for the truth, i.e., that the person does actually have greater freedom than he is willing to admit, even to himself, but he desires sexual stimulation and takes this means to obtain it.

In dealing with such problems in terms of morality one must recall, with Allers, that

> what matters is not the nature of man's sexuality as such, but how he experiences it, his attitudes towards it and the position he is prepared to accord it in his general system of life and in relation to ultimate values.[3]

One's morality in general and his attitude toward ultimate values in matters other than sex may well give a clue to the weight of his personal evaluation of responsibility. It is not a question of: Do these intrinsic factors have an influence? They do. The question is, How much?

Although the objective norm of morality is definite, and the human will is free, in the concrete there are many factors which can encroach on this freedom. It is important for the moralist to be aware of them, so that he will be able to pass a proper judgment in each individual instance. In doing so he must bear in mind that in most cases, perhaps more especially in cases of homosexuality, he is concerned not only with a sex act. The problem reaches the whole personality of the subject. Affectively the homosexual lives not in a world of men and women, but only in a world of men.

OBJECTIVE MORALITY OF INVERSION

The facts in regard to the objective morality of homosexual acts need no argument or further exposition. There has been a condemnation of such acts:

1. In both the Old and New Testaments of the Bible — some of these were described briefly in Clinic 1;
2. In the teachings of the Fathers of the Church;
3. In the Councils of the Church;
4. In the teachings on the Natural Law;
5. In the opinion of all men through recorded history.

SUBJECTIVE RESPONSIBILITY

There are several questions which must be answered before one is prepared to discuss individual subjective responsibility:

1. Is the homosexual responsible for the origin of his inversion?
2. Is the state of being an invert culpable?
3. If not responsible for his basic condition, is the homosexual responsible for his current individual acts?

In the attempt to answer these questions those factors which, by influencing the will, may reduce the culpability of the invert in comparison to the heterosexual will also be discussed.

IS THE HOMOSEXUAL RESPONSIBLE FOR THE ORIGIN OF HIS INVERSION?

This would certainly not be true if the formation of a homosexual personality took place before the subject had the use of reason. Such a theory of origin has been presupposed in our earlier clinics and such is the opinion of Father Gleason.[4] Father Buckley, on the other hand, seems to favor the opinion that homosexuality is an induced state or, as he calls it, "a bad habit fixation." Although he does not exclude the possibility of a pre-use-of-reason origin, he sums up the morality of the state of inversion as follows:

> In conclusion, therefore, it is our considered opinion that, after a careful examination of the main factors involved, there can be no doubt that the homosexual is generally in some degree responsible for his condition, either for its origin or at least being willing to remain as he is.[5]

In regard to this Father Harvey commented in his review of Father Buckley's book:

> [Father] Buckley assumes that most homosexuals can get rid of the very tendency itself by a process of re-education of the will. But many genuine inverts have not had a true interest in the opposite sex since the dawn of consciousness. They come to realize their condition sooner or later, but usually too late to do anything about the redirection of the instinct into heterosexual tendencies.[6]

Father Harvey then added:

> The homosexual condition is more than a bad habit fixation; it is a neurosis of personality, more difficult to control than a comparative bad habit in a normal person. It would be more fruitful advice to tell an invert that he has a moral responsibility to *control* his neurosis, for which there are adequate means, than to insist that he *eradicate* the same, which is rarely possible.[7]

I find myself in agreement with Fathers Harvey and Gleason. It is commonly held that the genuine homosexual is not responsible for being what he is. Generally, since he is already guilt-laden, it may be better to minimize his responsibility or even to inform him of his lack of personal guilt for being a homosexual, unless, of course, the facts of an individual case indicate otherwise.

IS THE STATE OF BEING AN INVERT CULPABLE?

The state of being a homosexual under practically all circumstances has in itself no more moral responsibility than the state of being heterosexual. If, for example, a young man feels a spontaneous erotic urge toward another man, it is no more immoral than it would be for a young man who experiences the same type of feeling for a young woman. The urge is impulsive and unsolicited. There is no human act and, therefore, no moral responsibility:

> Those who have to deal with the young may be reminded that *the symptoms of sexual awakening in the invert are parallel with those of the normal youth.* While susceptible to males and unsusceptible to females, he is— unless already polluted by gossip or companions of the street — innocent of those particular practices the inclination to which is commonly supposed to be the badge of inversion.[8]

Some may offer the objection that although the impulse might be *in se* involuntary, it might be voluntary *in causa.* Although it might be argued that in its first act homosexuality is voluntary, this would not be true for the fully developed homosexual state. In the first place most homosexuality starts at an age before the use of reason and even though the first act in the total process may have been voluntarily accepted the numerous subsequent steps leading to the final state were not. These subsequent steps, and indeed even the first step, were not *intended* to lead to a state of inversion. For example, suppose at the age of eight a child after some rejecting act on the part of his mother cries out, "I hate you, I hate you, I am never going to get married." Suppose further that this is the first step on a path leading to eventual homosexuality as a result of a persistent pattern of avoiding women. It is logical to believe that, although the first step was voluntary, it was not purposely directed toward homosexuality, and subsequent steps became habitual and to a larger extent involuntary. At no time during the formative period of the eventually complete state of inversion did the individual *intend* to be an invert. If anyone could be said to be responsible for the final result it would be those individuals forming his milieu during the growth process. This, however, is of purely academic interest.

As I have stated elsewhere with Father McGoldrick:

> The onset of mental disorders may be in childhood but may be delayed until adult life. The defective use of the intellect, the emotions or the will may begin at any time. More usually the individual is exposed in childhood to the first traumatic events. It may be then that he willingly accepts the protective devices and finds comfort as they bolster his defenses. Their use may be discontinued after this for a long time, but the foundation has been laid, and when the individual is confronted later in life with a similar situation, he reactivates these defenses, retreats, as it were, to previously prepared defenses. On the other hand, the first use of these mechanisms may occur in adult life. It is our belief that the individual at first willingly accepts these various devices for avoiding painful reality; these reactions, however, soon become habitual and are adopted as a way of life.[9]

IS THE INVERT RESPONSIBLE FOR CURRENT INDIVIDUAL ACTS?

The rule to follow in determining the morality of the actions of an individual with a pathological disposition is that, although the person may not be responsible for his present condition, he was probably in some measure responsible for setting off the series of actions which led to his present condition. Sexual inversion is a wrong way of thinking and feeling, and somewhere during the period of development, as the pattern of reaction was developed, a will

action came into play. The will may have been erroneous in the
beginning so that a habit was formed before it was demanded. Or the
will may have chosen the sex actions as a plan of action, although
recognized as illicit from the beginning. The fact that the will does
not come into play at the present time removes the imputability
of the present condition except, as the theologians say, *in causa*. This,
however, does not exculpate the homosexual for any action performed
as a result of his present basic pattern.

In this case I would accept the opinion of Father Duhamel:

> Even when a habit of sin has been contracted deliberately and sinfully,
> once the habitual sinner repents of the sin involved in contracting the
> habit and sincerely resolves to use efficacious means to correct the habit,
> the habit itself is considered involuntary and sinless. This means that,
> hereafter, and as long as he remains in the same good disposition, the
> individual acts placed under the influence of habit are no longer
> attributed to him *in causa*. This means, further, that the formal guilt of
> any future individual acts, placed under the influence of the acquired
> habit, must be judged from the individual acts themselves, i.e.,
> according to the amount of effective control he was able to exercise
> in each instance, considering all the internal and external circum-
> stances of the act.[10]

The following case illustrates the voluntary acceptance of the
homosexual act, although the initial stimulation was spontaneous and
involuntary:

PATIENT

When I was five, I was sitting one day on the kitchen floor, looking at
a wash-board which had a printed picture of the early pioneers across
the top. Perhaps the cramped way I was sitting set off the reaction, but
I found myself experiencing sexual pleasure as I looked at one of the
pioneers. I remember I was ashamed of the feeling, even while I enjoyed
it, and didn't want my mother who was nearby to know anything about it.
That was the beginning — in ignorance, with no one introducing me to
the sensations. I indulged in day-dreaming after that for a couple of years,
with desires. Then one day another boy introduced me to homosexual
acts; I was quite willing. We committed these acts from time to time —
maybe once a month, maybe less often; I don't remember. Curiously
enough, I was at the same time a rather pious boy, and was considered
such by other boys. And from the time I was about four or five I had
wanted to be a clergyman when I grew up. All through the years, this
desire never left me.

In one of my first confessions I was going to tell the priest about these
sins, but my courage failed at the last moment and I lied. But the knowledge that I was making bad confessions didn't trouble me much, and I

thought myself rather pious. At fourteen I left home to go to school. For four months I committed no sinful acts, but then began to slip into them; never with anyone else. (In fact, I may add that I was never tempted after this to do anything with others, and my relations with the other boys were always sound, and I had the highest respect for my closest friends, as they had for me.) Midway through this first year of preparation I made a clean breast of everything in a good general confession.

After the state has developed, the invert must realize that outside of the married state all fully deliberate sex acts are seriously immoral. It is here that the invert has his greatest problem. He realizes that within the framework of his disorder there can never be a legitimate sex act. He is, therefore, quite susceptible to a subtle campaign by other homosexuals who attempt to persuade him that, since his state precludes marriage and since he has such strong erotic urges, for him sex acts with other homosexuals are not only desirable but necessary. He must only avoid, they say, sexual relations with children and the use of force. Many inverts are able to rationalize that this is so and although they will agree at an intellectual level that such acts are immoral their continued activity indicates otherwise. In the face of continued acts the counselor can only attempt to persuade the homosexual that he must follow his reason which is intact and use his will which still has the power to control the situation. To accomplish this he must be persuaded that abstinence is the greater good. Since he is free, he is not bound to sin and, by the same token, he is not forced to do what is right. He is theoretically, at least, able to choose his course, and in the interest of his own future welfare he should be persuaded to choose the moral course. However, since the roots of the disorder are so deeply placed, it can hardly be expected that they can be uprooted simply by conscious acts of the will.

Father Duhamel sums this up by saying:

> There is a unanimous agreement among moral theologians that there is a diminution of freedom in the individual acts that are actually placed under the influence of an acquired sinful habit.[11]

ABBÉ ORAISON ON MORALITY

Not only his associates but professional people as well may mislead the invert in regard to his moral responsibility. Some authors, including Catholics, are extreme in their theories as to the lack of responsibility of the homosexual for his actions. Thus Abbé Oraison was criticized by Fathers Ford and Kelly because he held that

> . . . all mankind is so sexually immature and so dominated consciously or unconsciously by passion that in practice, and as a general rule, we must presume sexual sins to be only materially grave.* Man's unconscious profoundly influences his voluntary depriving him practically of the power of inhibiting his sinful sexual acts. . . .[12]

Commenting on this statement Fathers Ford and Kelly disagree:

> Underlying these conclusions of Abbé Oraison there seems to be a fundamental misconception, the idea that normality is illusory, that everyone is a victim of sexual pathology . . . but it is only in the topsy-turvy world of certain psychoanalysts that everyone is a pathological problem. . . .[13]

Father Duhamel also comments on this book. He agrees with Fathers Ford and Kelly:

> It is impossible to mention all that is objectionable in his book — which, however, contains many clear and helpful insights — but his fundamental principle seems to be a distortion of the notion of Original Sin with the corollary that almost no one is ever normal in the matter of sex. Practically all human beings are the victims of sexual pathology. There is, therefore, a presumption that sins of impurity are mortal sins only materially for the generality of mankind, and this presumption will yield to contrary proof only in very rare instances. This presumption is applied not only to sins of masturbation, but also to acts of homosexuality, fornication, adultery, and conjugal onanism. In the confessional, penitents are to be treated on the presumption that there has been no subjective mortal sin in the commission of these violations of an admitted objective sexual code.[14]

Quoting the address of Pope Pius XII to the psychotherapists, April 13, 1953, Fathers Ford and Kelly make clear the mind of the Holy Father concerning the theories advanced by some psychiatrists:

> It cannot be alleged that the psychic troubles and disorders which disturb the normal functioning of the psychic beings represent what normally happens. The moral struggle to remain on the right path does not prove that it is impossible to follow that path, nor does it authorize any drawing back.[15]

If any of the theories which hold that sexual conduct is determined independently of the will of the subject were correct, then the homosexual would be rid of all responsibility.

---

* "Material sin is a transgression of the divine law committed without knowledge of its sinfulness or without free consent; it is no true sin, since the act is not a willful transgression, e.g., taking the property of another in the belief that it is one's own."[16]

SUMMARY

The answers to the three questions asked on page 227 would, therefore, be:

1. Is the homosexual responsible for the origin of his inversion? — No, except possibly in some unique situation.

2. Is the state of being an invert culpable? — No.

3. Is the homosexual responsible for his current individual acts? — Yes, except under certain circumstances of diminished responsibility.

Having answered these three questions, we are now better prepared to discuss the subjective responsibility of the invert.

THE CONFESSOR AND THE INVERT

A good literary example of the homosexual's dilemma is found in a recent best-selling novel. In answer to a priest's reminder that homosexuality is a sin against nature, Nicholas Black, an invert, replies:

> What about my nature? I was born the way I am. . . . It was my nature to be drawn more to men than to women. I wasn't seduced in the shower room or blackmailed in the bar. That is what I am. I can't change it. I did not ask to be born like this. God knows I've suffered enough because of it. But who made me? According to you — God! What I want and what I do is according to the nature He gave me.[17]

One of the first questions proposed by the penitent anxious about his condition will probably be that of his moral responsibility. The question is a legitimate one, but it must be realized as Father Harvey has said that any answer which aspires to finality is useless; because — and this would probably be the best answer to be given — time and experience with this particular client are needed in order to form an opinion, even approximately, of *the part played by the condition and that played by the will.* During the course of counseling, the pastor can determine more and more clearly the part played by each. Instead, therefore, of hastily giving a theoretical answer which, although it might temporarily satisfy the client, would not correspond to the changing situation, the counselor must defer an answer and disengage, little by little, the positive elements when the person feels himself more and more free in revealing his opinion. It is more necessary to cultivate and strengthen the grip of conscience than to give an objective but theoretical analysis.[18]

It will be apparent that many inverts do not want to give up their practices because they foresee a certain amount of loneliness and rejection if they do so. The invert, if he is to receive help through religion, must, however, come to the realization of his own utter helplessness and place his confidence in God and God's grace. He must realize that he is like the alcoholic whose ability to will is weak and, left to himself, cure may be impossible. He must go outside himself and seek help from God. Even then, his attitude may bring to mind these words of St. Augustine:

> . . . But I wretched, most wretched, in the very commencement of my early youth, had begged chastity of Thee, and said, "Give me chastity and continency, *only not yet.*" For I feared lest Thou shouldst hear me soon, and soon cure me of the disease of concupiscence, which I wished to have satisfied, rather than extinguished. And I had wandered through crooked ways in a sacrilegious superstition, not indeed assured thereof, but as preferring it to the others which I did not seek religiously, but opposed maliciously. [Italics added.][19]

To be continent for some natural end or on the natural level alone may not be enough. Such natural measures are helpful only if based on the supernatural character of the continence and the holiness of chastity which arise from supernatural motives. God's grace, we are told, is sufficient for all men. It is up to man to accept it. God does not force the human will. He leaves it free. Hence, the invert, if he sincerely wishes a new sexual orientation, must be motivated to the extent that he is willing to accept not only psychotherapy but also the supernatural aid of grace. It is by grace that man's lower appetites are brought more or less perfectly under the control of reason, a reason which is in subjection to God.

It should be noted that the moralist's problem with homosexuality is with subjective rather than objective morality. Subjective morality is more difficult to evaluate than objective, because of the many concrete, situational, individual, cultural factors that enter into any judgment concerning subjective morality.

The Confessor and the Unconscious

It may be appropriate at this point to mention another aspect of subjectivity. It is important for the confessor to bear in mind that he is not a psychotherapist and that his interest is only in the conscious subjective judgments of his penitent. For this reason, there would be no value in the introduction of unconscious mental factors to the confessor. It could only result in confusion. The confessor is concerned only with conscious factors. The conscience is conscious. The confessor in arriving at a judgment is not concerned with repressed material. Such material may be helpful in determining the "why," but not in arriving at a decision on responsibility.

Responsibility for his act will be based upon the penitent's judgment of himself as acting rightly or wrongly. When reference is made to the question of right and wrong it applies to right and wrong of the objective order. That is to say, the man may have misapprehensions of objective reality; i.e., he has an erroneous subjective judgment of what reality is. The presence of such a misrepresentation of reality would not, in itself, relieve a man of responsibility. It would do so, however, if this misapprehension was due to mental instability or disease. It would undoubtedly relieve him of any responsibility if because of such a disturbance he sincerely believed, on the basis of his misrepresentations, that what he was doing was right. Such conscious factors are important to the confessor. He is not concerned, as confessor, with all of the unconscious factors which brought about the patient's condition. The confessor must bear in mind that, in any case, *unconscious factors, although they may influence conduct, do not coerce.* They do not determine conduct:

> Unconscious conflicts, associated as they are with fear, threat, hostility, hatred, sexuality and guilt from which serious complexes derive, are powerful motivating forces which cannot be dealt with by the conscious mind until they are brought up to that level.[20]

The introduction of the unconscious to the confessor for the purpose of determining responsibility recommended by many would not assist and could only confuse him. Consider, for example, a case in which the individual had been raised by a cruel punishing father. As he grew older he repressed some of this feeling but retained in consciousness a resentment of all authoritative figures. If this man in adult life should kill an authoritative figure, would he be relieved of responsibility merely because it is revealed that his crime was indirectly the result of a repressed hatred of his father? Some say it would.

For the confessor the man is guilty of murder. The principle would apply which was discussed above. The individual is responsible for acts performed as a result of a long-standing habit even though he may not be responsible for the habit itself. This individual may long have resented authoritative figures because of an initial attitude which started with the hatred of his father. The repression of this feeling toward his father may have contributed toward his present crime but it did not coerce. It will naturally depend on how sick this person is as a result of his repression, but, granted an absence of illness, he is responsible. In a civil court his repressed hatred would probably not be exculpating.

The Will and Responsibility

The ultimate answer to responsibility depends upon how seriously the freedom of the individual to act or not to act is impaired by his disorder. The definition of a mortal sin which we were taught in the catechism was that it was a sin which had three elements: (1) a serious matter, committed after (2) sufficient reflection and (3) with full consent of the will. At that time we were quite unaware of the many ramifications of these three elements which confront the confessor.

The Will

The confessor is frequently confronted especially with the last element. Not always finding an answer he asks: "When can we judge emotional stress in these cases to be so great that it diminishes freedom below the point where grave imputability is possible?" To some extent this is an insoluble problem, but as Father Ford has said, "we should like to clarify it, and move in the direction of solving it." There is no doubt, however, that any real progress in this direction will require intensive studies in all fields. There is much difference of opinion as to how free an individual is in regard to his acts.

Father Ford describes "normal" freedom of the will in these terms:

> I believe that the following description of free will in the philosophical sense would be admitted by theologians of all schools. It is the power, given certain prerequisites of knowledge and motivation, of saying "yes" or "no" freely to a proposed action, or of choosing freely between two alternative courses of action. Freely does not mean easily or without reluctance, although sometimes free choices are easily made. Freely means that at the time the choice was made the man could have made the opposite choice — even if with difficulty or repugnance.

Father Ford then suggests that when a confessor asks the question which has to do with sufficient advertence and deliberation —

"Did you realize fully that it was a grave sin?" — there is still the unanswered question of the freedom of the will. He continues:

It is like the "right and wrong" test of criminal law. Is it universally true that in the presence of sufficient advertence, there always follows automatically sufficient consent of the will?[21]

Most philosophers and moralists would probably hesitate to deny that with the use of reason unimpaired, with intellectual perception intact, the will can be anything but sufficiently free. They appeal to St. Thomas:

To whatever extent reason remains free and not subjected to passion, to that extent the movement of the will which remains does not tend with necessity toward the object to which passion inclines.[22]

Many psychiatrists might disagree. What appears in consciousness may appear to be a clear-cut concept. The subject may be able to discuss it coherently and intelligently. Unconsciously, however, due, for example, to compartmentation, he may react quite differently. I recall one teacher of ethics who was able very clearly and concisely to discuss the morality of perverse acts. His actions clearly showed, however, that by a mechanism of isolation he did not accept these concepts as applying to himself.

FACTORS LESSENING THE FREEDOM OF THE WILL

There are a variety of factors affecting the will which must be considered in evaluating the homosexual's decreased moral responsibility. The most important of these are:

1. Defective conceptual and evaluative cognition;
2. Concupiscence;
3. Degree of sexedness;
4. External environment factors;
5. The severity of associated psychiatric disorders;
6. Occasions of sin.

1. *Conceptual and Evaluative Cognition*

In forming his subjective judgments regarding his state, the invert is likely to have faulty conceptual or evaluative cognition. Conceptual cognition expresses *what the object of knowledge is.* Evaluative cognition expresses *the value that the object of knowledge has* for the individual. Although these are merely diverse aspects of the same object of knowledge, conceptual cognition is not sufficient for responsible action. There must also be present an ability to weigh and evaluate the substantial elements of an action. When we apply this principle to the homosexual it must be borne in mind that when the sexual fixation occurs in childhood there is likely, at least at an unconscious level, to be a fixation of the emotions related to sex at that time. Although the individual grows and matures in other ways, the sexual emotions remain fixated at this early level. At this level the attitude adopted toward pleasure may well have been "what is pleasant is good because it is good for me." As he grows older the homosexual may realize intellectually that this is an erroneous attitude, but emotionally and unconsciously he may cling to this concept. Under such circumstances there is no real insight, and the cognition of the invert in regard to his condition is, therefore, likely to be defective.

He may know that it is unnatural to have sexual desires for members of the same sex; he may agree, he may express himself as understanding, but unconsciously or even consciously he may persist in having such thoughts as:

1. God made me this way.
2. Maybe I am a mistake and they do not understand.
3. Maybe I am a woman in a man's body.
4. Maybe there is a third sex.

In the presence of such attitudes one could question even conceptual knowledge *in some cases.*

Evaluative cognition is more likely to be defective and in this case the thoughts are quite likely to be conscious:

1. I am confused. I look like a man but I feel like a woman.
2. The condition is stronger than I am.
3. I am powerless when the urge strikes me.
4. Such feelings are natural to my condition.
5. I am this way through no fault of my own and, therefore, I have an inherent right to act.
6. The inversion reaches into the very core of my being.[23]

> The conflicts underlying the habitual performance of sinful acts are *unconscious* and of a sexual or aggressive nature; they relate to either

the concupiscible or irascible appetites. These conflicts are varied and involve such problems as fears, hostility, hatred, rejection, severe doubt, despair, and self-destruction. [Italics added.][24]

In the presence of such attitudes it is quite likely that the evaluative cognition of the invert will be faulty. The question then confronts us: Does it arise because the invert *does not want to change* or because he is *unable to change?* If he is genuinely obstructed in his natural power of appreciation due to a chronic disorder, there would seem to be a definite decrease in his responsibility for his falls. It should, however, be a genuine indication for psychotherapy. If he does not want to change, there is little to be done about it.

2. *Concupiscence*

Concupiscence cannot be disregarded in forming an estimate of the invert's responsibility. Concupiscence is the spontaneous movement of the sensitive appetites and instincts insofar as they anticipate man's reason. It is imperative that such spontaneous movements be controlled by the intellect if conduct is to be moral. In some inverts the deviant drive may be so strongly entrenched that it may be difficult to control. To the extent that the appetites affect conduct beyond the control of the will the individual has a diminished responsibility. Such supremacy of instincts and emotions may lead to impulsive, unpremeditated conduct for which the individual would not be responsible. Such impulsivity is, however, more frequently a rationalization than a fact.

*The Will and Irresistible Impulses.** Such impulsivity is sometimes spoken of as bringing about an "irresistible impulse." This is an unfortunate term because the expression "irresistible impulse" connotes a distortion of the power of the will itself. This is an inaccuracy. It is not the power of will *itself* that has been distorted. If the patient had entertained different reality judgments he might have chosen to act in another manner. The distortion is not of the will, but of the whole person — as I hope to show by a brief outline of the psychosomatic unity of the human person.

Man is a being who possesses a vast number of capacities. These are divided into three broad genera: intellectual, sensile, vegetal. The

---

* Some parts of this section are taken from "A Psychiatrist Looks at the Durham Decision," *The Catholic University of American Law Review,* Vol. V, No. 1 (January, 1955), pp. 3–32.

intellectual activities are those of *intellect and will*. The sensile involve
the external and internal senses plus the whole gamut of emotions;
the vegetal involve his activities of nutrition, growth, and reproduction. All of these capacities necessarily tend toward their natural
goals which are called their natural goods. In the case of the will
there is only *one* irresistible object — the infinitely good. That is to
say, if the intellect recognized an object as being the infinite good,
the will would have no other choice than to accept it. On the other
hand, *if the intellect recognizes an object as less than infinitely good,
the will is free to accept or to reject the object.*[25]

The will tends to accept any good which is less than infinite if
the intellect does not recognize in the acceptance a threat to an even
greater good. This is the way in which intellect and will would act
in an emotionally mature individual. The intellect would have a
regulating and integrating role over the sensile and vegetal activities.

However, we must keep in mind that intellect and will are not
the only capacities of the whole human person. He is an emotional,
sensile, and vegetal being as well as intellectual. The person may
choose to cultivate his sensile life at the expense of the intellectual.
In such a case the person may establish fixed habits whereby his
emotional capacities react more readily than the intellectual, and
the emotional obtain their satisfaction at the expense of the person
as a whole.

The regulating and integrating rule of the intellect is never a
despotic one over the lower powers, even in the most perfectly
integrated human personality. Its rule is rather a democratic one;
that is to say, the lower powers have some autonomy of their own;
if they are not regulated, they will break out and take over the
person. But even here the question of responsibility is not to be
ignored. If an individual's life is a chaos of emotions, we cannot
say that he has lost his willpower. What should be said is that the
individual has not exercised his willpower, not that his will was
overrun. In determining guilt the question will arise: "To what
extent did the person *knowingly* allow his emotions to take the
ascendancy?"

If his emotional life is emphasized at the expense of his higher
powers, it may be due to a number of factors, such as poor training
by his parents. This would be a mitigating factor so far as guilt is
concerned. On the other hand, an individual may have allowed his

emotions to take over simply because he chose the path of least resistance. In this case he would be far more guilty than in the other.

In both of these last two cases we should speak of an "unresisted" urge but *never* of an "irresistible" urge.

In brief, the will is indirectly *influenced* by the emotions and unconscious factors but never *coerced*. The will acts on the basis of *conscious judgments* and inclines toward the judgment which is presented to it as good.

A great deal of the confusion on psychic determinism in modern psychiatry has arisen because Freud thought that he had shown once and for all that free will is an illusion. He based this on his explanation of a number of psychic activities, such as the connection of thought associations, the origin of neurotic symptoms, slips of the tongue, and acts of forgetting, among others. But anyone who understands Freud's theories, and who simultaneously understands the doctrine of free will, will immediately see that the instances offered in proof against free will do not pertain to the question. The conditions upon which an individual makes a free decision are all *in consciousness* at the time he makes the decision. That is to say, the premises upon which he decides to act or not to act are in his field of consciousness. These thoughts are *influenced* by other unconscious factors which are not directly available to the man making the decision. However much these conscious thoughts may be *influenced* by unconscious factors, it still remains true to say that the individual's decision is based upon those thoughts immediately available in consciousness. *This is true for both the psychotic and for his more normal confrere.* Every human being is influenced but not coerced by the unconscious. The difference between the normal man and the psychotic is the *degree of influence* which is exerted on his actions by the unconscious. In the normal man the power of reason *has control* over the urges arising from unconscious sources. In the psychotic, the power of reason yields its place more readily to the urges of the unconscious. Thus reason is unseated because its control has been usurped by the lower powers. Just why reason is overwhelmed in the psychotic depends on a large number of factors, the most important being the loss of proper subjective judgment which permits the effects of childhood trauma, more immediate environmental influences, psychic threats, faulty habits, and other traumatic psychological experiences to gain access to the conscious without the usual controls. As I have said before, normal and abnormal minds do not differ qualitatively but quantitatively. The sensitive conscience of a psychotic might lead to swift and terrifying behavior.

It should be clearly understood that I do not maintain that *all* acts of man are free. On the contrary, only those acts which follow deliberation are free acts. That is why the philosopher distinguishes between an *actus humanus* and an *actus hominis*. Human acts (*acta humana*) are those specific acts resulting after a man exercises his human power of deliberation. Acts of a man (*acta hominis*) are those actions which take place without deliberation, e.g., reflex activity, digestive activity, response to stimuli, growth. Habit and bodily appetites may influence the judgment which precedes the act of the will and consequently may strongly influence its action. The will in this latter case, although influenced, is not coerced. In regard to the lack of freedom in reference to certain acts, Mercier has this to say:

> . . . all acts performed by man are not free. Only those acts are free which are the fruit of reflection. A very large percentage of acts, then, even in the most serious life, are not free because done without thought; a larger percentage are suggested simply by the imagination, controlled by passion or self-interest, or are due to routine. In the second place, it is a mistake to imagine that free acts are purely arbitrary, proceeding from a will that acts without a purpose. Truly man may be unreasonable if he like. But in point of fact, in by far the majority of cases, men are not unreasonable, but allow themselves to be actuated by a purpose. Thus, not to speak of the last intention — the seeking after supreme happiness — the instinct of self-preservation, the instinct of propagation, the natural love of parents for children, of children for parents, the striving for well-being, or for personal interest, are all so many motors to the will to which it generally responds without making a deliberate choice.[26]

Freedom of will does not mean merely arbitrariness, as if the will simply moved at random without receiving influences. On the other hand, we should not say that these influences coerce the will into a position where it can choose only one alternative. We all know how often we have had the chance to choose between two motives, and we may have chosen something which at the time was less desirable than something else. For example, going to work at the office on a pleasant day instead of playing golf. Most of the arguments against freedom of the will are based on a nineteenth-century concept of Newtonian physics or upon the law of the conservation of energy. Behind the doctrine of psychic determinism is the nineteenth-century philosophy of mechanism which Freud adopted uncritically from his contemporaries. Freud himself was not a philosopher, as he pointed out somewhat ironically in his own autobiography. Nineteenth-century mechanism has been rejected because in more recent times even in the physical universe it can no longer be held that there is absolute determinacy.

It is a mistake for a philosopher to predicate of all reality some principle which applies to only a segment of reality, just as it would be for a botanist to say that since tomatoes and lemons are both fruit, anything he says about tomatoes will apply equally to lemons. This is why the philosopher who understands freedom of the will ignores the Heisenburg Principle as a proof of free will. Sheldon Glueck, as an authority, quotes Sir Arthur Eddington, who is a physicist, as giving evidence that free will is now a distinct possibility.

The following definition of unresisted urge (irresistible impulse) seems best: *An unresisted urge is one which, because of mental illness, so far causes the individual to lose his power of choice in regard to particular acts that, in spite of the fact that he may recognize an act as wrong, he feels so impelled to act that he is unable to adhere to what he considers right.*

Put in philosophical terms this could be expressed as follows: An unresisted urge is one which has developed so excessively at the expense of the other psychic powers that in comparison to this urge the other powers exert negligible influence upon reason when it is called upon to make a judgment. This urge occupies the focal point of consciousness. Because it occupies this central point, it becomes the basis upon which the intellect represents an object or some course of activity as desirable to the will.

In other words, this urge has developed to such a degree that its occupancy of the whole field of consciousness for the individual precludes the entrance into consciousness of other notions which might tend to represent the urge as undesirable. Since the urge is presented to the will only as something desirable to fulfill, the individual wills to satisfy the urge. This occurs not as an isolated temporary mental illness but as part of a continuing illness which both antedates and succeeds this particular act. Instances of acts of short duration are more likely to be the result of sudden passion or anger and are not properly considered under this title.

Emphasis has been placed on the ability of the invert to control his conduct. In many instances it is said that the invert has the same ability to control his impulses as does the average heterosexual individual.[27] This is apparently Father Buckley's opinion. In reviewing Father Buckley's book, Father Harvey made this very apt statement with which I agree:

> Also, Buckley contends that the invert is "generally as mentally healthy as a normal man and therefore the usual moral standards must be applied to his sexual activities." As soon as he discovers his condition, he is morally obliged to take adequate steps to rid himself of the condition. Would to God it were so simple for him![28]

3. *Degree of Sexedness*

An important but often forgotten fact involved in making such comparisons is that not all individuals are equally sexed. Even within the "normal" or average range of men and women, sexuality may range from a low drive to a very high or intense drive. This would apply regardless of the sexual orientation of the person. This gradation might be described in terms of one plus (1+) for the lowest "normal" sex drive. It is obvious that a person with a very strong sex drive (4+) will have greater difficulty controlling his sexual impulses than will an individual with a low sex drive (1+). This must always be taken into account when such generalizations are made as those of Father Buckley and the Wolfenden Commission.

4. *External Pressures*

There are pressures on the homosexual which are not brought to bear on the heterosexual individual. Among these are:

1. The fear (and possibility) of blackmail because of his condition.

2. Job insecurity, since many employers, including the federal government, will not hire homosexuals, and if they are discovered they are discharged.

3. He must always be careful of his choice of friends. This may lead to a lonely life with at times a desperate desire for a close confidant.

4. Unlike the heterosexual, no moral sexual outlet is ever possible for him.

5. Attempted seduction by other homosexuals is not uncommon.

6. He has to fight constantly the effects of his deviant sex drive.

7. He may be severely resentful of his condition which is present through no choice of his own.

8. He may resent the failure of his confessor to understand his problem.

9. He may resent his inability to have children.

It must also be borne in mind that no two individuals are exactly alike, and in regard to moral responsibility certainly very few inverts are alike.

In addition to these conscious factors, Father Hayden adds these comments about unconscious elements:

> Compulsive acts of masturbation, normal sexual acts, promiscuity and even perversions are often associated with obsessive fears, such as an unconscious fear of castration or genital mutilation. As a consequence a persistent performance of these acts is resorted to as a reassurance of genital intactness. Such fears frequently result from a direct threat of injury on the part of the parents and others when they see the small child engaged in the practice of masturbation. They may also result from a traumatic sexual experience with another person, child or adult.[29]

5. Associated Psychiatric Disorders

In a general way homosexuals may be grouped in terms of the severity of their disorder, but even within these groups there will be variations. Each penitent becomes an individual problem. At one end of the scale, representing probably a total lack of responsibility, is the homosexual who is psychotic. Certainly in the field of his disorder he would lack moral responsibility. In increasing order of responsibility, I would list the following types of inverts:

Responsibility types:

1. Psychotic inverts. These are usually schizophrenic.

2. Neurotic inverts whose neurosis is more likely to be the result rather than the cause of his inversion. In such cases there are likely to be intense anxiety and castration fears.

3. "Hard-core," or confirmed, homosexuals.

4. "Highly sexed" inverts, especially with a compulsive need for satisfaction.[30]

5. Habitual types of inverts who offer little resistance to their desires.

6. The "fatalistic" type of invert who feels that since he is what he is he cannot be changed.

7. The average true homosexual (2+ to 3+).

8. "Quiet" types of inverts who usually have a relatively low sex drive.

9. Low-sexed true homosexuals.

10. Bisexual individuals.

Among the hard-core or confirmed homosexuals would be the older men whose sex drive has been intensified by habitual indulgence. Such men can be seen in any large city, furtively looking around bars, trying to look younger than they are, looking too eagerly for new company, complaining about their friends, and posing so as to be seen in their best profile. An observer cannot help but look on them with some compassion when he reads on their faces all their unrealized frustrated potentialities for development. It is no argument to say that some of these men are filling some of the most responsible and most lucrative places in the social structure; they still have a look about them which any careful observer can pick out without difficulty.

6. *Occasions of Sin*

In addition to these personality elements there are other factors to be taken into consideration when speaking of the sexual acts of the genuine invert. Also to be considered is the matter of occasions of sin. Concerning this, Father Gleason says:

> It is well to remember also that this type of penitent may more often be in necessary occasions of sin than his normal counterpart, simply because he cannot reorganize society to permit him to live with the cultural and social protections that ordinary mores set up between the sexes. This fact may make one more lenient in judging the homosexual in certain situations.[31]

SUMMARY

Having in mind these various factors which affect the will, there can be no doubt that in some cases the responsibility of the homosexual for performing homosexual acts is diminished. It is practically nil in the psychotic individual. Whereas it is probably not reduced at all in the poorly sexed (1+) true homosexual. Because of this great variety of types, I do not believe that any general statement concerning the responsibility of all types of homosexuals could possibly be valid.

> Freedom depends on the control actually exercised by the will; this depends on the power of deliberation, the power to assess and weigh alternatives; and this, in turn, depends on the evaluative element in the cognition of the act proposed to the will.[32]

There are undoubtedly individuals of both sexual orientations who would experience greater difficulty than others in controlling their sexual impulses. Both Father Buckley and the Wolfenden Committee disagree, to some extent, with this conclusion:

> A very false emphasis has been put on this sense of frustration by irresponsible writers, and we condemn absolutely those who gratuitously hold that the homosexual is no longer a free agent when it comes to keeping his tendencies under control. The Wolfenden Committee also agrees with this judgment and says that homosexual impulses are not any less resistible than heterosexual.[33]

Father Buckley apparently is speaking from the standpoint of the moral theologian dealing with sin. The Wolfenden Committee, on the other hand, is a government committee dealing with the legal aspects of the problem. These viewpoints are not necessarily the same.

Father Duhamel takes a somewhat opposite point of view. Although he is speaking of masturbation and not specifically of the homosexual, it would seem that the principle applies:

> If all the elements that diminish imputability are carefully assessed in each case, I suggest that, *far more often than we have been generally willing to admit in the past,* there will be serious doubt whether the subjective guilt of mortal sin was actually contracted and, at times, there will be sufficient evidence to warrant the conclusion that there was no subjective moral guilt.[34]

Pastoral Practice

It is obvious that just because an act is qualitatively abnormal its agent is not automatically deprived of that use of reason and liberty required for responsibility. The invert should, however, be judged with these extenuating factors in mind. The confessor must avoid two extremes when an invert states in confession that he knows that what he is doing is objectively sinful but that the feelings are stronger than he is. Such a penitent is expressing some guilt but seeks to excuse himself by blaming the weakness on his will, which he reifies to some extent, rather than on himself. One extreme that the confessor should avoid under such circumstances is to immediately absolve him from all responsibility as though freedom were automatically and totally wiped out by the basic condition. Only moral nihilism could be the result of such an attitude. Objective moral laws do exist which are universally binding, founded upon immutable natures and essences. At the other extreme, the confessor must avoid equating objective disconformity to the moral law with subjective guilt. Factors of the existential, subjective, concrete situational order and psychological mechanisms must be taken into consideration and usually these factors cannot be easily established by the confessor. In judging the occasional fall of the invert the confessor must consider whether the invert is sincerely striving to conform with the moral code; is he seeking to do God's will or his own; does he make use of the usual spiritual aids to avoid future falls — prayer, the sacraments, cooperation with divine grace? But grace alone is not the whole cure. Neurosis and psychotic disorders are not ordinarily cured by grace alone but by psychiatric treatment. The homosexual needs psychotherapy to restore balance to his sex drives. He needs reeducation in regard to his sexual instincts. This is the work of the psychotherapist, not that of the confessor.

In his pastoral work the counselor has excellent opportunities to counsel such a penitent and to encourage him to seek proper medical treatment which, it is hoped, will restore to him the freedom he needs for accomplishing objectively the demands of a Christian moral life. Since the invert is looked upon by some as a social outcast, a person to be avoided, the confessor must give him encouragement by his own acceptance of him. This will enable him to do something positive, instead of cutting himself off from society and accentuating his fatalistic attitude. The most important point for the confessor to keep in mind is that he is a clergyman and not a psychiatrist. He must, however, cooperate with the psychiatrist if any effective treatment is to be hoped for. The confessor must bear in mind that not all psychiatrists may be suitable for this task. There are some who may do a great deal of damage. There are, however, many excellent psychotherapists, and the proper choice will make the treatment of inverts much easier.

Perhaps there is no better way to conclude this section than by presenting the word of Father Larere, addressed to all the clergy, in which he shows how much good can come from inversion:

There is no question on the objective plane of morality of modifying the Christian judgment passed on homosexuality; but we must turn in mercy towards those torn souls at grips with a fixed and determined habit, that we may cause them to find once again the way of salvation. And if there are few among them who can long sustain such tension of their whole being and accept the constant effort towards spiritualization to dominate this divorce between mind and body, it sometimes happens that souls are met with who have gained magnificent spiritual profit from such a struggle. Indeed, when once they have recognized the gravity of this deviation and accepted the painful struggle that has no ending, it happens that this anomaly becomes, for these men, the occasion of a very exalted spiritual life.[35]

Clinic 16 — Notes

1. M. R. Sapirstein, *Emotional Security* (New York: Crown Publishers, 1948), pp. 99–100.
2. Gerald Vann, O.P., "Moral Dilemmas," *Blackfriars*, Vol. XXXV (January, 1954), pp. 6–7.
3. Rudolph Allers, *The Psychology of Character* (New York: Sheed and Ward, 1943), p. 317.
4. George Hagmaeier, C.S.P., and Robert Gleason, S.J., *Counselling the Catholic* (New York: Sheed and Ward, 1959), p. 228.
5. Michael J. Buckley, D.D., *Morality and the Homosexual* (Westminster, Md.: The Newman Press, 1959), p. 159.
6. John F. Harvey, O.S.F.S., in *Theological Studies*, Vol. XXI, No. 3 (September, 1960), p. 491.
7. *Ibid.*, p. 494.
8. Anomaly, *The Invert* (Baltimore: The Williams and Wilkins Company, 1948), p. 132.
9. John R. Cavanagh, M.D., and James B. McGoldrick, S.J., *Fundamental Psychiatry* (Milwaukee: The Bruce Publishing Company, 1958), p. 181.
10. Joseph Duhamel, S.J., "Theological Aspects," Part I of *Theological and Psychiatric Aspects of Habitual Sin*, paper copresented with Dom Jerome Hayden, O.S.B., at the Eleventh Annual Convention of the Catholic Theological Society of America, June, 1956, Cleveland, Ohio. Published in the *Proceedings*, p. 131.
11. *Ibid.*
12. John Ford, S.J., and Gerald Kelly, S.J., "Psychiatry and Moral Responsibility," *Theological Studies*, Vol. XV (1954), p. 60. See also, by the same authors, *Contemporary Moral Theology* (Westminster, Md.: Newman Press, 1958), Vol. 1, pp. 175–176. The statement is quoted from Marc Oraison, *Vie Chretienne et Problemes de la Sexualite* (Paris: Lethielleux, 1952).
13. *Contemporary Moral Theology*, p. 175.
14. Duhamel, *op. cit.*, p. 142.
15. *Contemporary Moral Theology*, p. 177 ff.
16. Donald Attwater, *A Catholic Dictionary* (New York: The Macmillan Company, 1961), 3 ed., p. 463.
17. Morris L. West, *The Devil's Advocate* (New York: William Morrow and Company, 1959), p. 23.
18. Father Harvey comments in "Homosexuality as a Pastoral Problem," *Theological Studies*, Vol. XVI, No. 1 (March, 1955), pp. 106–107: "But, supposing the penitent himself raises the question of his responsibility for each fall, what then? It is best to tell him that no categorical answer may be given. Do not tell him that he is completely responsible. Presume some freedom, and therefore

some responsibility. Time and experience will determine how free the will is in the face of this malady in its mature form. The case is analogous to that of the full-fledged alcoholic. Without encouraging him to rationalize in any way, help him to get a grip on himself. He must regain the consciousness of being the master of his own actions. After that, responsibility can be discussed in detail."

19. St. Augustine, *The Confessions,* Book VIII, Sec. 17.
20. Dom Jerome Hayden, O.S.B., "Psychiatric Aspects," Part II of *Theological and Psychiatric Aspects of Habitual Sin,* paper copresented with Rev. Joseph Duhamel, S.J., at the Eleventh Annual Convention of the Catholic Theological Society of America, June, 1956, Cleveland Ohio; published in the *Proceedings,* p. 162.
21. John C. Ford, S.J., *Proceedings* of the Second Institute for the Clergy on Problems in Pastoral Psychology, June 24–28, 1957, pp. 201 and 204.
22. St. Thomas Aquinas, *Summa Theologica,* I, IIae, qu. 10, a. 3.
23. See Harvey, *op. cit.,* p. 87.
24. Hayden, *op. cit.,* p. 153.
25. In the opinion of Father Woroniecki, "Human liberty is the *dominion* of the will over its own act" in regard to every imperfect good ("Pour une bonne definition de la liberte humaine"), *Angelicum,* Vol. XIV (1937), p. 151.
26. Cardinal Mercier, *Manual of Scholastic Philosophy* (London: K. Paul Trench, Trubner and Co. Ltd., 1916), Vol. I, p. 275.
27. See Buckley, *op. cit.,* and *The Wolfenden Report,* Authorized American Edition (New York: Stein and Day, 1963).
28. Harvey, *loc. cit.,* p. 494.
29. Hayden, *op. cit.,* p. 154.
30. There are some cases on record of male homosexuals who had overt contacts with hundreds of partners (R. v. Krafft-Ebing, *Psychopathia Sexualis* . . . Rebman, New York, 1906). This promiscuity and the insatiable need to seek repeated orgiastic experiences bring to mind Freud's (. . . [1917], *Introductory Lectures on Psycho-Analysis,* Allen, London, 1922) compassionate statement when speaking of the difficult life of the pervert: "In reality, perverts are more likely to be poor devils who have to pay most bitterly for the satisfaction they manage to procure with such difficulty" (see Paul Friedman, "Sexual Deviations," Chapter 29 in the *American Handbook of Psychiatry,* Silvano Arieti (ed.) [New York: Basic Books, Inc., 1959], p. 596).
31. Hagmaier and Gleason, *op. cit.,* p. 229.
32. Duhamel, *op. cit.,* p. 137.
33. Buckley, *op. cit.,* pp. 159–160. See also *The Wolfenden Report, loc. cit.*
34. Duhamel, *op. cit.,* p. 145.
35. Rev. Charles Larere, "Passage of the Angel Through Sodom," in *New Problems in Medical Ethics* (Westminster, Md.: Newman Press, 1955), p. 120.

Pastoral Counseling of Inverts

Although some knowledge of the general principles of counseling are presumed in the reader, it might be well to summarize some general considerations. It is first important to make a distinction between types of counseling.[1]

Pastoral counseling is a comparatively new term. In its technic it partakes of some of the elements of all forms of counseling. It is essentially eclectic in its methods and its practitioner is not bound to any one school. It is pragmatic and expedient in its approach, elastic and adaptable in its method. It would be called "guidance" by some, but depending on circumstances it may at times use a counseling approach. It differs from other methods of counseling in that instead of the counselor-counselee approach of the directive-nondirective counselor, it specifically includes God in the counseling relationship. It is clear that the counselor-God-counselee relationship would differ in many respects from the one-to-one "secular" counseling relationship. The term *secular counselor* is used to distinguish the counselor with specialized training, whether he be clerical or lay, from the pastor without such specialized training. The pastor, although he may not aim at being a specialist in counseling, does need knowledge and insight beyond his theological training before he can consider himself more than an amateur in the field.

Pastoral counseling differs from "secular" counseling in its aims, in its methods, and in its technics. It is a three-way relationship of which God is the third member. "Consequently," according to Father Curran, "pastoral counseling, as I conceive it, is a unique kind of relationship between the person and the counselor, a relationship which implies and introduces God as a third party."[2] As stated above, pastoral counseling is essentially eclectic. It accepts the best from all other methods. It may at times be directive, authoritarian, and nonpermissive, although at others it may be permissive, nondirective, and accepting. It must always have in mind the pastor's primary religious goal.

It is clear that the pastor's primary function is the salvation of souls and that his primary duties are of a religious nature. His counseling activities, therefore, will be secondary to these purposes and will be aimed primarily at making his parishioners more accessible to his pastoral ministrations. There will therefore be, for the pastor, two aspects of counseling:

a) Primary — that directly aimed at the accomplishment of his pastoral function.

b) Secondary — that which indirectly aids his parishioner and thus makes him more accepting of the pastor's primary ministrations.

Father Bier says that pastoral counseling must be related to the pastor's overall aims if it is to be distinct from secular counseling.[3]

THE PASTOR AS COUNSELOR

The pastor, as counselor, must be prepared to listen with all available patience, he must direct with all available wisdom, he must correct and admonish with kindness, he must delve into a difficulty with diligence and prudence. The pastoral counselor must extend his field beyond the confessional to the rectory parlor and office whenever it becomes necessary. When the pastor extends his interests from the purely religious field into the area of general living, he enters the counseling field, if, in doing so, he refrains from offering solutions to the problems brought to him; in renouncing "the imparting of advice in favor of an attempt to get people to understand themselves, he begins to adopt what is essentially a counseling approach."[4]

From this brief description we can deduce that very frequently, in contrast to the "secular" counselor, the pastor offers guidance or direction rather than counseling. The pastor, as pastor, frequently cannot be nondirective, completely permissive, or indiscriminately accepting. The relationship between the pastor and the parishioner frequently cannot be client-centered or counselor-centered, but must be theocentric. Only by stepping out of his priestly role can the pastor practice secular counseling. *He may wear two hats; he may be a professional (secular) counselor, and he may be a pastor. He cannot be both simultaneously.*

Ordination by the grace of office does not make the pastor a counselor. His purpose as a pastor is to shepherd the souls entrusted to his care. He uses the customary pastoral means to achieve this end, e.g., teaching revealed doctrine and doctrines connected with revelation, offering the sacrifice of the Mass, and administering the Sacraments. His main duty is not helping people in emotional or mental trouble, but rather the salvation of souls. The pastor may use specific technics which he has acquired from the mental health field, but he does so only in order to reach an individual and help him through pastoral means. Though the pastor can, and should frequently, be permissive — he may, for example, urge his client to discuss any matter whatsoever, in whatever way he wishes to do so — he must also at times, however, have an attitude of authority in pointing out the Church's laws and teachings as applied to the client's problem. The pastor must bear in mind that he is primarily a clergyman, and, though some knowledge of mental illness and its treatment will be helpful to him, this is not his primary concern. His conviction must be that he counsels, not primarily mentally disturbed persons who happen to be members of his congregation, but members of his congregation who happen to be emotionally or mentally disturbed.

With these general principles clear, I shall now discuss the specific aspects of counseling the invert.

COUNSELING THE INVERT

Because of the numerous demands for counseling the homosexual, the pastor must learn early that only those inverts who are genuinely concerned over their condition *per se* are likely to benefit from his services. The homosexual who seeks advice because he has gotten into the hands of the police is seldom looking for more than a temporary refuge. This is also true of the homosexual who, although he seeks help, persistently continues to maintain his homosexual friendships and to perform sex acts. The best candidate for counseling and/or psychotherapy is the individual who is in conflict with his inversion and who has developed enough anxiety as a result of the conflict that he is likely to persist in his therapeutic efforts (see p. 269).

> Provided he accepts his position philosophically and mixes with others of like mind, the homosexual can leave behind the emotional turmoil

that originally drove him away from women. Neurotic conflict only
remains evident in those who do not fully accept either homosexual
or heterosexual adjustment.[5]

The best test of sincerity is the willingness to forego sexual activity.
It is possible, even in some cases in which the individual was poorly
motivated in the beginning, to awaken a desire for a change. In
most such cases it is necessary to combat a fatalistic attitude on the
part of the invert which produces a feeling that nothing can be done
to change the direction of his sex drive and that because of this he
is justified in persisting in his sexual activities.

The fact that all homosexuals have a feeling of isolation from
their fellows, which produces a feeling of loneliness, brings about
the need for a confidant. Since, by the very fact of his office, the
clergyman is more inclined to view the moral rather than the
psychological aspects of the case, he must be careful, as a rule, not
to actively condemn the individual's activity before good rapport
is established.

THE PASTOR IS THE FIRST CONTACT

The pastor today, as always, is looked upon by many of his
parishioners as having a ready solution for almost any problem.
To most people the pastor is the one most available for a discussion
of the problems which they hesitate to take to others because of their
personal nature. The pastor is frequently, therefore, the first to come
in contact with these troubled individuals. Dr. Robert Felix, director
of the National Institute of Health in the United States Public
Health Service, estimates that perhaps 40 percent of people take
their personal problems first to a clergyman.[6]

An effective spiritual rapprochement often rests in the initial
greeting. It is a very difficult moment for the invert when he faces
up to admitting his perversion, especially if it is for the first time.
The counselor must, therefore, be understanding, but discreet and
considerate, in his first questions. He must awaken confidence before
going on to speak of spiritual remedies. "With many homosexuals,
the fact of being able to speak of it openly for the first time without
seeing a pharisaic look or the look of naïve astonishment on the face
of his listener, is the beginning of rapport. The clergyman should
aim, therefore, at creating to the fullest possible extent an atmosphere
of confidence."[7]

There is, perhaps, no other admission so painful to make as that of being homosexual; to admit that one is hyper-erotic is at least to state *ipso facto* and sometimes even with a touch of satisfaction, that one's instinct is normally orientated.[8]

HOMOSEXUAL ACTS ARE OBJECTIVELY IMMORAL

It has been established that homosexuality is objectively immoral; it is directly opposed not only to the divine positive law, but also to the natural law. Granted this fact, there is still the need for pastoral counseling. Before any further discussion is ventured on the point of counseling, a correction of the following statement should be made:

It requires a voluntary act on the part of the homosexual to perform a homosexual act. The homosexual has the same ability, and should be expected to abstain from sexual activity outside of marriage in the same manner that the heterosexual person is expected to abstain from sexual activity outside of marriage.[9]

I said this in *Fundamental Marriage Counseling* in 1963. Since then I have changed my mind slightly. It is still true that it takes a voluntary, conscious, and deliberate action to perform a homosexual act. It is still true that the invert should be expected to abstain from homosexual acts. The statement should be altered only to the extent that *all* homosexuals do not have the same ability as *all* heterosexuals to abstain from the sex act outside of marriage. On reflection and additional experience, I am now convinced that *some* homosexuals have *some degree* of decreased responsibility for *some* of their acts. This matter is discussed fully in Clinic 15.

The counselor may find that the homosexual client believes he has no control over his desires, that he must take pleasure in them, and that they necessarily lead him, willy-nilly, to commit overt homosexual acts. In such a situation it should be explained to him that merely because he is a homosexual his sex drive is not necessarily stronger than that of any "average" heterosexual his own age. Rather, just as chastity is morally and practically possible for a heterosexual, so with divine help it is possible and absolutely necessary for the invert. If the homosexual client has goodwill, is otherwise mentally well balanced, and really wants to obey the law of God, then the counselor has real ground for confidence that, if his client keeps away from the people with whom he has committed acts, before long he will be living a chaste life. The counselor should not hesitate to communicate this confidence which, given the above qualification, is not merely a pietistic optimism, to his invert client. Whatever habits of solitary acts and acts with others the client may have contracted, if he has goodwill, honesty, and love of God he can, in most instances, overcome them and lead a celibate life. When the client is otherwise seriously neurotic the counselor will have less hope for his client's spiritual care, but he may have the opportunity to suggest that, along with his own work, the invert consult a psychiatrist. When the client is not firmly persuaded of the undesirability of overt homosexuality, the counselor should warn him that, though he is not responsible for being a homosexual — for his abnormal sex drive, he is responsible for what he allows himself to do with it. In a word, the counselor should so talk to him that he will reach a determination to give up homosexual acts and any inner complacency he might have had about homosexual desires.

PSYCHIATRIC CARE SHOULD BE ADVISED

Because of the emotional pressures that often accompany homosexuality there is undoubtedly a high incidence of deep psychological disorders among inverts. In such cases a pastor would best fulfill his role by recognizing such disorders and encouraging the client to seek psychiatric treatment. He should not, however, discontinue his own help of a spiritual nature to aid the invert in controlling his tendencies.

Certainly it is not the job of the pastoral counselor to attempt a thorough probing of the homosexual's problems. Since he is not trained for "depth psychology" there is a real danger that he may do more harm than good. Writers on the clergyman's guidance of homosexuals agree that the counseling situation should be a supportive one. The understanding attitude of the clergyman will go a long way in helping the homosexual overcome the feeling that his anomaly has made him a social outcast and in establishing some hope where previously there may have been only despair.

Often, however, psychiatrists are met who distrust this collaboration. To understand their reserve, you must first of all appreciate the instability of the first therapeutic results and the obligation of keeping the full confidence of the subject. But the distrust of the physician may arise also from unfortunate experiences in which the pastoral counselor, ignorant of psychic and especially of psychoanalytical therapeutic technics, has thwarted, sometimes unconsciously, the therapeutic plan. Mutual collaboration has become easier as knowledge of depth psychology and the problems of the human mind have become more current among the clergy.

In this regard Father Tobin commented:

> The priest or spiritual counselor often will play an ancillary, auxiliary role in the therapy of homosexual individuals. Spiritual values may help to develop and sustain the proper motivation for treatment.[10]

Westwood, however, was not too sure about the favorable effect of religion. He noted that 61 percent of his contacts had turned at one time to their church for help.[11] Yet, only 6 percent reported that they had obtained help with their homosexual problem from their religion, while 5 percent more stated that their religious beliefs had afforded them some comfort. Unfortunately, 87 percent reported no help or comfort from religion[12] and, furthermore, 88 percent had adjusted to their condition.[13]

THE AIM OF PASTORAL COUNSELING

What should a priest hope to accomplish in his guidance of the homosexual? Father Buckley puts it this way:

> The aim of all pastoral care of the homosexual should be ultimately his re-orientation to heterosexuality and where this is impossible an adjustment to his condition in the only way acceptable to Catholic moral theology — a life of chastity.[14]

It is generally agreed that there is little hope of sexual reorientation for a true invert through pastoral counseling. A clergyman should be content to set as his ultimate aim the adjustment of the homosexual to a life of chastity. A more immediate aim and one which is a means to this adjustment should be to help the client understand his own conflicts. A lack of this self-knowledge, an inability to see outside of his narrowed emotions, is the cause of a great many difficulties involved in homosexuality. Regarding this more immediate aim, Father William C. Bier, S.J., says, "The generic aim of counseling of whatever kind is to help people to help themselves by gaining understanding of their inner conflicts."[15]

Lest any clergyman become discouraged with recidivism while counseling the homosexual, let him keep in mind these words of Father Leo Trese:

Indeed it is quite conceivable that one might be a homosexual and become a saint, since it is by the conquest of temptation that sanctity is developed, under God's grace. Since "the greater the temptation the greater the merit," the homosexual who achieves self-discipline is doubly admirable, since he must do so despite the lack of safeguards which shelter the person of normal impulses.[16]

THE QUALITIES OF THE COUNSELOR

Not everyone is equipped to counsel. Since, however, the pastor by his office is forced into counseling situations, there are certain qualities which he must seek to develop. Among these would be the ability to accept individuals professionally, regardless of their personalities, with patience and self-confidence. He must be accepting without condemning or condoning. He must be prepared to be empathic and not sympathetic. He must be prepared to distinguish between the invert who wishes to use the clergyman for his own purposes and the one who is genuinely seeking help. He must be prepared to make a differential diagnosis between true homosexuality, the obsession of being a homosexual, and the homosexual delusions of the schizophrenic (see p. 100). He must be able to reassure the normally sexed girl who fears that because she dated a male homosexual this proves she is also a homosexual. He must be prepared to accept the fact that many homosexuals have no desire to be cured and that, even in those who do, there is a marked tendency to recidivism. He must be prepared to recognize his own professional deficiencies and to make prompt referrals to others more qualified than himself if he gets beyond his depth.

Homosexuals who turn to a pastor should be able to expect at least to be heard and treated in a spirit of Christian charity. There is no justification for regarding them as a class to be abhorred, as depraved and degenerate.[17] They, like all sick people, deserve to be understood and to be given the same sympathetic assistance that is willingly given to other types of people. Scorn, contempt, and undue severity will only increase the feeling of inferiority that predominates in many homosexuals despite an outward appearance of self-satisfaction or defiance. Kindness does not mean weakness on the part of the pastor, who should insist on the giving up of all homosexual practices and relations. Unless the client shows definite signs of his intention to do so, the case is well-nigh hopeless; but even then the counselor should try to form in the client the right intention, particularly by educating him to the use of supernatural means. When natural means fail, divine grace may still prevail.

The clergyman is in a position to help remove the undue fear and guilt which are often an integral part of the homosexual's mental outlook. Especially consoling would be the assurance that the client need feel no guilt because of his homosexual inclinations since they are ordinarily beyond the scope of responsibility. A clergyman can help the invert regain a sense of his own individual worth which may have been lost over the years.

BASIC TENETS OF COUNSELING

For the professional counselor no hints on how to conduct his interview are necessary. Because, however, many clergymen are forced into counseling situations without previous training, I would like to set up some basic ground rules for the untrained counselor. This is not intended as a shortcut to the achievement of counseling skill. It is merely an attempt at "self-help" for those who must counsel because of the office they hold, even though they have had no training.

1. Treat the client as a person with dignity.
2. Bear in mind that many inverts do not want to be cured.
3. Do not raise false hopes as to the value of treatment.
4. Accept the client as he is.
5. Do not be surprised if the client seeks to avoid discussing the real problem.
6. Do not interrupt the efforts of the client to tell his story.
7. Ask questions only if necessary.
8. Be flexible in your approach.
9. Encourage the client to discuss himself rather than his symptoms.
10. Encourage the client to discuss his feelings.
11. Do not moralize, criticize, or blame until you have heard the whole story.
12. Be slow in offering advice.
13. Make no promises.
14. The untrained counselor should avoid long and frequent personal interviews with a true invert.

SPECIFIC COUNSELING OF THE INVERT

There are some specific points about counseling the homosexual which should serve as guidelines for the pastoral counselor. It is important to bear in mind the distinction between counseling and therapy:

> Counseling is a definite dynamic interpersonal relationship in which the counselor, who should be more mature, more educated, and more experienced, applies common sense in assisting another individual who is troubled to reach a beneficial self-solution of a mutually defined problem which is within the "normal" range of behavior, thinking, or feeling.[18]

Therapy is defined in Webster's *New International Dictionary* as: "Treatment of disease; therapeutics; now used chiefly in compounds (compound words)." Psychotherapy is the application of a remedy for emotional or mental illness. Crotty makes this distinction between psychotherapy and counseling:

> Counseling should be distinguished from psychotherapy; the latter being a term referring to techniques employed by persons working with the mentally ill, those persons with deep, difficult to uncover, emotionally laden psychological problems; the former concerned with procedures employed with relatively normal people who have personal problems which they feel are beyond self-solution.[19]

No clergyman, unless he has adequate training, should attempt therapy. This is beyond his capability. In making referrals of cases in which he feels such treatment is necessary or desirable, he must be careful to recommend a psychiatrist of whom he has assurance that his principles and practice do not offend against morality. Above all, it would be inadvisable for any clergyman who may have either latent or overt homosexual tendencies of his own to counsel the invert.

The good judgment of the counselor must be the guide to procedure as the situation unfolds. There are certain recommendations, however, which will serve to guide his counsel.

1. The first step is that *the individual must be urged to admit to himself that he is a true homosexual.* This step must never be omitted because without such a frank admission further steps in treatment are quite likely doomed to failure. This also gives the counselor an opportunity to make his own prognosis which will include an estimate of the individual's sincerity.

As a rule there is little doubt in the mind of either the counselor or the client that homosexuality exists in the subject. The invert merely does not like to express it in words. As in Alcoholics Anonymous where the first step consists in the admission by the individual that he is powerless in the face of his adversary, so too in homosexuality the individual must admit that "I am a homosexual and I find myself in need of help in the face of my perverse sex drive." The counselor should dwell on this point — "Are you a homosexual?" — until the client has decided that he is or is not. If the subject refuses to come to a conclusion about his condition, there is nothing to treat.

> This is a *sine qua non* to successful or even relatively profitable treatment. Most homosexuals do not want to recover. Many of them are only looking for a chance to prove their inability to behave otherwise and so to be accepted as they are. . . . The patient must become convinced that his fault is not determined by an hereditary constitution and that he can get well. Furthermore, one must show him moral, social, and psychological reasons *why* he should get well.[20]

2. An early concern of the counselor will be to *break down gradually in the client the idea of the deterministic nature of his condition,* an idea with which he is often obsessed. "It is stronger than I am; I can do nothing against it." The pastor must exercise patience, as was said before (but cannot be said enough), for he is faced with a will that cannot yet exercise itself until the counseling process shall have given back to the subject a little of his autonomy. However, some instruction of the invert on the supernatural action of grace may be of help to him. The pastor may, then, systematically remove from him all false, childish conceptions of the "magic power" of grace; if not, the faults which still continue for a time to burden his life will occasion doubts of the efficacy of spiritual aid, such aid being thought of too frequently as a "psychological remedy."

While the counselor is concentrating on relieving the fatalistic attitude, he must at the same time avoid overoptimism. If, for example, assurance of the nonfatalistic nature of homosexuality is followed by informing the invert that his sexual deviation is not so difficult to control, there is danger that he will lose confidence at the first lapse. Rather, he must be told that cure is not instantaneous and that a fall does not mean abandonment by God or impossibility of change. He must be assured that with God's grace not only a cure

but even sanctity can be attained, since it is by conquest of temptation that sanctity is developed under God's grace.

When the invert makes the objection that his is an abnormal
drive, Dr. Odenwald may be quoted as saying, "his abnormal drive
is probably no stronger than an exaggerated heterosexual drive."[21]
Furthermore, we know as a matter of fact that the alcoholic and
other addicts have proved that abnormal urges can be controlled.
The counselor must be careful in discussing the defenses of the
invert patient never to permit his own attitude to suggest that the
homosexual cannot help himself nor control himself. Such an attitude, however slight or unwitting, would give the homosexual
sufficient excuse for considering himself incurable and thus not
responsible.

3. *All homosexual activity must stop.* Falls from grace will occur
in many cases, but not in all. The homosexual must be persuaded
that he has the ability to remain continent. He will frequently argue
that, since he is a homosexual through no choice of his own and
since he can never in the nature of things have a normal sexual
outlet, therefore he is different and homosexual activity is permitted him. The answer to this is obvious. The homosexual, just as
the heterosexual, is not permitted sexual activity outside of marriage.
Just as we expect the heterosexual person to be continent outside
of marriage, so, too, the homosexual.

4. *All of his previous homosexual companions must be avoided.*
This is of the utmost importance because these individuals are a real
source of temptation. In forming new friendships, individuals who
are sexually attractive should be avoided. The invert should live
alone. He should not work with boys and, if possible, should avoid
entry into the military service. The question of entry into the religious
life has been discussed in Clinic 11.

One of the principles of conduct that an invert should formulate
is that, because of his special condition, there is no value in allowing himself to form or to continue romantic friendships (i.e., those
in which sexual attraction is a determining element) with people
of his own sex, no matter how chaste the relationship may be. Even
if the invert is continent in these friendships, it is, nevertheless, a
human love which can never be fully realized or satisfied licitly.
It will, therefore, inevitably lead to anxiety and repression. Mean-
while, he dissipates energy on frustrated emotion which he could

fruitfully apply to some other area of his daily life. Even if the invert's romantic friendships do not lead him into sin, they are still imprudent in that they orient him to unachievable goals. He should, therefore, give them up, as depressing as this may be. The counselor should explain to his invert client the virtue of perfect Christian chastity, "that is, for love of God to abstain for the rest of one's life from sexual pleasure,"[22] and that even though he is himself incapable of marriage, his wholehearted obedience to the commandment of chastity (according to one's state in life) will be meritorious.

This is the theory, but what may be done from the practical point of view? The unity of willpower and determination to give up the practice should urge him to give up the persons, places, and things which for him are occasions of sin. He must refuse any contact at all with his former associates. If this cannot be done for some grave reason, then the invert must take every means available to render that occasion of sin as remote as possible. The void that results from such a severance should be filled with new interests, new work, new hobbies, works of charity for others. He should be advised to make new friends of those who view life healthily, to get into fields that will allow a release for his energies in a healthy manner. He should live and work with others who will help him to get over his feelings of inferiority. Such help will increase his courage and confidence when he sees an improved ability to accomplish.

Complete withdrawal from accepted social circles may, on the other hand, also be damaging for the homosexual. Thus:

> The uninformed confessor has a tendency to demand that the invert avoid every contact which might possibly be a source of stimulation for him, e.g., swimming, sports, stag society, artistic circles, male friendships. In many cases such involvements help to drain off a more basic urge for physical contact. To stifle these outlets could very well precipitate the penitent into more frequent and more overt homosexual activity.[23]

The client, then, should not be discouraged from his social activities but avoid only those persons or places which are for him a proximate occasion of sin.

The counselor must remember in his efforts to seek safe, social activity for his client that female company should be suggested cautiously because it may increase anxiety, tension, and frustration. Professor Jean Lhermitte has said:

> Is it possible, however, to attempt the cure of this tendency by the
> cultivation of female company without going, be it clearly understood,
> to the extent of having sexual relations? Certainly, because the experi-
> ence carries no risks; but in spite of his efforts, the real homosexual
> experiences only disgust for and aversion to women.

The professor is of the opinion that the prohibition need be less
strict for the woman homosexual. Not because he thinks the woman
will change, but

> it is legitimate to think that maternity will develop her sentiments of
> attachment to home, and thus effect a union which the abnormal man
> is certainly incapable of realizing.[24]

5. *The invert should be urged to keep silent about his condition.*
The counselor should urge the invert to keep his handicap to himself, and never let himself be tempted to talk about it to anyone,
even to his closest friends or to members of his family. It should
be discussed only with professionals who have a need to know. On
this point Anomaly is firm.[25]

Other rules for keeping the condition from coming to the notice
of others as written by Anomaly are:

Don't

1. write admissions to inclinations.
2. masquerade in women's clothes.
3. be too meticulous in clothing, wear jewelry, etc.
4. allow voice or intonation to be feminine.
5. stand with hand on hip or walk mincingly.
6. be identified with groups.
7. believe love is the same as friendship.
8. become involved in marked intimacies with men.
9. let enthusiasm for certain males become noticeable.
10. occupy self with pastimes that are feminine.

Do

1. hold frank conversations with suitable persons, avoiding mental repression.
2. encourage every symptom of sexual normalization.
3. cultivate self-esteem.
4. become deeply engrossed in a congenial occupation or hobby.
5. observe discretion and practice self-restraint.

The invert can never be sure that if he and his confidant have
an argument in the future the information he once imparted will

not be held over his head or thrown back at him as a taunt, or that, even if no such rift occurs, the confidant will not let it slip out to a third person. There is no need for the invert's telling even a priest, unless he should have to confess a homosexual sin with another person. Even if he deliberately indulges in impure thoughts that have as an object a person of his own sex, he need not say more in confession (unless he is asked) than that he had impure thoughts, without describing their precise species; in a word, for his own good he should keep the fact of his sexual misdirection to himself, except when he needs to tell a counselor or a psychiatrist.

6. *A search must be made for psychological factors and an effort made to develop insight into them.* Even if the counselor succeeds in giving the patient an insight into the acquired nature of his condition and into his own potentialities, there is still a long road for him to travel because insight alone will not be enough to make him discontinue his homosexual tendencies, which may be deeply ingrained through many years of habit formation.

One of the reasons for tracing the psychological development of the disorder is to establish insight into the acquired nature of the illness and into the client's own capabilities of self-control. The client should be shown the relationship of his psychic tendencies toward members of his own sex, once it is discovered after a discussion of his development. Once the client begins to become more and more convinced of the accidental rather than essential nature of his illness through this development of insight, he is ready for further insight.

> The patient may well be convinced of the acquired nature of his illness, of the possibility of a cure, and of the desirability of a cure . . . but he is still faced with the problem of breaking this long-existing habit of homosexual practices.[26]

7. *The part the will plays must be stressed continually.* Only the homosexual who sincerely desires to be cured is likely to persist in the counseling. It should be made clear that while he may not be able to control his indeliberate desires, he can control his actions and deliberate desires by an act of the will. Further, the counselor must make an effort to arouse in the invert a desire for normality. He must be persuaded that with effort he can change his sexual orientation which is psychogenic and not the result of heredity or other physical causes.

After pointing out the part of the will, the counselor must inspire in his client supernatural motivation. He must be urged to adopt a new attitude (provided he does not already have it) which includes a love of God and a dedication to His service. In this way he may find a new incentive, a new inner peace, and a stronger desire for normality. Inverts who have this attitude may not find their way to counselors.

8. The invert should *avoid alcohol* which tends to limit his control and may lead to relapses.

9. The counselor must help to *supply a socially and morally acceptable sublimation.* Since the only course open to the homosexual until he develops a heterosexual orientation is that of celibacy, St. Augustine's ideas on this reorientation may be useful to him. These may be summed up briefly as follows:

> 1) the realization that chastity is a supernatural gift, 2) the achievement of unity of purpose in his own will, 3) the decision to devote his life to an ascetical ideal, 4) constant prayer for healing grace.[27]

The client must be convinced of God's love for him and persuaded that he can live with his inclination in a life of peaceful self-control and sublimation. The priest should encourage sublimation by providing opportunities for works of charity and personal sacrifice.

> The priest can help his penitent focus his perspective so that his whole life is not clouded and colored by the one problem. The invert can be helped to develop the many positive talents he is sure to have, and be proud of them. In doing so he can actually minimize the obsession with sexuality which can so poison the mind with guilt, fear and helplessness that all other creative and compensating activities become stifled or sterile.[28]

COMMENT

The pastoral counselor has an important role to play in helping the distressed invert. He is literally on the front line and should, therefore, be well informed on "spiritual first aid." A good basic knowledge of the natural history of the homosexual is an important part of such training. Actual therapy should be left to the professional counselor.

CLINIC 17 — NOTES

1. Some parts of the next few pages are paraphrased from *Fundamental Pastoral Counseling*, John R. Cavanagh, M.D. (Milwaukee: The Bruce Publishing Company, 1962), pp. 8–22.

2. Rev. Charles A. Curran, "A Catholic Psychologist Looks at Pastoral Counseling," *Pastoral Psychology*, February, 1959, p. 13.
3. William C. Bier, S.J., "Goals in Pastoral Counseling," *Pastoral Psychology*, February, 1959, pp. 10–11.
4. *Ibid.*, p. 9.
5. Donald J. West, *The Other Man* (New York: Whiteside, Inc., and William Morrow and Company, 1955), p. 154.
6. Quoted by William C. Bier, S.J., *op. cit.*, p. 9.
7. Rev. Charles Larere, "Passage of the Angel Through Sodom," article in *New Problems in Medical Ethics*, Dom Peter Flood, O.S.B. (ed.) (Westminister, Md.: The Newman Press, 1953), p. 116 (Vol. I).
8. Paul Le Moal, M.D., "The Psychiatrist and the Homosexual," article in *New Problems in Medical Ethics*, Vol. I, p. 70.
9. John R. Cavanagh, M.D., *Fundamental Marriage Counseling* (Milwaukee: The Bruce Publishing Company, 1963), p. 196.
10. Rev. William J. Tobin, *Homosexuality and Marriage* (Rome: Catholic Book Agency, 1964), p. 73.
11. Gordon Westwood, *A Minority: A Report on the Life of the Male Homosexual in Great Britain* (London: Longmans, Green and Co. Ltd., 1960), p. 51.
12. *Ibid.*, p. 52.
13. *Ibid.*, p. 61.
14. Rev. Michael J. Buckley, *Morality and the Homosexual* (Westminster, Md.: The Newman Press, 1960), p. 184.
15. William C. Bier, S.J., *op. cit.*, p. 10.
16. Leo Trese, "Muted Tragedy," *The Commonweal*, 51 (February 17, 1950), p. 512.
17. John F. Harvey, O.S.F.S., in *Theological Studies*, Vol. XVI, No. 1 (March, 1955), p. 86.
18. John R. Cavanagh, M.D., *op. cit.*, p. 17.
19. Charles Crotty, "Marriage Counseling and Psychology," *Bulletin of the Guild of Catholic Psychiatrists*, Vol. VI, No. 4 (October, 1959), p. 12.
20. Robert Odenwald, M.D., "Counseling the Homosexual," *Priest*, Vol. IX (December, 1953), p. 941.
21. *Ibid.*, p. 944.
22. Pope Pius XII, *On Holy Virginity*, an encyclical, Rome, March 25, 1954.
23. George Hagmaier, C.S.P., and Robert Gleason, S.J., *Counselling the Catholic* (New York: Sheed & Ward, 1959), p. 102.
24. Jean Lhermitte, "Problems of Sexual Morality," *New Problems in Medical Ethics*, Vol. I, p. 67.
25. Anomaly, *The Invert* (Baltimore: The Williams and Wilkins Co., 1948), p. 133.
26. Odenwald, *op. cit.*, p. 942.
27. Harvey, *op. cit.*, p. 99.
28. Hagmaier and Gleason, *op. cit.*, p. 110.

Treatment

The treatment of homosexuality has been regarded with pessimism in the past. This difficulty arose partly from a failure of the therapist to define his objectives and partly from an inadequate concept of the proper therapy for the condition. A rational therapy for inversion requires a solid etiological foundation. Until recently even a rational hypothesis has been lacking. Even today, although the psychic origin of the disorder is generally recognized, it is most likely that the causative factors which lead to the various forms of homosexual adaptation are not all the same. The treatment, therefore, must be flexible and the therapist must be willing to alter his method to suit the case. For each case, after a preliminary diagnostic survey (see p. 89), the therapist should discuss with the patient what he hopes to accomplish. This is necessary because the direction of the therapy is related to the aim which is sought.

THE AIM OF THERAPY

Confusion concerning the results of the treatment of inverts has frequently followed from a failure on the part of the therapist to state what he hoped to achieve by his therapy. The professional counselor or psychiatrist should aim at "cure," not merely "acceptance." The ends of therapy should be:

1. A new orientation on the part of the invert so that he adopts a completely heterosexual attitude;

2. A new orientation which would include an acceptance of heterosexuality but with no basic change in his homosexuality;

3. An acceptance of his condition with the decision to remain abstinent.

Cory, with other therapists, has adopted complete change of orientation as the ideal:

The present writer, following Freud and being under certain misapprehensions, misunderstandings, and limited experience, formerly
urged but no longer espouses an orientation toward adjustment within
the framework of homosexuality, rather than an expenditure of energy
in the effort to effectuate a change. This preference for adjustment
seems to have been mistakenly chosen by many modern therapists
(particularly Freudians, such as Dollard), and is also espoused, for
entirely different reasons, by most homosexuals.[1]

In defining his goals the therapist must also determine his prognosis of two factors: (1) Will the patient persist in his treatment?
(2) Is he likely to achieve the goal decided upon?

In regard to his persistence in the treatment, the following factors are important:

1. *Not likely to persist*
   a) No concern over problem
   b) Threat of punitive measures is present
   c) Lack of strong personal motivation
   d) Pressured by relatives to seek help
   e) Less than high school education
   f) No previous heterosexual acts (Bieber)
   g) Chronically established pattern
   h) Men less likely to persist than women
2. *More likely to persist*
   a) Anxious, fearful, or ashamed over his condition
   b) Strongly motivated with a sincere desire to change
   c) No firmly established pattern
   d) Previous heterosexual acts
   e) Better than high school education
   f) Women more likely to persist
   g) Loneliness
   h) Desire for normal marriage and children

The financial factor must always be borne in mind. The treatment is expensive because of its duration. Age must also be considered — the younger the individual at the time he seeks treatment, the better the prognosis. Two factors play a part here: the
shorter duration of the pattern and the greater adaptability of youth.

In planning treatment the therapist cannot hope for success of his
therapy if it includes technics which are morally unacceptable to
the patient. One should not, for example, suggest heterosexual intercourse to the unmarried patient. Heterosexual petting attempts cer-

tainly cannot be recommended to the priest-homosexual. Moll, for example, suggested a form of treatment which he called "association therapy." His aim was to shift the sexual attention from boys to boyish-looking girls.[2] This has rather clear-cut moral drawbacks.

Treatment may be divided into two types:
1. That involving some physical method;
2. That in which the method is purely psychological.

PHYSICAL METHODS

1. *Imprisonment*

Imprisonment as a method of treatment of homosexuality has failed over the years because the homosexual was sent to prison more often for punishment than for treatment. In many instances, at least until very recent years, no treatment was given in the prison setting. No means were provided for rehabilitation.

Homosexuality in prisons. There have been many misconceptions concerning homosexuality in prisons. Next to the belief that all homosexuals are effeminate, the most common misconception about inversion is that homosexuality is rampant in prisons. There is a reason for this misconception. It is the confusion of homosexuality with criminality. Since acts committed by the overt homosexual are subject to criminal prosecution, the argument runs: If homosexuals are criminals, then criminals are homosexuals — at least they are homosexual by the time they come out of prison because they have been too long removed from the company of women, and they must have had their sex some way.

Facts refute these erroneous concepts. Suppose we look at the reports of two men who have been intimately associated with psychiatric work in prisons.

Robert Lindner, Ph.D., states that no criminal, homosexual, sexual psychopath, or sexual pervert of any kind ever becomes one as a result of his prison confinement. What actually happens is that these repressed tendencies come to light during confinement because of the very nature of prison life. In Lindner's own words, there is "an unmasking rather than a fashioning."[3] By this Lindner means that prisoners have their lives regulated so completely that they lose any characteristics of adult maturity they might have had, and they regress to more infantile stages. That is why, he adds, it is a "kind of lunacy" for the general public or prison officials to be surprised when prisoners begin adopting infantilistic modes of adjustment in all fields, including sex.

To confuse the homosexual with the criminal and to confuse the criminal with the homosexual is to display a lack of understanding about homosexuality and a naïve grasp of the nature of sex.

There is perhaps a lower percentage of criminals among homosexuals than in any other group of human beings. In any particular prison the number of true homosexuals is approximately the same as for the general population.

Perhaps another reason why prisons are thought to be crowded with homosexuals is because homosexuals, when they are present in the prison population, stand out so prominently that their presence cannot be overlooked. Prisons are close quarters, and life in a prison is like life in a goldfish bowl. Almost anything that happens is noticed. It is practically impossible for two prisoners to engage in any kind of relationship without being observed by either prison officials or fellow prisoners.

When Kinsey reports that 30 to 85 percent of prisoners perform some kind of homosexual acts he fails to distinguish between homosexual acts and the acts of a homosexual. For example, Kinsey fails to make this distinction in this statement:

> The judge should bear in mind that the penal or mental institution to which he may send the male has something between 30% and 85% of its inmates engaging in the sort of homosexual activity which may be involved in the individual case before him.[4]

For this reason, as I have indicated before, Kinsey's figures cannot be accepted without great reservations.

Lindner remarks that the real trouble-maker in a prison is not the homosexual but the sexual psychopath.

Charles E. Smith, M.D., studied one hundred homosexual prisoners in the Federal Penitentiary at Springfield, Missouri.[5] Only fifteen out of the hundred were sentenced for offenses directly connected with their homosexuality. Nine were cases of sodomy. The other six were sentenced for misuse of the United States mails for solicitation. The specific violation was that the letters were obscene. Among the remaining eighty-five one was a "pimp" and another was a middle-aged man who had raped a thirteen-year-old girl. Most of these homosexuals were sentenced for crimes that are frequently committed on impulse.

Only six of the hundred prisoners were free of any mental deviation other than homosexuality. Forty-two were diagnosed as psychopathic personalities (sociopathic personality disorder, see p. 33). Twenty-one were diagnosed as schizoid personalities. Seventeen had some form of neurosis. Seven suffered from a schizophrenic psychosis. One suffered from an involutional psychosis. Six were mentally deficient.

Most prison officials find it necessary to segregate homosexual prisoners because they so frequently either seek out other prisoners for sex contacts or are sought out. In many instances the homosexual is resented by the other prisoners and physical violence is often inflicted on him. Homosexual murders are not infrequent in prison.

Psychotherapy of Prisoners. In recent years, psychotherapy, both group and individual, has been introduced in some prisons. This is especially true in those states which have adopted "Sexual Psychopath Laws." Although these laws do not apply specifically to homosexuality, they do include it.

Pacht, who has worked with the Wisconsin Sex Crimes Law, is cautiously optimistic after nine years of experience with psychotherapy in a prison setting. The reeducative therapy described by Pacht and his co-workers may be broken down into three phases. It must be remembered that all of their subjects were in confinement with an indeterminate sentence.

According to Pacht:

> The *initial phase* is devoted to creating a climate which allows the establishment of a therapeutic relationship. This period may encompass several months to a year. Only after the development of such a relationship can the individual begin to examine his behavior without resorting to defensiveness or intra-punitive mechanisms.

The *second phase* in this system is employed in working through nuclear conflicts. "During this period, therapy focuses upon those factors in the background of the individual that have contributed to the development of deviant trends." The day-to-day behavior of the subject in the prison setting is carefully observed and correlated with the therapy.

The *last phase* of therapy is devoted to problems of separation from the prison and planning for the future.

This is often a very complicated process. Returning to the free world from a closed institution presents an additional burden to the stresses of community attitude, vocational problems, family attitudes, and separation from the therapist.[6]

2. Castration

Castration as a treatment of sexual deviations is not new. Denmark was apparently the first country to enact a special castration law. This law was first passed in 1925 and revised about ten years later.

Considerable interest was displayed concerning castration as a treatment of sex offenders in Europe during the 1930's. This was exemplified by resolutions adopted at the Berlin meetings of the International Penal and Penitentiary Congress in 1935 where the section on prevention of crime held, *inter alia,* that:

2. The favorable preventive-therapeutic results from castration achieved relative to sexual disorders in cases involving a leaning toward criminality, ought to cause all States to amend or supplement their respective laws, so as to facilitate the performance of such operations upon demand or with the consent of the person concerned in order to free that person from a disordered sexual inclination which might bring in its train the committing of sexual crimes. (Compulsory castration is also provided for.)[7]

Most of the Scandinavian countries have enacted laws which permit castration. Finland was the last to be added to the list.

The frequency of the procedure in Denmark was reported by Sand and Le Maire. They stated that "in the period 1929–1939, there were 4,190 sexual crimes in Denmark, of which comprehensive records were available on 3,476, including recidivists. A total of 3,185 individuals were involved in these crimes, and of this group 139 were ultimately castrated. Le Maire has analyzed the records in detail to discover the relationship between the crimes and the motives, stated in terms of the offenders' psychological condition, and the numbers of castrates in these categories."[8]

In general the attitude in the United States is strongly opposed to castration. In some sporadic cases it has been employed, however, in different sections of the country:

Castration has been proposed to some of the legislative commissions seeking more effective policy in the handling of sex offenders, but nowhere has it been taken seriously in this country.[9]

The use of the procedure is not likely to become widespread in the United States.

From the psychiatric standpoint castration is not likely to produce its desired effect unless the patient recognizes the desirability of the procedure and the likelihood of its beneficial results. If the procedure is imposed against the subject's will, it is more likely to be harmful than helpful. If consent to the procedure is required, it would serve to minimize possible abuses in the administration of the law in this regard. Even so, certain pressures are inevitable, even though these be of a psychological nature and applied by the patient on himself.

Moral Aspects of Castration. Is castration morally permissible as a method of treatment of homosexuality? An affirmative answer is given by some Catholic moralists, presuming that the necessary requirements are present. They reason that castration is an act with a double effect, one good and one bad, and that it may be permitted as a last resort after all other treatments have failed. They then deem the conditions required for the permissibility of such an act to be fulfilled. The cure of the abnormal sexual drive is the good effect which is expected, whereas permanent deprivation of the function of reproduction is the evil effect; in addition, the operation may produce a variety of psychosomatic effects. It is argued that, if the good effect does not outweigh the bad effect, at least it balances it. Although at first sight this may appear to be a solution to the problem, actually it does not meet the principles of the double effect. The good effect does not follow equally or immediately from the bad, and as a matter of fact there is no certain guarantee of a good effect at all, but only a probability.

Doctor Odenwald and Father VanderVeldt both express some reservations concerning the validity of this argument.[10] A first reservation concerns the good effect. Several serious investigations have proved, indeed, that castration may considerably and lastingly reduce the sexual urge in such a way that the subject more easily controls himself, but the operation does not present an absolute, or even probable, guarantee that such a reduction will be effected. This, it would seem, is where the application of the principle of the double effect is weakest — if not altogether lacking. However, this is not the main point. The main concern regards the character of the operation itself. The prime requirement for the permissibility of an act with a double effect is that the act itself be licit. In most surgical operations this condition is fulfilled; the act itself is good, inasmuch as it removes a diseased organ which endangers the health of the entire organism. It is argued that similar conditions prevail in the operation of orchidectomy; castration, it is said, is not in this case a mutilation, but the removal of a sick part of the body. This is not true, however, in the case of homosexuality. It rests on the premise that homosexuality has an organic cause, presumably an endocrine disturbance. But this premise is gravely doubtful. It is true that the androgen-estrogen ratio in male homosexuals as a *group* is lower than it is in heterosexuals as a *group*. But a surgeon does not operate on groups; he operates on an individual.

Suppose an indubitably male homosexual has androgen values below normal and estrogen values above normal. One might argue that in such cases the lowered androgen-estrogen ratio is the cause of the individual's sexual disorder. This has never been demonstrated. In fact, the administration of sex hormones seems not to alter the prevailing sex drive except by increasing it.

It would seem, therefore, in view of the unproved etiology that an orchidectomy cannot be licit.

It must be emphasized that this discussion deals with only the moral aspects of castration considered as a possible therapeutic measure. It leaves undecided the legal question of whether the state has the right to order castration of a delinquent homosexual as a punishment for his crimes and as a protective or preventive measure for the benefit of society.

3. Behavior Therapy

A number of new psychotherapeutic methods known as "Behavior Therapy" have been developed in recent years. Based on a common theory, the procedures themselves vary from aversion conditioning to desensitization:[11]

A brief account of this rationale may be stated as follows: the position adopted by this theory is that neurotic behavior is acquired. The process of acquisition implied in the theory is derived from modern learning theory. If neurotic behavior is regarded as being acquired, then it must follow that such behavior will be subject to the established laws of learning. Current knowledge about the learning process concerns not only the acquisition of new habit patterns but also their elimination. The elimination of learned responses occurs either by the extinction process or by inhibition.[12]

Rachman, reporting in 1961 from England, described the use of behavior therapy in a small number of cases. He felt that the method might prove valuable but emphasized that the treatment must stress positive sexual behavior and not merely attempt to eliminate the abnormal.

Stevenson and Wolpe[13] reported the use of the method in two cases of homosexuality.

The largest series of cases was that of Freund and Srnec, who reported forty-seven cases in all. Unfortunately, they had no control series.

Freund's treatment consisted of two phases. *Phase I* involved the administration of "an emetic mixture by subcutaneous injection." While the unpleasant effects of the injection were being experienced the patient was shown slides of dressed and undressed males. In *Phase II* of the treatment the patient was shown films of nude and seminude females approximately seven hours after the administration of testosterone. Follow-up studies after three and five years indicated that 51 percent of the patients showed no improvement, 14.9 percent showed temporary improvement, and only 25.5 percent were permanently improved; the remaining 8.5 percent were not adequately documented and were excluded from the final analysis.[14]

Feldman and McCulloch, also reporting from England, described their method of aversion therapy. They aimed to develop in their patients an aversion to previously attractive males and to develop an attraction to previously unattractive females. They described the treatment of twelve patients with a follow-up of nine months in their longest case.[15]

Their technic consisted in showing the patient a series of photographs of attractive males. If he did not put aside the picture in eight seconds, an electric shock was given until he did remove the picture. When the picture was put aside the shock ceased. They would then introduce female pictures after the male was removed. These would then be associated with the relief of anxiety after the shock.

They state that McGuire and Vallance[16] were the first to use Faradic current for this purpose.

Feldman *et al.* report one case in which eight booster sessions were given over nine months. Before treatment this patient had a Kinsey rating (q.v.) of 4 to 5; after treatment this rating was reduced to 1.

Summary. There is little so far to recommend the use of behavior therapy.

4. *Hypnosis*

Hypnosis has been tried through several generations. R. Krafft-Ebing,[17] A. P. F. von Schrenck-Notzing,[18] and A. Meares[19] all felt it had very limited and short-lived value. The danger of transference is very great and for the passive homosexual there may be considerable erotic satisfaction from the therapy. It is not a recommended form of therapy.

5. *Shock Therapy*

Owensby in 1940 reported on the use of pharmacological shock therapy in the treatment of inversion:

> Of a series of 15 homosexuals of both sexes successfully treated with the pharmacologic shock therapy during the past three years, only two have resumed their former practices. These relapses occurred in patients who did not remain under observation for a sufficient period of time to complete the psychiatric measures believed essential for the success of any method employed in an attempt to correct homosexuality. Many years will have to elapse before a correct evaluation of this method of treatment can be made but certainly its employment has been followed by remission of three years duration in 13 patients.[20]

I know of no series of cases in which electroshock was used. There is no reason why electroshock should have a beneficial effect on this condition. It might possibly have an effect on some of the depressive manifestations associated with homosexuality as in Patient III (see p. 76).

6. *Drug Therapy*

No drug has been found that is specific for the disorder. Various hormones have been tried. Their effect, however, was to accentuate the prevailing sexual drive rather than to divert it. Drugs have been used principally by those who accepted a constitutional genesis.

PRIMARILY PSYCHOGENIC THERAPIES

Hirschfeld suggested what he called "adaptive therapy."[21] By this he meant that the subject was aided in adapting to his condition and learning to live with it. Ellis suggested sublimation.[22] Aside from these early suggestions, Freud's rejection of psychoanalysis did much to delay the adoption of psychotherapeutic depth technics. His much quoted letter of 1935 in which he expressed marked pessimism about the results of psychotherapy in homosexuality did not encourage others to try. The letter, which was written to an American woman who had sought advice about the treatment of her homosexual son, was as follows:

Dear Mrs. ——

I gather from your letter that your son is a homosexual. I am most impressed by the fact that you do not mention this term yourself in your information about him. May I question you, why you avoid it? Homosexuality is assuredly no advantage, but it is nothing to be ashamed of, no vice, no degradation, it cannot be classified as an illness; we consider it to be a variation of the sexual function produced by a certain arrest of sexual development. Many highly respectable individuals of ancient and modern times have been homosexuals, several of the greatest men, among them (Plato, Michelangelo, Leonardo da Vinci, etc.). It is a great injustice to persecute homosexuality as a crime, and cruelty, too. If you do not believe me, read the books of Havelock Ellis.

By asking me if I can help, you mean, I suppose if I can abolish homosexuality and make normal heterosexuality take its place. The answer is, in a general way, we cannot promise to achieve it. In a certain number of cases we succeed in developing blighted germs of heterosexual tendencies which are present in every homosexual, in the majority of cases it is no more possible. It is a question of the quality and the age of the individual. The result of treatment cannot be predicted.

What analysis can do for your son runs in a different line. If he is unhappy, neurotic, torn by conflicts, inhibited in his social life, analysis may bring him harmony, peace of mind, full efficiency whether he remains a homosexual or gets changed. If you make up your mind he should have analysis with me!! I don't expect you will!! He has to come over to Vienna. I have no intention of leaving here. However, don't neglect to give me your answer.

Sincerely yours with kind wishes
Freud[23]

Insight Psychotherapy

Today, intensive psychotherapy or psychoanalysis is the method of choice. Results with this method are the most satisfactory so far, but even here the results leave much to be desired.

Albert Ellis reported on the treatment of 28 male and 12 female homosexuals. These patients were seen in from 5 to 220 psychoanalytic sessions. It was found that in terms of the ability to engage in satisfactory "sex-love" relationships with members of the other sex, 36 percent were "distinctly" improved and 39 percent were "considerably" improved. Thirty-three percent of the Lesbians were "distinctly" improved and 66 percent were "considerably" improved. In this series he gave no Kinsey rating either before or after treatment.

In commenting on these results Dr. Ellis felt that the following aspects of his technic were important in bringing about the improvement:

1. The therapist was quite accepting and noncritical in relation to the patients' homosexual desires and acts in themselves, but at the same time insistent on unmasking the neurotic motivations behind exclusive, fetishistic, and obsessive-compulsive homosexuality.
2. The therapist did not insist that the patients overcome all their homosexual tendencies, but accepted many of these tendencies as normal or idiosyncratic. He emphasized the patients' becoming more heterosexual rather than less homosexual.
3. The therapist showed, by his manner and verbalizations, that he himself was favorably prejudiced toward heterosexual relationships.
4. Special attention was usually concentrated on the patients' general antisexual attitudes and an active attack was made on his feelings of sexual guilt and shame.
5. In every instance there was as much focusing on the individual's general feelings of inadequacy as on his sex problems. A major goal of therapy was always the achievement of general ego-strengthening, on the assumption that exclusive homosexuality often follows from, and is in turn the further cause of, severe feelings of worthlessness.
6. Wherever possible, the patients were persuaded to engage in sex-love relationships with members of the other sex and to keep reporting back to the therapist for specific discussion of and possible aid with these love relationships.[24]

Others reporting on the results of treatment, for example, Woodward,[25] Knight,[26] and Curran and Parr,[27] gave a guarded and not too optimistic prognosis. Allen was more hopeful. He felt that the condition was durable.[28] A more favorable prognosis was given by Hadfield,[29] Hadden,[30] Poe,[31] Ovesey,[32] and Bieber.[33] All of these authors expressed the opinion that psychotherapy offers promise.

Curran and Parr reported that there was no significant difference between their therapy cases and their controls. Only three out of thirty-eight homosexual cases studied showed some change toward heterosexuality after psychotherapy.[34]

Knight reported that two of twelve treated cases were considered cured.[35]

Hadden employed group therapy with homosexual patients. He was unwilling to think in terms of cure "because we regard homosexuality as only a symptom and its suppression without definite personality reorganization is of little value. . . . We should aim at personality reorganization rather than symptom control."[36] In such group efforts it is desirable to have patients of a similar age and without too rigid a pattern.

The most recent figures on the results of psychoanalytic treatment are those given by Bieber *et al.*:

> Of 106 homosexuals who undertook psychoanalysis, either as exclusively homosexual or bi-sexual, 29 (27 percent) became exclusively heterosexual;
> (a) Of the 72 H-patients who began treatment as exclusively homosexual, 14 (10 percent) became heterosexual.
> (b) Of the 30 H-patients who began treatment as bi-sexual, 15 (50 percent) became heterosexual.

In this study it was felt that results depended to some extent on the length of treatment. The results of treatment as related to duration were as follows:

1. Only 2 patients of 28 (7 percent) who had fewer than 150 hours became heterosexual.
2. 9 of 40 (23 percent) of those patients who had 150–349 hours of analysis became heterosexual.
3. 18 of 38 (47 percent) of the patients who had 350 or more hours of analysis became heterosexual.[37]

Prevention

In view of the multiplicity of factors involved in the etiology of inversion, prophylaxis is difficult. A look at the variety of possibilities of psychiatric trauma listed in Clinics 4 and 5 helps to some extent in seeing the size of the problem. Certainly a happy marriage and a happy home life where children are wanted and treated equally, lovingly, and with proper attention to their sexual upbringing would be important contributory factors in prevention. One finding of Bieber and his group is of special importance:

> We have come to the conclusion that a constructive, supportive, warmly-related father precludes the possibility of a homosexual son. . . . Most mothers of homosexual sons were possessive of them.[38]

Improved knowledge of proper parent-child relations, although not easily obtained, would be useful, since parents could then avoid some at least of the more obvious mistakes (see Clinic 5). Better education of the public and especially of adolescents would help to alleviate the possibility of seduction. This type of instruction has been avoided until recently. In fact the whole subject of sex education has only been treated with any degree of adequacy in recent years. Education of the general public, including professional people, on the subject of homosexuality has been lacking and is still inadequate.

It seems inadequate, too, to sum up the prevention of homosexuality in these terms: that what is required is a happy marriage, a happy home with children who are contented, accepted, and loved. Yet this is the environment which produces citizens who are mentally and physically healthy and who perpetuate these things in their children.

CLINIC 18 — NOTES

1. Donald W. Cory, "Homosexuality," in *The Encyclopedia of Sexual Behavior*, Albert Ellis and Albert Abarbanel (eds.) (New York: Hawthorn Books, Inc., 1961), Vol. I, p. 492.
2. A. Moll, *Libido Sexualis. Studies in the Psychosexual Laws of Love Verified by Clinical Sexual Case Histories* (New York: Am. Ethnological Press, 1933).
3. Robert Lindner, "Sex in Prison," *Complex*, Vol. VI (Fall, 1951), p. 6.
4. Alfred C. Kinsey *et al.*, *Sexual Behavior in the Human Male* (Philadelphia: Saunders, 1948), p. 664.
5. Charles E. Smith, "The Homosexual Federal Offender: A Study of 100 Cases," *Journal of Criminal Law and Criminology*, Vol. XLVI, No. 5 (January–February, 1954), pp. 528–591.
6. Asher R. Pacht, Ph.D., Seymour L. Halleck, M.D., and John C. Ehrmann, Ph.D., "Psychiatric Treatment of the Sex Offender," in *Current Psychiatric Therapies*, Jules H. Masserman, M.D. (ed.) (New York: Grune and Stratton, 1962), Vol. II, p. 177.
7. Quoted by Paul W. Tappan, Ph.D., "Treatment of the Sex Offender in Denmark," *The American Journal of Psychiatry*, Vol. CVIII, No. 4 (October, 1951), pp. 244–245.
8. Quoted by Tappan, *op. cit.*, p. 245.

9. Tappan, *op. cit.*, pp. 244–245.
10. Robert Odenwald, M.D., and James H. VanderVeldt, O.F.M., *Psychiatry and Catholicism* (New York: McGraw-Hill, 1957), p. 435.
11. See S. Rachman, Ph.D., "Sexual Disorders and Behavior Therapy," *The American Journal of Psychiatry*, Vol. CXVIII, No. 3 (September, 1961), pp. 235–240.
12. *Ibid.*, p. 235.
13. I. Stevenson and J. Wolpe, *American Journal of Psychiatry*, Vol. 116 (1960), p. 737.
14. K. Freund, in *Behavior Therapy and the Neuroses* (London: Pergamon Press, 1960). See also Freund and Srnec in *Sbornik Lekarsky*, officialni Publikancni Organ Lekarske Fakulty University Karlovy V Praze (reported in the *International Journal of Sexology*, Vol. VII, No. 2 [November, 1953], pp. 92–93).
15. M. P. Feldman, Ph.D., and M. J. MacCulloch, M.B., "A Systematic Approach to the Treatment of Homosexuality by Conditioned Aversion: Preliminary Report," *American Journal of Psychiatry*, Vol. 121, No. 2 (August, 1964), pp. 167–171.
16. R. L. McGuire and M. Vallance, *British Medical Journal*, 1 (1964), p. 151.
17. R. v. Krafft-Ebing, *Psychopathia Sexualis, with Special Reference to the Antipathic Sexual Instincts. A Medico-Forensic Study* (New York: Rebman, 1906).
18. A. P. F. von Schrenk-Notzing, *Therapeutic Suggestion in Psychopathia Sexualis (Pathological Manifestations of the Sexual Sense) with Especial Reference to Contrary Sexual Instincts* (Philadelphia: Davis, 1895).
19. Ainslie Meares, M.D., *A System of Medical Hypnosis* (Philadelphia and London: W. B. Saunders, 1961).
20. Newdigate M. Owensby, M.D., "The Correction of Homosexuality," *The Urologic and Cutaneous Review*, Vol. XLV (August, 1941), p. 496.
21. M. Hirschfeld, "Homosexuality," in *Encyclopaedia Sexualis: A Comprehensive Encyclopaedia-Dictionary of the Sexual Sciences*, V. Robinson (ed.) (New York: Dingwall-Rock, in collaboration with *Med. Rev. of Rev.*, 1936), pp. 321–324; see also *Sexual Anomalies and Perversions: Physical and Psychological Development and Treatment* (New York: Emerson, 1944).
22. H. Ellis, *Studies in the Psychology of Sex*, Vols. I and II (New York: Random House, 1942).
23. Paul Friedman, "Sexual Deviation," in *American Handbook of Psychiatry*, Chapter 29, pp. 606–607. Friedman gives as his source of the letter: E. Jones, *The Life and Work of Sigmund Freud, The Last Phase: 1919–1939*, Vol. III (New York: Basic Books, Inc., 1957).
24. Albert Ellis, "The Effectiveness of Psychotherapy With Individuals Who Have Severe Homosexual Problems," *Journal of Consulting Psychology*, Vol. XX, No. 3 (1956), p. 194.
25. Mary Woodward, "The Diagnosis and Treatment of Homosexual Offenders," *British Journal of Deliquency*, 9 (July, 1958), pp. 44–59.
26. R. P. Knight, "Evaluation of the Results of Psychoanalytic Therapy," *American Journal of Psychiatry*, 98 (1941), pp. 434–436.
27. Desmond Curran and Denis Parr, "Homosexuality: An Analysis of 100 Male Cases Seen in Private Practice," *British Medical Journal*, 1 (1957), pp. 797–801.
28. Clifford Allen, M.D., *Homosexuality* (London: Staple Press, 1958), p. 111.
29. J. Hadfield, "The Cure of Homosexuality," *British Medical Journal*, 1 (June 7, 1958), pp. 1323–1326.
30. Samuel B. Hadden, "Attitudes Toward and Approaches to the Problem of Homosexuality," *Pennsylvania Medical Journal*, 60 (September, 1957), p. 1195; also "The Treatment of Homosexuality by Individual and Group Therapy," *American Journal of Psychiatry*, 114 (March, 1958), p. 810.
31. J. S. Poe, "The Successive Treatment of a 40-Year-Old Passive Homosexual," *Psychoanalytic Review*, 29 (1952), pp. 22–23.

32. Lionel Ovesey, Willard Gaylin, and Herbert Hendin, "Psychotherapy of Male Homosexuality," *Archives of General Psychiatry,* 9 (July, 1963), pp. 19–31.
33. Irving Bieber *et al., Homosexuality: A Psychoanalytic Study* (New York: Basic Books, Inc., 1962), p. 300.
34. Curran and Parr, *op. cit.,* pp. 797–801.
35. Knight, *op. cit.,* pp. 434–446.
36. Samuel B. Hadden, "Homosexuality: Observations on Its Psychogenesis and on Its Treatment by Group Therapy," paper read at the Third International Congress of Group Therapy, Milan, Italy, July 20, 1963, p. 9.
37. Bieber *et al., op. cit.,* p. 301.
38. *Ibid.,* pp. 311, 315.

Bibliography

ARTICLES

Air Force Regulation No. 35–66: "Discharge Processing Where Homosexual Acts or Tendencies Are Involved (Effective April 14, 1959)," Department of the Air Force, Washington, D. C., March 17, 1959.

Allen, C., "On the Cure of Homosexuality," *Int. J. Sexology*, 1952, pp. 5, 148–150.

———— "The Meaning of Homosexuality," *International Journal of Sexology*, Vol. VI, pp. 207–212.

Allers, Rudolph, "Sex and Morals," *Commonweal*, LIII, December, 1950.

Arieff, A. J., and Rotman, D. B., "Psychiatric Inventory of 100 Cases of Indecent Exposure," *Archives of Neurology and Psychiatry*, 47 (1942), pp. 495–498.

Armon, V., "Some Personality Variables in Overt Female Homosexuality," *J. of Proj. Techniques*, Vol. 24 (1960), pp. 292–309.

"Artificial Insemination" (editorial), *Justice of Peace and Local Government Review*, Vol. 109 (1945), pp. 194, 448 f.

Barahal, H. S., "Testosterone in Psychotic Male Homosexuals," *Psychiatric Quarterly*, 14 (1940), pp. 319–330.

Barr, Murray L., and Hobbs, G. Edgar, "Chromosomal Sex in Transvestites," *Lancet* i (1954), p. 1109.

Barton, G. A., "Sodomy" in *Encyclopedia of Religion and Ethics*, XI:672, New York, 1921.

Bauer, J., "Homosexuality as an Endocrinological, Psychological, and Genetic Problem," *Journal of Criminal Psychopathology*, 2 (October, 1940), 188–197.

Benda, Clemens E., "Existential Psychotherapy of Homosexuality," *Rev. Existential Psychol. Psychiat.*, 3:133–152, May, 1963.

Bendel, R., "The Modified Szondi Test in Male Homosexuality, 1," *International Journal of Sexology*, Vol. 8 (1955), pp. 226–227.

Bender, L., and Paster, S., "Homosexual Trends in Children," *Amer. J. Ortho-psychiat.*, 11:730, 1941.

Berg, C., "The Problem of Homosexuality. Part 1," *American Journal of Psychotherapy*, Vol. 11 (1957), pp. 65–79.

Bergler, Edmund, "The Myth of a New National Disease, Homosexuality, and the Kinsey Report," *Psychiatric Quarterly*, Vol. 22, No. 1 (1948), p. 66.

Bergmann, M. S., "Homosexuality on the Rorschach Test," *Bulletin, Menninger Clinic*, Vol. 9 (1945), pp. 78–93.

Beukenkamp, C., "Phantom Patricide," *Archives of General Psychiatry*, Vol. 3 (1960), pp. 282–288.

Bier, William C., S.J., "Goals in Pastoral Counseling," *Pastoral Psychology,* February, 1959, pp. 10–11.

Bowman, Karl M., M.D., "The Problem of the Sex Offender," *The American Journal of Psychiatry,* Vol. 108, No. 4 (October, 1951), pp. 250–257.

Bowman, Karl M., M.D., and Engle, Bernice, M.A., "Medicolegal Aspects of Transvestism," *The American Journal of Psychiatry,* Vol. CXIII, No. 7 (January, 1957), pp. 583–588.

——— "The Problem of Homosexuality," *J. Soc. Hyg.,* Vol. 39 (January, 1953), pp. 2–16.

——— "A Psychiatric Evaluation of the Laws of Homosexuality," *The American Journal of Psychiatry,* Vol. 112, No. 8 (February, 1956), pp. 577–583.

Bradshaw, W. V., "Homosexual Syphilis Epidemic," *Texas Journal of Medicine,* 57 (November, 1961), pp. 907–909.

Brambilla, F., "Endocrinal and Chromatinic Pictures of Male Homosexuality," *Sessuologia,* Vol. IV, No. 3 (July-September, 1963), pp. 170–174. Translated Summary, *Sessuologia,* Vol. IV, No. 4 (October-December, 1963), p. xii.

Brody, Morris W., "An Analysis of the Psychosexual Development of a Female — With Special Reference to Homosexuality," *Psychoanalytic Review,* 30 (1943), pp. 47–58.

Bromberg, Walter, M.D., "Sex Deviation and Therapy," *Journal of Social Therapy,* Vol. 1, No. 4, October, 1955, pp. 203–210.

Brown, D. G., "The Development of Sex-Role Inversion and Homosexuality," *J. Pediat.,* 50:613, 1957, pp. 613–619.

Buki, Rudolph A., M.D., "The Use of Psychotropic Drugs in the Rehabilitation of Sex-Deviated Criminals," *The American Journal of Psychiatry,* Vol. 120, No. 12 (June, 1964), pp. 1170–1175.

Cameron, N., "Paranoid Conditions and Paranoia," *The American Handbook of Psychiatry,* Silvano Arieti (ed.), Vol. I (New York: Basic Books, 1959), pp. 508–539.

Chang, J., and Block, J., "A Study of Identification in Male Homosexuals," *J. Consult. Psychol.,* Vol. 24 (1960), pp. 307–310.

Chapman, A. H., and Reese, D. G., "Homosexual Signs in Rorschachs of Early Schizophrenics," *J. Clinical Psychol.,* Vol. 9 (1953), pp. 30–32.

Chesser, Eustace, "Society and the Homosexual," *International Journal of Sexology,* Vol. VII (1954), pp. 213–216.

Clark, Leman, "Adhesions Between Clitoris and Prepuce," Chapter 25 in *Advances in Sex Research,* Hugo Beigel (ed.), (New York: Harper & Row, Inc., 1963), pp. 233–235.

Coates, S., "Homosexuality and the Rorschach Test," *Brit. J. Med. Psychol.,* Vol. 35 (1962), pp. 177–190.

Coburn, Monsignor Vincent P., "Homosexuality and the Invalidation of Marriage," *The Jurist,* Vol. XX, No. 4 (October, 1960), pp. 4441–4459.

Connery, John R., S.J., "Notes on Moral Theology," *Theological Studies,* Vol. XVI, No. 4 (December, 1955), p. 586.

Coogan, Matt J., "Wisconsin's Experience in Treating Psychiatrically-Deviated Sexual Offenders," *The Journal of Social Therapy,* Vol. I, No. 2 (January, 1955), pp. 3–6.

Coppen, A. J., "Body Build of Male Homosexuals," *British Medical Journal,* Vol. II (1959), pp. 1443–1445.

Cory, Donald Webster, "Homosexuality in Prison," *Journal of Social Therapy,* Vol. I, No. 3 (April, 1955), p. 137.

Crotty, Charles, "Marriage Counseling and Psychology," *Bulletin of the Guild of Catholic Psychiatrists,* Vol. VI, No. 4 (October, 1959), p. 12.

Curran, Rev. Charles A., "A Catholic Psychologist Looks at Pastoral Counseling," *Pastoral Psychology* (February, 1959), p. 13.

Curran, D., and Parr, D., "Homosexuality," *British Medical Journal,* Vol. 5022, April 6, 1957, pp. 797–801.

Darke, Roy A., "Heredity as an Etiological Factor in Homosexuality," *Journal of Nervous and Mental Disease,* Vol. 107, No. 3 (March, 1948), pp. 251–268.

David, H. P., and Rabinowitz, W., "Szondi Patterns in Epileptic and Homosexual Males," *J. Consult. Psychol.,* Vol. 16 (1952), pp. 247–250.

Davidman, Dr. Howard, "What You Should Know About Homosexuality," *State of Mind* (published by CIBA, Summit, N. J.), Vol. 2, No. 4 (April, 1958).

Davids, A., "Rorschach and TAT Indices of Homosexuality in Overt Homosexuals, Neurotics and Normal Males," *The Journal of Abnormal and Social Psychology,* Vol. 53, No. 2 (1956), pp. 161–172.

Davidson, W., and Winn, S., *Postgraduate Medical Journal,* 35 (1959), p. 494.

"A Delicate Problem," *Newsweek,* June 14, 1954, p. 99.

"Depravity and Unbelief," from a legal correspondent, *The Tablet,* Vol. 202, December 19, 1953, p. 606.

Deutsch, Helene, "Homosexuality in Women," *Psychoanalytic Quarterly,* October, 1932, pp. 484–510.

Devereaux, G., "Retaliatory Homosexual Triumph Over the Father," *Int. J. Psycho-Anal.,* Vol. 41 (1960), pp. 157–161.

Dinerstein, Russell, H., and Glueck, Bernard C., "Sub-Coma Insulin Therapy in the Treatment of Homosexual Panic States," *J. of Social Therapy,* Vol. 1, No. 4, October, 1955, p. 182.

Dixon, A. D., and Torr, J. B. D., "Chromosomal Sex and Abnormal Sex Development," *British Medical Journal,* Vol. I (1948), pp. 222–228.

Dougherty, W. J., "Epidemiological Treatment of Syphilis Contacts," *Journal of the Medical Society of New Jersey,* 59 (November, 1962), pp. 564–567.

Due, F. D., and Wright, M. E., "The Use of Content Analysis in Rorschach Interpretation. I. Differential Characteristics of Male Homosexuals," *Rorschach Research Exchange,* Vol. 9, No. 4 (1945), pp. 169–177.

Duhamel, Joseph S., S.J., "Theological Aspects," Part I of *Theological and Psychiatric Aspects of Habitual Sin,* paper copresented with Dom Jerome Hayden, O.S.B., at the Eleventh Annual Convention of The Catholic Theological Society of America, June, 1956, Cleveland, Ohio. Published in the Proceedings.

Ellis, A., "Are Homosexuals Necessarily Neurotic?" *One* (1955), 3 (4), pp. 8–12.

———— "On the Cure of Homosexuality," *Int. J. Sexology* (1952), 5, 135–138.

———— "The Effectiveness of Psychotherapy With Individuals Who Have

Severe Homosexual Problems," *J. Consult. Psychol.*, 20, No. 3 (1956), pp. 191–195.

———— "A Homosexual Treated With Rational Psychotherapy," *J. Clin. Psychol.*, 15; 338–343, 1959.

"Employment of Homosexuals and Other Sex Perverts in Government," Interim Report submitted to the Committee on Expenditures in the Executive Departments by Its Subcommittee on Investigations pursuant to S. Res. 280 (81st Congress), December 15 (legislative day, November 27), 1950. United States Government Printing Office.

Fein, L. G., "Rorschach Signs of Homosexuality in Male College Students," *J. Clin. Psychol.*, Vol. 3 (1950), pp. 248–253.

Feldman, M. P., Ph.D., and MacCulloch, M. J., M.B., "A Systematic Approach to the Treatment of Homosexuality by Conditioned Aversion," *American Journal of Psychiatry*, Vol. 121, No. 2 (August, 1964), pp. 167–171.

Finger, F. W., "Sex Beliefs and Practices Among Male College Students," *Journal of Abnormal and Social Psychology*, Vol. 42 (1947), pp. 57–67.

Finney, Joseph Claude, M.D., Ph.D., "Homosexuality Treated by Combined Psychotherapy," *Journal of Social Therapy*, Vol. 6, No. 1, First Quarter, 1960, pp. 27–34.

Ford, J. C., S.J., and Kelley, G., S.J., "Psychiatry and Moral Responsibility," *Theological Studies*, 16 (1955), pp. 86–108.

Fraiberg, S. H., "Homosexual Conflicts," in Lorand, Sandor, and Schneer, Henry I., *Adolescents* (New York: Hoeber, 1961).

Freud, Anna, "Clinical Observations on the Treatment of Manifest Male Homosexuality," *Psychoanal. Quart.*, 1951, pp. 20, 337–338.

———— "Problems of Technique in Adult Analysis," *Bull. Phil. Assn. Psychoan.*, 4:44–69, 1954.

Freud, Sigmund, "The Psychogenesis of a Case of Homosexuality in a Woman," translated by Barbara Low and R. Gabler, *Collected Papers of Sigmund Freud*, Vol. II (London: Hogarth Press, 1920).

Freund, K., and Pinkava, V., "Homosexuality in Man and Its Association With Parental Relationships," *Rev. Czech. Med.*, Vol. 7 (1961), p. 32.

Friedman, P., "Sexual Deviations," in *American Handbook of Psychiatry* (Silvano Arieti, ed.), Vol. I (New York: Basic Books, Inc., 1959).

Fromm, E. D., and Elonen, A. S., "The Use of Projective Techniques in the Study of a Case of Female Homosexuality," *J. Proj. Tech.*, Vol. 15 (1951), pp. 185–230.

Gedda, L., "Genetic Aspects of Homosexuality," *Sessuologia*, Vol. IV, No. 3 (July–September, 1963), pp. 108–119. Translated Summary, *Sessuologia*, Vol. IV, No. 4 (October–December, 1963), p. ix.

Gershwan, Harry, "Consideration of Some Aspects of Homosexuality," *American Journal of Psychoanalysis*, 13 (1953), pp. 82–83.

Giese, Hans, M.D., "Differences in the Homosexual Relations of Man and Woman," *International Journal of Sexology*, May, 1955, pp. 225–227.

———— *Jahrbuch Psychol. Psychother.*, 1953 (1), pp. 223–225.

Gilby, Thomas, O.P., "Not All That Anomalous," *Blackfriars*, Vol. XLI, No. 486 (November, 1960), pp. 402–408.

Glass, S. J., Duel, H. J., and Wright, C. A., "Sex Hormone Studies in Male Homosexuals," *Endocrinology*, Vol. 26, 1940, pp. 590–594.

Gleason, Robert W., S.J., "Homosexuality: Moral Aspects of the Problem," *The Homiletic and Pastoral Review*, Vol. LVIII, No. 3, December, 1957, pp. 272–278.

Glick, B., "Homosexual Panic: Clinical and Theoretical Considerations," *Journal of Nervous and Mental Diseases*, Vol. 129 (1959), p. 20.

Glueck, B. C., "Psychodynamic Patterns in the Homosexual Sex Offender," *The American Journal of Psychiatry*, Vol. 112 (1955–1956), pp. 584–590.

Gough, H. P., "Diagnostic Patterns on the M.M.P.I.," *Journal of Clinical Psychology*, Vol. 2 (1946), pp. 23–47.

Grams, A., and Rinder, "Signs of Homosexuality in Human Figure Drawings," *J. Consult. Psychol.*, Vol. 22 (1958), p. 394.

Graner, D., "Homosexuality and the Paranoid Psychoses as Related to the Concept of Narcissism," *Psychoanalytical Quarterly*, Vol. 22 (1955), p. 516.

Graver, D., "Homosexuality in Paranoid Schizophrenics as Revealed by the Rorschach Test," *J. Consult. Psychol.*, Vol. 18 (1954), pp. 459–462.

Greco, M. C., and Wright, J. C., "The Correctional Institution in the Etiology of Chronic Homosexuality," *Amer. J. Orthopsychiat.*, 14:295, 1944.

Greenspan, H., and Campbell, J. D., "The Homosexual as a Personality Type," *American Journal of Psychiatry*, Vol. 101 (1945), p. 682.

Greenspan, Jack, "Sex of the Persecutor in Female Paranoid Patients," *Arch. Gen. Psychiat.*, 9:217–223, September, 1963.

Grygier, T. G., "Psychometric Aspects of Homosexuality: A Pilot Study in Psychological Measurement," *The British Journal of Delinquency*, Vol. 9, No. 1 (1958), pp. 59–61.

Guttmacher, Alan F., "The Role of Artificial Insemination in the Treatment of Human Sterility," *Bulletin of the New York Academy of Medicine*, Vol. 19 (1943), p. 590.

Hacker, Helen Mayer, "The Ishmael Complex," *The American Journal of Psychotherapy*, Vol. VI, No. 3 (July, 1952), pp. 494–513.

Hadden, Samuel B., "Attitudes Toward and Approaches to the Problem of Homosexuality," *Pennsylvania Medical Journal*, 60 (September, 1957), 1195–1198.

———— "Homosexuality: Observations on Its Psychogenesis and on Its Treatment by Group Psychotherapy." Paper read at the Third International Congress of Group Therapy, Milan, Italy, July 20, 1963.

———— "The Treatment of Homosexuality by Individual and Group Therapy," *American Journal of Psychiatry*, 114 (March, 1958), p. 810.

Hadfield, J. A., "The Cure of Homosexuality," *British Medical Journal*, Vol. I (1958), 1323–1326.

Haines, William H., M.D., "Homosexuality," *Journal of Social Therapy*, Vol. 1, No. 3, April, 1955, p. 132.

———— "Some Sexual Deviations," *Journal of Social Therapy*, Vol. 3, No. 1, First Quarter, 1957, pp. 39–45.

———— "The Sex Offender in Illinois," *Journal of Social Therapy* (double issue), Second Quarter, Vol. 3, No. 2, 1957, and Third Quarter, Vol. 3, No. 3, 1957.

Hamburger, C., Sturup, G. K., and Dahl-Iverson, E., "Transvestism," *Journal of the American Medical Association*, Vol. CXIII, No. 7 (January, 1947), p. 583.

Hammond, W., "The Disease of the Scythians (Morbus Feminarum)," *American Journal of Neurology*, Vol. 3 (1882), p. 339.

Harmon, L. R., and Wiener, D. N., "Use of the M.M.P.I. in Vocational Advisement," *Journal of Applied Psychology*, Vol. 29 (1945), pp. 132–141.

Harper, Robert A., "Psychological Aspects of Homosexuality," Chapter 20 in *Advances in Sex Research*, Hugo Beigel (ed.) (New York: Harper & Row, Inc., 1963), pp. 187–197.

———— "Psychological Aspects of Homosexuality." Paper delivered at the meeting of the Society for the Scientific Study of Sex, New York, May 22, 1959.

Harrington, Rev. Paul V., "Indications and Proof of Non-Consummation," *The Linacre Quarterly*, Vol. 19 (August, 1952), p. 61.

———— "The Impediment of Impotency and the Condition of Male Impotence," Part I, Vol. 25 (August, 1958), pp. 100–110. Part II, *The Linacre Quarterly*, Vol. 25 (November, 1958), p. 143.

Harvey, John F., O.S.F.S., "Counseling the Homosexual," *The Homiletic and Pastoral Review*, January, 1962, pp. 328–335.

———— "Homosexuality and Marriage," *Homiletic and Pastoral Review*, December, 1961, pp. 227–234.

———— "Homosexuality as a Pastoral Problem," *Theological Studies*, Vol. XVI, No. 1 (March, 1955), pp. 86–108.

———— Review of *Morality and the Homosexual* by Michael J. Buckley, *Theological Studies*, Vol. XXI, No. 3 (September, 1960), pp. 491–495.

———— *The Moral Theology of the Confessions of St. Augustine*, Washington, D. C., Catholic University, 1951, pp. 83–85, 94–110, 147–154.

———— *Proceedings of the Second Institute for Clergy on Problems in Pastoral Counseling*, Fordham University, 1957.

Hayden, Dom Jerome, O.S.B., "Theological and Psychiatric Aspects of Habitual Sin," *Proceedings of the Eleventh Annual Convention*, Catholic Theological Association (June 25, 26, 27, 1956), Cleveland, Ohio.

Helmer, William J., "New York's 'Middle-class' Homosexuals," *Harper's Magazine*, March, 1963, pp. 85–92.

Hersko, Marvin, Ph.D., "Incest: A Three-Way Process," *Journal of Social Therapy*, Vol. 7, No. 1, First Quarter, 1961, pp. 22–31.

"The Hidden Problem," *Time*, December 28, 1953, p. 29.

Holemon, R. Eugene, M.D., and Winokur, George, M.D., "Effeminate Homosexuality: A Disease of Childhood," *American Journal of Orthopsychiatry*, Vol. XXXV, No. 1, 35:48–56, January, 1965.

Holzberg, Jules D., "Sex Differences in Schizophrenia," Chapter 27 in *Advances in Sex Research*, Hugo Beigel (ed.) (New York: Harper & Row, Inc., 1963), pp. 241–247.

"Homosexuality in America," *Life* (International), 1964, Vol. XXXVII, No. 2, pp. 44–58.

"Homosexual Offences," *Scots Law Times*, August 9, 1949, pp. 84–85.

"Homosexuality, Prostitution and the Law: The Report of the Roman Catholic Advisory Committee," *The Dublin Review*, Summer, 1956 (No. 471), pp. 57–65.

Hooker, Evelyn, "The Adjustment of the Male Overt Homosexual," *J. Proj. Tech.*, 21:18–31, 1957.

————— "Male Homosexuality in the Rorschach," *J. Proj. Tech.*, Vol. 22 (1958), pp. 33–54.

Horney, K., "The Flight From Womanhood: The Masculinity Complex in Women," *International Journal of Psychoanalysis*, Vol. 7 (1926), p. 324.

————— "On the Genesis of the Castration Complex in Women," *International Journal of Psychoanalysis*, Vol. V (1924), p. 50.

————— "The Problem of Female Masochism," *Psychoanalytic Review*, 22 (1935), p. 241.

Huffman, Arthur V., "Problems Precipitated by Homosexual Approaches on Youthful First Offenders," *Journal of Social Therapy*, Vol. 7, No. 4, Fourth Quarter, 1961, pp. 216–223.

————— "Sex Deviation in a Prison Community," *Journal of Social Therapy*, Vol. 6, No. 3, Third Quarter, 1960, pp. 170–181.

Johnson, Adelaide, and Robinson, David B., "The Sexual Deviant (Sexual Psychopath) — Causes, Treatment and Prevention," *Journal of the American Medical Association*, 164, August 3, 1957, pp. 1559–1565.

Kahn, Eugen, and Lion, Ernest G., "Clinical Note on Self-fellator," *American Journal of Psychiatry*, 95:131–133, July, 1938.

Kalinowsky, Lothar, "Effects of Somatic Treatments on the Sexual Behavior of Schizophrenics," Chapter 26 in *Advances in Sex Research*, Hugo Beigel (ed.) (New York: Harper and Row, Inc., 1963), pp. 236–240.

Kallman, Franz J., *American Journal of Human Genetics*, Vol. IV (1952), pp. 136–146.

————— "Comparative Twin Studies on the Genetic Aspect of Male Homosexuality," *Journal of Nervous and Mental Disease*, 115 (1952), 283–298.

Karpman, B., "Sex Life in Prison," *Journal American Institute of Criminal Law*, 38:475–486 (January–February, 1948).

Kates, Elizabeth M., "Sexual Problems in Women's Institutions," *Journal of Social Therapy*, Vol. 1, No. 4, October, 1955, pp. 187–191.

Katz, Sander, "Comparative Sexual Behavior," *Complex*, 5 (Spring, 1951), pp. 16–25.

Kempe, G. Th., "The Homosexual in Society," *British Journal of Delinquency*, 5 (1954), pp. 4–20.

Ketterer, Warren A., M.D., "Venereal Disease and Homosexuality," Special Communication in the *Journal of the American Medical Association*, Vol. 188, No. 9 (June 1, 1964), pp. 811–812.

Kickham, Charles J. E., M.D., F.A.C.S., "The Impediment of Impotency and the Condition of Male Impotence" (Medical Aspects), *The Linacre Quarterly*, Vol. 26 (February, 1959), pp. 13–22.

Kinsey, Alfred C., "Criteria for a Hormonal Explanation of the Homosexual," *J. Clin. Endocrinol.*, 1:424–428, 1941.

Klaf, Franklin S., M.D., "Evidence of Paranoid Ideation in Overt Homosexuals," *Journal of Social Therapy*, Vol. 7, No. 1, First Quarter, 1961, pp. 48–52.

————— "Female Homosexuality and Paranoid Schizophrenia. A Survey of 75 Cases and Controls," *Archives of General Psychiatry*, Vol. 4 (1961), p. 84.

Klaf, Franklin S., M.D., and Davis, Charles A., M.D., "Homosexuality and Paranoid Schizophrenia: A Survey of 150 Cases and Controls," *The American Journal of Psychiatry*, Vol. CXVI, No. 12 (June, 1960), pp. 1070–1075.

Knight, R. P., "Evaluation of the Results of Psychoanalytical Therapy," *American Journal of Psychiatry*, Vol. 98 (1941), pp. 434–436.

Kolb, Lawrence C., M.D., "Therapy of Homosexuality," in *Current Psychiatric Therapies*, Jules H. Masserman, M.D. (ed.), Vol. 3 (New York: Grune & Stratton, Inc., 1963), pp. 131–137.

Kolb, L. C., and Johnson, A. M., "Etiology and Therapy of Overt Homosexuality," *Psychoanalytic Quarterly*, Vol. 24 (1955), pp. 506–515.

——— "Etiology and Therapy of Overt Homosexuality," *Psychoanal. Quart.*, 24:506–515, 1955.

Kubie, Lawrence S., "The Drive to Become Both Sexes." Paper read at Am. Psychoanalyt. Assoc. Meeting, St. Louis, Missouri, 1954.

Kurland, M. L., "Paedophilia Erotica," *Journal of Nervous and Mental Diseases*, Vol. 131 (1960), p. 394.

Laidlaw, Robert W., "A Clinical Approach to Homosexuality," *Marriage and Family Living*, Vol. XIV, No. 1 (February, 1952), pp. 39–45.

Lang, T., "Studies on the Genetic Determination of Homosexuality," *Journal of Nervous and Mental Diseases*, Vol. 92 (1940), pp. 55–64.

Lapponi, G., "Determination of Nuclear Sex. Technical Note and Findings Obtained From a Large-Scale Survey," *Sessuologia*, Vol. IV, No. 3 (July–September, 1963), pp. 120–123. Translated Summary, *Sessuologia*, No. IV, No. 4 (October–December, 1963), p. ix.

Laycock, S. R., "Homosexuality. A Mental Hygiene Problem," *Canad. Med. Assoc. J.*, Vol. 63 (1950), p. 245.

Lewinsky, Hilde, "Features From a Case of Homosexuality," *Psychoanalytic Quarterly*, Vol. XXI (1952), pp. 344–354.

Lieberman, Daniel, M.D., and Siegel, Benjamin A., Ph.D., "A Program for 'Sexual Psychopaths' in a State Mental Hospital," *The American Journal of Psychiatry*, Vol. 113, No. 9 (March, 1957), pp. 801–807.

Lindner, Robert, "Sex in Prison," *Complex*, Vol. VI (Fall, 1951), p. 6.

Lindzey, G., Tejessy, C., and Zamansky, H. S., "Thematic Apperception Test: An Empirical Examination of Some Indices of Homosexuality," *J. Abnorm. Sociol. Psychology*, Vol. 57 (1958), pp. 67–75.

Lurie, L. A., "Endocrine and Disordered Sexual Behavior," *British Medical Journal*, 1 (March 9, 1957), p. 574.

——— "The Endocrine Factor in Homosexuality," *American Journal of Medical Science*, 208 (1944), 176–186.

MacKinnon, J., "The Homosexual Woman," *Amer. J. Psychiat.*, 103:661, 1947.

McGuire, R. L., and Vallance, M., "Aversion Therapy by Electric Shock: A Simple Technique," *British Medical Journal*, 1 (1964), p. 151.

Maia, I., "A Contribution to the Study of Homosexuality in the Rorschach Test," *Arch. Dep. Assist. Psicop.*, S. Paulo, 25–26, 1, 265–280, 1959–1960.

Marcozzi, A., "Value of Homosexual Behavior in Adolescence," *Sessuologia*, Vol. IV, No. 3 (July–September, 1963), pp. 175–177. Translated Summary, *Sessuologia*, Vol. IV, No. 4 (October–December, 1963), p. xii.

Marcozzi, A., Pomini, P., and Caprioli, N., "Determination of Urinary 17-Ketosteroids in Females With Homosexual Tendencies," *Sessuologia*, Vol. IV, No. 3 (July–September, 1963), pp. 178–179. Translated Summary, *Sessuologia*, Vol. IV, No. 4 (October–December, 1963), p. xii.

Marone, Silvio, "Homosexuality and Art," *International Journal of Sexology,* Vol. VII, No. 4 (May, 1954), pp. 175–188.

Merloo, J. A. M., "The Concept of Psychopathy," *American Journal of Psychiatry,* Vol. 16 (1962), p. 645.

Mesnikoff, Alvin M., Rainer, John D., Kolb, Lawrence C., and Carr, Arthur C., "Intra-familial Determinants of Divergent Sexual Behavior in Twins," *Am. J. of Psychiat.,* Vol. 119, No. 8, February, 1963, p. 732.

Mohr, J. W., Ph.D., Turner, R., M.D., and Ball, Richard B., M.B., "Exhibitionism and Pedophilia," *Corrective Psychiatry and Journal of Social Therapy,* Vol. 8, No. 4, Fourth Quarter, 1962, pp. 172–186.

Money, John, "Components of Eroticism in Man. I: The Hormones in Relation to Sexual Morphology and Sexual Desire," *Journal of Nervous and Mental Disease,* 132 (1961), 239–248.

——— "Components of Eroticism in Man. II: The Orgasm and Genital Somesthesia," *Journal of Nervous and Mental Disease,* 132 (1961), 289–297.

——— "Sex Hormones and Other Variables in Human Eroticism," in W. C. Young (ed.), *Sex and Internal Secretions,* third edition (Baltimore: Williams and Wilkins, 1961), Chapter 22.

Moore, Thomas V., "The Pathogenesis and Treatment of Homosexual Disorders," *Journal of Personality,* Vol. 14, No. 1, September, 1945, pp. 47–83.

Muscardin, L., "Research Into Some Morphological Features in a Group of Homosexuals," *Sessuologia,* Vol. IV, No. 3 (July–September, 1963), pp. 150–154. Translated Summary, *Sessuologia,* Vol. IV, No. 4 (October–December, 1963), p. xi.

Nedoma, K., "Homosexuality in Sexological Practice," *Int. J. Sexology,* 1951, pp. 4, 219–224.

Neustadt, R., and Myerson, A., "Quantitative Sex Hormone Studies in Homosexuality, Childhood and Various Neuropsychiatric Disturbances," *American Journal of Psychiatry,* 97 (1940), pp. 524–551.

"New Shocker," *Newsweek,* May 29, 1950, p. 18.

Nielson, Nils, "What Is Homosexuality?" *International Journal of Sexology,* Vol. 6, No. 3 (February, 1953), p. 188.

Nitsche, C. J., Robinson, J. F., and Parsons, E. T., "Homosexuality and the Rorschach," *J. Consult. Psychol.,* Vol. 20 (1956), p. 196.

Norman, J., "Evidence and Clinical Significance of Homosexuality in 100 Unanalyzed Cases of Dementia Praecox," *Journal of Nervous and Mental Diseases,* Vol. 107 (1948), p. 484.

Odenwald, R. P., "Counseling the Homosexual," *Priest,* 9, December, 1953, pp. 940–944.

Ovesey, Lionel, "The Homosexual Conflict," *Psychiatry,* Vol. XVII, No. 3 (August, 1954), pp. 243–250.

Ovesey, Lionel, Gaylin, Willard, and Hendin, Herbert, "Psychotherapy of Male Homosexuality," *Archives of General Psychiatry,* 9 (July, 1963), pp. 19–31.

Owensby, Newdigate M., M.D., "The Correction of Homosexuality," *The Urologic and Cutaneous Review,* Vol. XLV (August, 1941), pp. 494–496.

Pacht, Asher R., Ph.D., Halleck, Seymour L., M.D., and Ehrmann, John C., Ph.D., "Psychiatric Treatment of the Sex Offender," in *Current Psychiatric Therapies,* Jules H. Masserman, M.D. (ed.), Vol. 2 (New York: Grune & Stratton, 1962), pp. 173–179.

Pantom, J. H., "A New M.M.P.I. Scale for the Identification of Homosexuality," *J. Clin. Psychol.*, Vol. 16 (1960), pp. 17–21.

Pare, C. M. B., "Homosexuality and Chromosomal Sex," *Journal of Psychosomatic Research*, 1 (1956), pp. 247–251.

Pascal, G. R., *et al.*, "A Study of Genital Symbols on the Rorschach Test: Presentation of a Method and Results," *The Journal of Abnormal and Social Psychology*, Vol. 45 (1950), pp. 286–295.

Poe, John S., "The Successful Treatment of a 40-Year-Old Passive Homosexual Based on an Adaptational View of Human Behavior," *The Psychoanalytic Review*, Vol. XXIX, No. 1 (January, 1952), pp. 23–33.

Pritchard, M., "Homosexuality and Genetic Sex," *J. Ment. Sci.*, 108:616–623, September, 1962.

Puxon, M., "Not as Other Men," *Solicitors' Journal*, 101:735 (September 28, 1957).

Group for the Advancement of Psychiatry, *Psychiatrically Deviated Sex Offenders*, Report No. 9, New York, February, 1950.

Raboch, J., and Nedoma, K., "Sex Chromatin and Sexual Behavior: A Study of 36 Men With Female Nuclear Pattern and of 134 Homosexuals," *Psychosomatic Medicine*, Vol. XX (1958), p. 55.

Rachman, S., Ph.D., "Sexual Disorders and Behavior Therapy," *The American Journal of Psychiatry*, Vol. CXVIII, No. 3 (September, 1961), pp. 235–240.

Rado, Sandor, "A Critical Examination of the Concept of Bisexuality," *Psychoanalytic Medicine II*, October 4, 1940, pp. 459–467.

Ramsey, G. V., "The Sexual Development of Boys," *The American Journal of Psychiatry*, Vol. 56 (1943), pp. 217–234.

Reitzell, J. M., "A Comparative Study of Hysterics, Homosexuals and Alcoholics Using Content Analysis of Rorschach Responses," *Rorschach Research Exchange*, Vol. 13 (1949), pp. 127–141.

"Report on Homosexuality With Particular Emphasis on This Problem in Governmental Agencies," formulated by the Committee on Cooperation With Governmental (Federal) Agencies of the Group for the Advancement of Psychiatry, Report No. 30, January, 1955. 3617 W. 6th Ave., Topeka, Kans.

Ricco, D., and Petiziol, A., "Psychological Examinations in Homosexuality," *Sessuologia*, Vol. IV, No. 4 (October-December, 1963), pp. 215–218. Translated Summary, *Sessuologia*, Vol. IV, No. 4, p. xiii.

Rickles, N., "Exhibitionism," *Journal of Nervous and Mental Diseases*, 95 (1942), pp. 11–17.

Ritty, Charles J., J.C.L., "Possible Invalidity of Marriage by Reason of Sexual Anomalies," *The Jurist*, Vol. XXIV, No. 4 (October, 1963), pp. 394–422.

Roberts, Leigh M., and Pacht, Asher R., "Termination of Inpatient Treatment for Sex Deviates: Psychiatric, Social and Legal Factors," *The American Journal of Psychiatry*, Vol. 121, No. 9 (March, 1965), pp. 873–880.

"Roman Catholic Advisory Committee on Prostitution and Homosexual Offences and the Existing Law" (*Dublin Review*, 230:60–65, Summer, 1956).

Rosenzweig, S., and Hoskins, R. G., "A Note on the Ineffectualness of Sex-hormone Medication in a Case of Pronounced Homosexuality," *Psychosom. Med.*, 3:87–89, 1941.

Salzman, Leon, "The Concept of Latent Homosexuality," *Am. Journal of Psychoanalysis*, Vol. XVII, No. 2, 1957, pp. 161–169.

Saul, J. L., and Beck, A. T., "Psychodynamics of Male Homosexuality," *International Journal of Psychoanalysis,* Vol. 42 (1961), pp. 43–48.

Sawyer, G. I. M., "Homosexuality: The Endocrinological Aspects," *The Practitioner,* 72 (April, 1954), 374–377.

Scott, P. D., "Homosexuality, With Special Reference to Classification," *Proc. Roy. Soc. Med.,* 50:655–660, 1957.

——— "Psychiatric Aspects of the Wolfenden Report," *British Journal of Delinquency,* Vol. 9 (1958), p. 1.

Severinghaus, E. L., and Chornyak, J., "A Study of Homosexual Adult Males," *Psychosom. Med.,* 7:302–305, 1945.

"Sexual Offenders and Social Punishment," published for the Church of England Moral Welfare Council, 1956, ed. D. S. Bailey.

Sherwin, R. V., "Sodomy. A Medico-legal Enigma," *International Journal of Sexology,* Vol. 5 (1951), p. 10.

——— "Some Legal Aspects of Homosexuality," *International Journal of Sexology,* Vol. 4 (1950), p. 22.

Slater, Eliot, "The Sibs and Children of Homosexuals," *Journal of Nervous and Mental Disease,* 107 (1948), pp. 251–268.

Slater, E., and Slater, P., "A Study in the Assessment of Homosexual Traits," *British Journal of Medical Psychology,* Vol. 21 (1947), p. 61.

Smith, Alexander B., Ph.D., Bassin, Alexander, Ph.D., "Group Therapy With Homosexuals," *Journal of Social Therapy,* Vol. 5, No. 3, Third Quarter, 1959, pp. 225–232.

Smith, C. E., "Homosexual Federal Offender: A Study of 100 Cases," *Journal, American Institute of Criminal Law,* 44:582–591 (January–February, 1954).

Socarides, C., "Meaning and Content of Paedophiliac Perversion," *Journal of the American Psychoanalytic Association,* Vol. 7 (1959), p. 84.

Srnec, Dr. J., and Freund, Dr. K., "Treatment of Male Homosexuality Through Conditioning," *Int. J. Sexology,* 1953, pp. 7, 92–93.

Stevenson, I., and Wolpe, J., "Sexual Disorders and Behavior Therapy," quoted from Rachman, S., Ph.D., *American Journal of Psychiatry,* Vol. CXVIII, No. 3 (September, 1961), pp. 235–240.

Tappan, Paul W., "Sentences for Sex Criminals," *Journal of Criminal Law, Criminology and Police Science,* Vol. 42 (1951), pp. 332–336.

——— "Treatment of the Sex Offender in Denmark," *The American Journal of Psychiatry,* Vol. CVIII, No. 4 (October, 1951), pp. 24–49.

Teodori, U., and Morabito, F., "Endocrinological Aspects of Homosexuality," *Sessuologia,* Vol. IV, No. 3 (July-September, 1963), pp. 156–164. Translated Summary, *Sessuologia,* Vol. IV, No. 4 (October–December, 1963), pp. xi–xii.

Thompson, Clara, "Changing Concepts of Homosexuality in Psychoanalysis," *Psychiatry* (10) (1947), pp. 183–189.

Thompson, G. N., "Electroshock and Other Therapeutic Considerations in Sexual Psychopathy," *Journal of Nervous and Mental Disease,* 109 (1949), p. 531.

Tocca, M., and Micheli, F., "The Validity of Hormonale Exploration in the Diagnosis of Homosexual Conditions," *Sessuologia,* Vol. IV, No. 3 (July–September, 1963), pp. 165–169. Translated Summary, *Sessuologia,* Vol. IV, No. 4 (October-December, 1963), p. xii.

Trese, Leo, "Muted Tragedy," *The Commonweal,* Vol. LI (February 17, 1950), p. 512 ff.

"The Unspeakable Crime," *Time,* November 16, 1953, p. 36.

Vague, J., Favier, G., and Nicolino, J., "Somatic Aspects of Male and Female Homosexuality," *Sessuologia,* Vol. 4 (1963), pp. 124–149. Translated Summary, *Sessuologia,* Vol. 4, No. 4 (October–December, 1963), pp. x–xi.

Vann, Gerald, O.P., "Moral Dilemmas," *Blackfriars,* XXXV (January, 1954), pp. 6–7.

Waxenburg, Sheldon E., "Some Biological Correlatives of Sexual Behavior," in George Winokur (ed.), *Determinants of Sexual Behavior,* p. 57. Annual conference on community mental health research, 4th, Washington University, Social Sciences Institute. "Determinants of Human Sexual Behavior," ed. by George Winokur, 11, 1963, pp. 7–25, Thomas, C. C. (Charles C. Thomas, Publisher, 301–327 E. Lawrence Ave., Springfield, Illinois).

Wayne, D. M., Adams, M., and Rowe, L. H., "A Study of Military Prisoners at a Disciplinary Barracks Suspected of Homosexual Activities," *Milit. Sun.,* Vol. 101 (1947), pp. 499–534.

Weil, A., "Concerning the Anatomic Fundamentals of the Congenital Homosexual," *Arch. Frauenk-Eugen.,* 10, pp. 23–26.

———— "The Substance of the Expression of Homosexuals About Their Specific Constitution," *Arch. f. Entwickungsmechanik der Organismen,* 49 (1921), p. 538.

Weissman, P., "Structural Considerations in Overt Male Bisexuality," *Int. J. Psychoan.,* 43:159–168, 1962.

West, D. J., "Parental Figures in the Genesis of Male Homosexuality," *Int. J. Soc. Psychol.,* Vol. 5 (1959), pp. 85–97.

West, Louis J., Doidge, William T., and Williams, Robert L., "An Approach to the Problem of Homosexuality in the Military Service," *The American Journal of Psychiatry,* Vol. 115, No. 5 (November, 1958), p. 393.

Wheeler, W. M., "An Analysis of Rorschach Indices of Male Homosexuality," *Rorschach Research Exchange* and *J. Proj. Tech.,* Vol. 13 (1949), pp. 97–126.

Whitaker, L., Jr., "The Use of an Extended Draw-a-Person Test to Identify Homosexual and Effeminate Men," *J. Consult. Psychol.,* Vol. 25, No. 6 (1961), pp. 482–485.

Willink, H. U., "Legal Aspects of Artificial Insemination," *The Practitioner,* Vol. 158 (1947), p. 349.

Wolfson, William, and Gross, Alfred, "A Footnote to the Etiological Study of the Homosexual Syndrome," *International Journal of Sexology,* 6 (February, 1953), pp. 178–179.

Woodward, M., "Diagnosis and Treatment of Homosexual Offenders," *British Journal of Delinquency,* Vol. 9 (1958), pp. 44–58.

Wortis, J., "Intersexuality and Effeminacy in a Male Homosexual," *American Journal of Orthopsychiatry,* 10 (1940), pp. 567–569.

———— "Note on Body Build of Male Homosexual," *American Journal of Psychiatry,* 93 (1937), p. 1121.

Wright, C. A., Glass, S. J., and Deuel, H. J., "Sex Hormone Studies in Male Homosexuality," *Endocrinology,* Vol. 26 (1940), pp. 590–594.

Zamansky, H. S., "A Technique for Assessing Homosexual Tendencies," *J. Pers.,* Vol. 24 (1956), pp. 436–448.

BOOKS

Allen, Clifford, M.D., *A Textbook of Psychosexual Disorders* (London: Oxford University Press, 1962).
——— *The Sexual Perversions and Abnormalities: A Study in the Psychology of Paraphilia* (London: Oxford University Press, 1949).
——— *Homosexuality* (London: Stape Press, 1958).
Allers, Rudolph, M.D., *The Psychology of Character* (New York: Sheed and Ward, 1943).
American Handbook of Psychiatry (2 vols.), Silvano Arieti (ed.) (New York: Basic Books, Inc., 1959).
Anomaly, *The Invert* (Baltimore: The Williams and Wilkins Company, 1948).
Attwater, Donald, *A Catholic Dictionary*, 3rd ed. (New York: The Macmillan Company, 1961).
Bailey, D. S., *Homosexuality and the Western Christian Tradition* (London: Longmans, 1955).
de Beauvoir, Simone, *The Second Sex* (New York: Alfred A. Knopf, 1953).
Berg, Charles, M.D., and Allen, Clifford, M.D., *The Problem of Homosexuality* (New York: The Citadel Press, 1958).
Berg, C., and Krich, A. M. (eds.), *Homosexuality* (London: Allen, 1958).
Bergler, Edmund, *Homosexuality: Disease or Way of Life* (New York: Hill & Wang, 1957).
——— *1000 Homosexuals* (Paterson, N. J.: Pageant Books, Inc., 1959).
Bergler, E., and Kroger, W. S., *Kinsey's Myth of Female Sexuality* (New York: Grune and Stratton, 1954).
Bieber, Irving, *et al.*, *Homosexuality* (New York: Basic Books, Inc., 1962).
Bills, N., *The Personality Structure of Alcoholics and Paranoids As Revealed by Their Responses to the Thematic Apperception Test,* Unpublished Thesis, Western Reserve University, 1953.
Biot, Rene, M.D., and Galimard, Pierre, M.D., *Medical Guide to Vocations* (London: Burns & Oates, 1955).
Boss, M., M.D., *Sinn und Gehalt der Sexuellen Perversionem* (The Meaning and Content of the Sexual Perversions) (Berne: Medizinischer Verlag Hans Huber, 1947). Reviewed in *Psychoanalytic Quarterly,* Vol. XVII (1948), p. 106.
Bouscaren, T. Lincoln, S.J., and Ellis, Adam C., S.J., *Canon Law* (Milwaukee: The Bruce Publishing Company, 1957), 3rd ed.
British Medical Association, *Homosexuality and Prostitution,* London, 1955.
British Medical Association and Magistrates' Association, *The Criminal Law and Sexual Offenders,* London, 1949.
Buckley, Rev. Michael J., *Morality and the Homosexual* (Westminster, Md.: The Newman Press, 1959).
Cavanagh, John R., M.D., *Fundamental Pastoral Counseling* (Milwaukee: The Bruce Publishing Company, 1962).
Cavanagh, John R., M.D., and McGoldrick, James B., S.J., *Fundamental Psychiatry* (Milwaukee: The Bruce Publishing Company, 1958, 1966).
Chesser, Eustace, *Live and Let Live* (New York: Philosophical Library, Inc., 1958).
Choisy, Maryse, *Psychoanalysis of the Prostitute* (New York: Philosophical Library, 1961).

Clark, William L., and Marshall, William L., *A Treatise on the Law of Crimes* (Chicago: Callaghan and Company, 1912).

Cole, William G., *Sex and Love in the Bible* (New York: Association Press, 1959).

Cory, Donald W., *The Homosexual in America* (New York: Greenberg, 1951).

———— *The Homosexual Outlook* (London: Peter Nevill, 1953).

———— *Homosexuality: A Cross Cultural Approach* (New York: Julian Press, 1956).

Crime in the United States, 1961, edited by the Federal Bureau of Investigation, United States Department of Justice.

Davidson, Henry A., *Forensic Psychiatry* (New York: The Ronald Press, 1952).

Davis, K. B., *Factors in the Sex Life of Twenty-Two Hundred Women* (New York: Harper, 1929).

Diagnostic and Statistical Manual of Mental Disorders, prepared by the Committee on Nomenclature and Statistics of the American Psychiatric Association (Washington, D. C.: A.P.A. Mental Hospital Service, 1952).

Dickinson, R. L., and Beam, Laura, *The Single Woman* (New York: Reynal, 1934).

Drummond, Isabel, *The Sex Paradox* (New York: Putnam's, 1953).

Ellis, H., *Studies in the Psychology of Sex* (London: Heinemann, 1950).

Encyclopaedia of Mental Health, Albert Deutsch and Helen Fishman (eds.) (New York: Franklin Watts, Inc., 1963), 6 vols.

The Encyclopaedia of Sexual Behavior, Albert Ellis and Albert Abarbanel (eds.) (New York: Hawthorn Books, Inc., 1961), 2 vols.

Encyclopaedia Sexualis, B. Robinson (ed.) (New York: Dingwall-Rock, Ltd., 1936).

English, Horace B., and English, Ava C., *A Comprehensive Dictionary of Psychological and Psychoanalytical Terms* (New York: Longmans, Green and Company, 1958).

English, O. Spurgeon, and Finch, Stuart M., *Introduction to Psychiatry* (New York: W. W. Norton and Co., 1954).

Epstein, Louis, *Sex Laws and Customs in Judaism* (New York: Block, 1948).

de Fabregues, Jean, *Christian Marriage* (New York: Hawthorn Books, Inc., 1959).

Farnham, M. F., *The Adolescent* (New York: Harper & Brothers, 1951).

Fenichel, O., *The Psychoanalytic Theory of Neurosis* (New York: Norton, 1945).

Flood, Dom Peter, O.S.B. (ed.), *New Problems in Medical Ethics* (Westminster, Md.: The Newman Press, 1953).

Ford, Clelland S., and Beach, Frank A., *Patterns of Sexual Behaviour* (London: Eyre and Spottiswoode, 1952).

Ford, John F., S.J., and Kelly, Gerald, S.J., *Contemporary Moral Theology* (Westminster, Md.: The Newman Press, 1958), 2 vols.

Foster, Jeannette H., *Sex Variant Women in Literature* (New York: Vantage Press, 1956).

Freud, Sigmund, *Collected Papers,* Vol. III, trans. A. and J. Strachey (London: Leonard and Virginia Woolf, 1925).

————— *New Introductory Lecture on Psycho-Analysis* (New York: W. W. Norton Company, Inc., 1933).

————— *Three Contributions to the Theory of Sex*, in *The Basic Writings of Sigmund Freud*, A. A. Brill (ed.) (New York: Modern Library, 1938).

Freund, K., *Behavior Therapy and the Neuroses* (London: Pergamon Press, 1960).

Gardet, Louis, *Mohammedanism*, trans. William Burridge, Vol. 143, of the *Twentieth Century Encyclopedia of Catholicism* (New York: Hawthorn Books, 1961).

Gassert, Robert G., S.J., and Hall, Bernard H., M.D., *Psychiatry and Religious Faith* (New York: The Viking Press, 1964).

Gemelli, A., *Artificial Insemination* (Milan, Italy: Catholic University of the Sacred Heart, n.d.).

Glover, E. (ed.), *The Problem of Homosexuality* (London: Institute for the Study and Treatment of Delinquency, 1957).

Gide, A., *Corydon* (Paris: Gallimard, 1925).

Goldschmidt, R., *The Mechanism and Psychology of Sex Determination* (London: Methuen and Company, Ltd., 1924).

Guttmacher, M. S., and Weihofen, H., *Psychiatry and the Law* (New York: W. W. Norton Co., Inc., 1952).

Hagmaier, George, C.S.P., and Gleason, Robert, S.J., *Counselling the Catholic* (New York: Sheed and Ward, 1959).

Hall, Radcliffe, *The Well of Loneliness* (New York: Covici, 1928).

Hamilton, Gilbert V., *On the Cause of Homosexuality* (two essays, the second in reply to the first) (New York: G. Legman, 1950).

————— *Research in Marriage* (New York: A. C. Boni, 1929).

Henry, George W., *All the Sexes* (New York: Rinehart, 1955).

Hinsie, Leland E., M.D., and Shatzky, Jacob, Ph.D., *Psychiatric Dictionary* (New York: Oxford University Press, 1953).

Hirschfeld, M., *Sexual Anomalies and Perversions* (London: Encyclopedic Press, 1952).

————— *Sexual Pathology* (New York: Emerson Books, Inc., 1940).

Hoch, P. H., and Zubin, J. (eds.), *Psychosexual Development in Health and Disease* (New York: Grune and Stratton, 1949).

Jacoby, George W., *The Unsound Mind and the Law* (New York: Funk and Wagnalls Co., 1918).

Jones, E., *Life and Work of Sigmund Freud*, Vol. 2 (New York: Basic Books, 1956).

————— *The Life and Work of Sigmund Freud, The Last Phase: 1919–1939*, Vol. III (New York: Basic Books, Inc., 1957).

Jung, C. G., *Contributions to Analytical Psychology* (London: Routledge & Kegan Paul, Ltd., 1948).

Kardiner, Abram, *Sex and Morality* (Charter Book, No. 107) (New York: The Bobbs-Merrill Company, Inc., 1954).

Karpman, Benjamin, *The Sexual Offender and His Offense* (New York: Julian, 1954).

Kelly, Gerald, *Modern Youth and Chastity* (St. Louis: The Queen's Work Publishing Company, 1941).

Kinsey, A. C., et al., *Sexual Behavior in the Human Female* (Philadelphia: Saunders, 1953).

—— *Sexual Behavior in the Human Male* (Philadelphia: Saunders, 1948).

Kirch, A. M. (ed.), *The Homosexuals* (New York: The Citadel Press, 1954).

Krafft-Ebing, R. v., *Psychopathia Sexualis* (New York: Physicians and Surgeons Book Co., 1934).

Kroger, William S., and Freed, Charles S., *Psychosomatic Gynecology* (Philadelphia: W. B. Saunders Co., 1951).

Levin, Meyer, *Compulsion* (New York: Simon & Schuster, 1956).

Levinson, Samuel A. (ed.), *Symposium on Medico-Legal Problems* (Philadelphia: J. B. Lippincott Co., 1948).

Licht, Hans, *Sexual Life in Ancient Greece* (Pseudo for Paul Brandt) (London: G. Routledge & Sons, Ltd., 1932).

Lindman, Frank T., and McIntyre, Donald M., Jr. (eds.), *The Mentally Disabled and the Law* (Chicago: The University of Chicago Press, 1961).

Lloyd, Charles W. (ed.), *Human Reproduction and Sexual Behavior* (Philadelphia: Lea & Febiger, 1964).

Lorand, S., and Balint, M. (eds.), *Perversions, Psychodynamics and Therapy* (New York: Random House, 1956).

Masserman, Jules H. (ed.), *Current Psychiatric Therapies* (New York: Grune & Stratton, Inc., 1962), Vol. II.

Masters, R. E. L., *The Homosexual Revolution* (New York: The Julian Press, Inc., 1962).

Mather, John S., and Seaman, Donald, *The Great Spy Scandal* (London: Purnell & Sons, Ltd., 1956).

Mead, Margaret, *Male and Female* (New York: William Morrow and Company, 1949).

Meares, Ainslie, M.D., *A System of Medical Hypnosis* (Philadelphia and London: W. B. Saunders Company, 1961).

Mercier, Cardinal, *Manual of Scholastic Philosophy* (London: K. Paul Trench, Trubner and Co., Ltd., 1916).

Moll, A., *Libido Sexualis. Studies in the Psychosexual Laws of Love Verified by Clinical Sexual Case Histories* (New York: American Ethnological Press, 1933).

—— *The Sexual Life of the Child* (New York: The Macmillan Company, 1912).

Moore, Dom Thomas Verner, *The Nature and Treatment of Mental Disorders* (New York: Grune & Stratton, 1951).

Oliven, John F., M.D., *Sexual Hygiene and Pathology* (Philadelphia and Montreal: J. B. Lippincott Company, 1955).

Ploscowe, M., *Sex and the Law* (New York: Prentice-Hall, Inc., 1951).

Ploss, Hermann Heinrich, Bartels, Max, and Bartels, Paul, *Woman* (London: William Heinemann, Ltd., 1935), 3 vols.

The Proceedings for the Institute for the Clergy on Problems in Pastoral Psychology (New York: Fordham University Press, 1956), pp. 140–191.

Quinn, Rev. Joseph J., *Rotal Jurisprudence With Regard to Functional Impotence in the Male* (Washington, D. C.: The Catholic University of America, October 23, 1956).

Rees, Judge Tudor, and Usill, Harley V. (eds.), *They Stand Apart* (New York: The Macmillan Company, 1955).

Risk, James E., *The Law of Catholic Marriage* (Chicago: Callaghan & Company, 1957).

Ruitenbeek, Hendrik M. (ed.), *The Problem of Homosexuality in Modern Society* (New York: E. P. Dutton & Co., Inc., 1963).

Sakel, Manfred, *Schizophrenia* (New York: Philosophical Library, 1958).

Sapirstein, M. R., *Emotional Security* (New York: Crown Publishers, 1948).

Schofield, M. G., *Society and the Homosexual* (London: Gollancz, 1952), first American edition (New York: Dutton, 1953).

von Schrenck-Notzing, A. P. F., *Therapeutic Suggestion in Psychopathia Sexualis (Pathological Manifestations of the Sexual Sense) With Especial Reference to Contrary Sexual Instincts* (Philadelphia: Davis, 1895).

Statistical Abstracts of the United States, 1959 (80th Annual Edition), prepared under the direction of Edwin D. Goldfield, Chief, Statistical Reports Division, U. S. Department of Commerce (U. S. Government Printing Office, Washington, D. C.).

Stekel, William, M.D., *The Homosexual Neurosis* (New York: The Physicians and Surgeons Book Company, 1934).

St. John-Stevas, Norman, *Life, Death and the Law* (Bloomington, Ind.: Indiana University Press, 1961).

Sullivan, Harry S., *The Interpersonal Theory of Psychiatry,* Helen Swick Perry and Mary Ladd Garvel (eds.), (New York: Norton, 1953).

Tobin, Rev. William J., *Homosexuality and Marriage* (Rome, Italy: The Catholic Book Agency, 1964).

VanderVeldt, James H., O.F.M., and Odenwald, Robert, M.D., *Psychiatry and Catholicism* (New York: McGraw-Hill Book Company, 1957).

Waring, Paul, and Bryce, Dean Travis, *Homosexual Freedom,* privately published, 1961.

Weinstock, Herbert, *Tschaikovsky* (New York: Alfred A. Knopf, 1943).

West, D., *Homosexuality* (London: Duckworth, 1955).

―――― *The Other Man* (New York: Whiteside, Inc., and William Morrow & Company, 1955).

West, Morris L., *The Devil's Advocate* (New York: William Morrow & Company, 1959).

Westwood, G., *A Minority. A Report on the Life of the Male Homosexual in Great Britain* (London: Longmans, 1960).

―――― *Society and the Homosexual* (London: Gollancz, 1952).

Winokur, George (ed.), *Determinants of Human Sexual Behavior* (Springfield, Ill.: Charles C. Thomas, 1963).

The Wolfenden Report, Authorized American Edition With Introduction by Karl Menninger, M.D. (New York: Stein and Day, 1963).

Psychosexual homosexuality, 20
Psychotherapy, and insight, 279; prognosis of, 279 f; technic of, 279
Pygmalionism, 188

Racial characteristics, 75 f
Rape, 190
Reification, 53
Religious life and homosexuality, 147 ff
Responsibility, for acts, 235; and homosexual types, 245; moral, 225 ff; pastoral practice on, 247 f; and will, 236

Sadism, 185; description of, 185 ff
Salzman, Leon, on definition of homosexuality, 18
Sapphism, 25 f
Satyriasis, 181
Scale rating for homosexuals, 89 f
Schizophrenia, paranoid, differential diagnosis, 98
Scopophilia, 182
Scythians, disease of, 94
Seduction, 190
Sex act, classification of, 205; *contra naturam*, 191 f; legally permissible, 205 f; quantitative disturbances of, 180 ff
Sexedness, degree of, 244
Sexual disturbances against nature, 189
Sexuality, Freudian concept of development, 35 ff; period of sexual latency, 36 f
Sexual offense, definition of, 203
Shock therapy, 277
SIR (Society for Individual Rights), 220
Social and business relations, Patient VII on, 123
Social Understanding, The National

League for, 220
Societies, international, 222 f
Sodom and Gomorrah, 3
Sodomy, 26, 192; penalties for, 193; U. S. Code on, 193

Tertullian on homosexuality, 7
Therapy, 260; adaptive, 278; aim of, 268 ff; behavior, 275 f; distinct from counseling, 260; drug, 277 f; physical methods, 270 ff; primarily psychogenic, 278; prognostic indications, 269
Thompson, Clara, on "wastebasket" term for homosexuality, 30
Transsexualism, 26, 95 f
Transvestitism, 26; differential diagnosis, 92
Treatment of inversion, 268 ff
Tribadism, 26
Triolism, 191

United States Mission, 221
Unresisted urge, 243

Vaginismus, 182
Venereal disease and homosexuality, 86 f
Voyeurism, 26, 182 f

Will, factors lessening freedom, 237; and irresistible impulses, 239; occasions of sin and freedom, 246; and responsibility, 236; responsibility types and freedom, 245
Wolfenden Report, Catholic viewpoint on, 202; on homosexuality as a disease, 31; on incidence of homosexuality, 13; on inversion, 24